Women, Aging & Myths

TEN STEPS TO LOVING YOUR LONG LIFE

PATRICK RODEN

Cover created by Patrick Roden; image purchased from Adobe Stock.

Editing and Interior Design by Skye Blue Press.

ISBN-13: 978-1-955674-37-9 (hardcover)

ISBN-13: 978-1-955674-38-6 (paperback)

ISBN-13: 978-1-955674-39-3 (ebook)

Library of Congress Control Number: 2022920728

Printed in the United States of America

First Edition 2022

Skye Blue Press

Vancouver, WA

https://skyebluepress.com

Acknowledgments

Any person who creates a book will tell you that it begins first in the mind —then in the physical, and never without context. Many of the ideas along this journey were formulated in the context of the following people and experiences.

Julie Roden, my wife/life partner, I am grateful you are on my team, honey. Nancy Rollins Gantz, RN Ph.D., you were my first boss and you set a high bar that never was equaled again in my career. Harry Rick Moody, who wrote the books that taught me about aging. Without his ideas, I would be rudderless.

To Portland State University, where my Gerontology education started. Fielding University, for accommodating, yet uncompromising academics. Ken Dycthwald, my role model, a guy who single-handedly made aging cool again; the book, *Age Wave*, was my launching pad. Louis Tennenbaum, the lone voice, the pioneer who showed me the way. Laurie Orlov, who brought aging-in-place technology to the masses with attitude! Dr. Doug Robertson, who introduced me to andragogy and was hands down the best teacher/example of self-directed learning I have encountered. Mary Furlong, who told me silver could be turned into gold—I believed her, and I still do. Mike Waters, who gave me my first opportunity to share these ideas in public. Joe Coughlin, of MIT AgeLab, who is a role model for messaging with style.

Ramiah Ramasubramanian, for richly informing my ideas and supporting a better version of myself. Jim Krueger, for modeling a gentler side of masculinity. Mavis Lindgren, who started it all by living the theories I studied and showed by example "possibility aging." Francis Gabe, the genius who invented the self-cleaning house, designed to free women from drudgery to realize their higher calling. Jim McCully, the blind man who taught me to see. Zita, Ann, and Pat, without you, I would not be here; you are the reason I am.

Good Samaritan Nursing Home (Eugene, Oregon, where I was Certified Nursing Assistant) and all the residents who were family during my undergraduate years. Halsey, who gets me up in the morning and reminds me each day to live in the moment and that a good day involves walks, cuddles, and treats.

I no doubt neglected to mention other instrumental figures on my gerontology path; you are the countless unknowns that make up the scaffolding by which I strive to build a better world in which to age. Special thanks to George F. Campbell, "Cousin George."

I am forever in your debt and will continue to pay it forward as long as I live.

To the women in my life . . .

To my wife, Julie, a wicked smart businesswoman with a loving heart.
To Aunt Ann, the epitome of successful aging, on the job till 90 years of age, open to new adventures—always.
To my mother-in-law, Karen, who is a seeker of knowledge and the most curious person I have ever met.
To Zita, who showed that creativity is the greatest gift.

Contents

Introduction

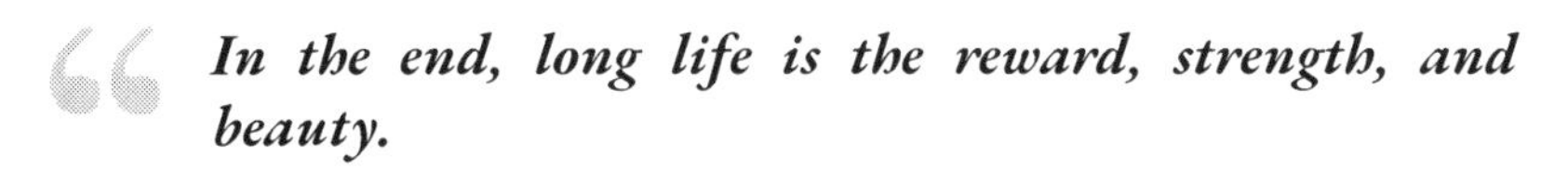

> ***In the end, long life is the reward, strength, and beauty.***
>
> —GRACE PALEY

Dear Reader,

I created this book with you in mind. For over thirty-five years working in the female-dominated nursing profession alongside women of all ages, ethnic groups, and economic strata, there has not been much concerning women's stories I have not heard. I have been privy to many life-lessons worthy of sharing.

Often, I have been called upon to be an active sounding board for a plethora of women's concerns, the topics of which vary—but a reoccurring theme is aging.

The topic of aging generally, and women's aging specifically, really began for me when I was an infant, crawling around the floors of a nursing home run by my grandmother, the head nurse. The experience imprinted on me so profoundly that it became my life's work. Growing up, of course, I had the joy of loving older women who were the family matriarchs, and although many have passed, their influence will be with me forever.

An experience I had in the early fall of 1992, as a Portland marathon medical volunteer, was when I met an extraordinary senior named Mavis Lindgren. She changed the course of my life and set me on this path of studying a new kind of aging—"Possibility Aging." This book contains many concepts and ideas (condensed) that I have unearthed over decades of study, researching, and experiencing this new kind of old. Advanced Aging ("oldest-old") is predominately a women's issue because of longevity trends, so that is the focus. However, there is a robust offering for men here because men have much to learn from women's experiences growing older.

This book aims to identify some of the "myths" surrounding women's aging and provide actionable steps to counter them. I have designed each of the ten steps to make your experience of aging more satisfying and enjoyable. The topics covered are not exhaustive and will undoubtedly be incomplete in some key areas; having noted this, I trust the ideas, concepts, and resources shared will benefit you, the reader, for being exposed to them. The information presented here on aging includes topics from the early 1990s and extends through the present. This was strategic to show how the past thinking has evolved over the decades and influences current trends.

There are four main sections:

1. Women, aging, and culture
2. Domestic universe of home (aging in place)
3. Health/wellness
4. Human potential and unfinished business

At the end of each chapter a myth is debunked, and a step is offered to support loving your long life. The theme that runs throughout the work is optimizing women's longevity advantage. The concluding chapter (11) profiles ten remarkable women, each uniquely taking on a specific aging myth. They are all examples of empowered female aging.

Years ago, a nurse practitioner buddy was on the circuit, giving talks on menopause, and I always thought that was bold and even foolhardy on some level. He understood the objective clinical aspects of the topic—but could not claim to understand the subjective side. Fast forward to the present, and here I am authoring a book on women and aging. Whether bold or foolhardy, I, too, have sailed into waters I cannot entirely appreciate subjectively—I acknowledge that. As mentioned, men get old, but women get older; therefore, aging into the 'oldest-old' category is a women's issue.

My education in Gerontology has provided the theoretical underpinnings to venture into these waters. Still, acting on the caregiving side of countless older women (family and professionally) has earned insights worth sharing. And it does not hurt to have been working in female-dominated professions for over three and a half decades. Yes, this is a not-so-thinly-veiled attempt to get "cred" for knowing the topic without first-hand experience of being an aging woman. I will never fully appreciate your struggles, victories, or experiences—but that should not stop me from striving to gain understanding as best I can. Listening has been an invaluable tool for learning.

In this work, there is intentional neglect of relevant topics. I avoided some essential issues such as menopause, violence against women/elder abuse, sexism, gender bias, transgender women's aging, LGBTQ, equal wages, ethnic/racial discrimination, and women aging in prison. Also, affordable care, fair housing, grandparenting, relationships, dating, and workplace COVID burnout, to mention a few aspects of aging women's lives. These are all worthy of delving into and seeking solutions. Other authors have tackled these with academic rigor and grace, and I have only the highest respect for those who bring knowledge and understanding to improve the human condition.

I am honored you invested the time to read this book.

> ***Our lives are like the talents in the parable of the three stewards. It is something that has been given to us for the time being, and we have the opportunity and privilege of doing our best with this precious gift.***
>
> —GEORGE VAILLANT

Vaillant's words sum up my objectives for this work, and the deepest desire is for you to live every stage of life fully—and love your long life. I want to thank all the women who have invited me into their conversations; the experience has enriched my life beyond measure.

Best Long Life,

Patrick

CHAPTER 1

The Myth of Ageless Aging

MYTH: Successful Aging is Ageless Aging

Grandma Wears Running Shoes

The night's chill lingered in the air as the early morning silence was broken by the trills of tiny songbirds. The sun began to rise on that crisp October morning in 1992. Suddenly, the squeaking brakes of a rental truck and the clanging of folding chairs shattered the serenity. With military precision, the volunteers set up the first aid station at the 18-mile marker. I was one of those volunteers, and this was the Portland Marathon.

It took an hour to set up and go through my checklist. The first aid kit was in order, and the communications were working. We were ready. Soon, the elite runners would fly through, followed by a seemingly endless sea of participants. The conditions were perfect: a bright, clear, indigo sky and golden fall leaves. We were anticipating an inspiring day.

The morning had been uneventful at our station. The usual blisters, Vaseline applied to the chafed skin, hydration to the dehydrated, and lots of moral support. A pregnant woman reached the 18-mile point and could go no further, so we loaded her into the ambulance. They taxied her to the finish line and her anxiously awaiting husband.

It was now late afternoon, and the sea of runners had dwindled to a trickle of determined souls. The frequent and now familiar static that preceded a message from the EMS broke the airwaves. An older woman was reported to be down near the 18-mile mark, which was in our territory. I waited for a person fitting the description to pass, and no one did. Strapping on my first aid kit, I set out to investigate. Running upstream, I thought, how old could they mean? Whoever it was, she had run 18 miles and this was a marathon, after all. I figured she was fifty or maybe sixty, tops.

As I rounded the bend, I saw a young woman attending the injured runner who resembled Mother Teresa in running shorts! The young woman explained that a runner had cut in front of the injured woman, knocking her down as she stepped toward the curb. As I listened, I assessed the situation. Her injuries comprised a fractured wrist and a slight bump on the head.

"Her name is Mavis," the young woman said.

"Mavis, I would like to escort you to the first aid station," I said. "We need to—"

"Young man, I'm going to finish this race," she interrupted. After a few seconds of negotiating, I held up her injured arm, and we briskly took off for the first aid station (or so I thought).

Amazed, I blurted out, "How old are you?"

"I'm eighty-five," Mavis said. She pointed to the number pinned to the front of her T-shirt. "Every year, they give me the number of my age. This year I am number 85."

"What do you mean, every year?" I asked.

Mavis Lindgren had run all over the world. She had appeared on TV and radio, and been featured in magazines such as Runner's World, Sports Illustrated, and The New York Times. She had also been written about in the books *Age Wave* (Ken Dychtwald) and *Grandma Wears Running Shoes* (Patricia Horning Benton). She was no stranger to Portland, either. All along the course, people held signs that encouraged her, and they cheered her every step! Two middle-aged women ran up and hugged her, exclaiming that they wanted to be just like her when they grew up.

Mavis and I reached the finish line arm-in-arm, right into interviews for the six o'clock news (I have the video). The following year, I was asked to escort her through the entire race, and it became a tradition. She retired from running at ninety years old, after the 1997 Portland marathon. It was her seventy-fifth and final 26.2-mile outing. Phil Knight of Nike had a custom pair of "Air Mavis" running shoes made especially for her last marathon. Her two daughters and grandchildren accompanied us, and it was an emotional finale to an illustrious running career.

What makes her story even more exceptional to me is that at age sixty-two, Mavis led a sedentary life. She spent most of her time reading, writing, and knitting. She had suffered four bouts of pneumonia in five years. As a retired nurse, she knew antibiotics were not the long-term solution. Something had to change. A doctor urged her to join an early bird walking group. At age seventy, encouraged by her son, she ran her first marathon!

Two years later, she established a record of 4:33.05. For the next eight years, she held the world's best time for women seventy and over. And at eighty-four, she finished the Los Angeles marathon in six hours and forty-five minutes—the fastest woman in her age category.

After I started running, I never had another cold.

—*MAVIS LINDGREN*

Mavis Lindgren & Patrick Roden

Asked what his message was, Gandhi replied, "My life is my message." The same could have been said about Mavis Lindgren—she never denied her age and lived fully within it.

> ***The old Americans I studied do not perceive meaning in aging itself; rather, they perceive meaning in being themselves in old age.***
>
> —SHARON R. KAUFMAN

Since January 1, 2011, the demographic transition became evident for baby boomers, the oldest being 65. This often-stated fact is becoming hackneyed now, but the reality is still settling in for many; however uneasy it makes us all feel. For the next decade, ten thousand baby boomers a day would reach that milestone.

This has led to an interest in aging that our culture has never experienced before. *Newsweek* contributing author Susan Jacoby reports, "As we age, physical and financial hardships mount as people move beyond the relatively hardy 60s and 70s (young-old), and the territory gets harsher into the 80s and 90s (old-old). The incidence of Alzheimer's disease is 50% for those over 85, and two-thirds of Americans older than 85 are women, who usually become poorer with age."

Further, Jacoby notes that age-defying hope and hype do nothing to address the overwhelming political issues of paying for Medicare and social security. Nor does it address the various personal decisions that need to be made about aging in place, retirement, or end-of-life issues that are just offshore, brewing. Jacoby also warns that many of us must prepare for the possibility that not the best, but some of the worst years of our lives may lie ahead if we live to the oldest-old age group. The message is clear: age comes at a cost.

There is no shortage of information on the topic of aging; some are legitimate, some are snake oil. Problems arise when we encounter definitions such as *successful aging means little or no loss in function compared to youth.* Statements like this are at the heart of the problem; the danger is the lack of acknowledgment concerning change. Holding on tenaciously to youth or middle-aged values of physical beauty, competition, and ambition into older ages can lead to a psychiatric breakdown in the future.

A more mentally healthy approach focuses on the evolving aspects of the aging self instead of on the losses. Defining aging as merely the absence of youth blinds us to what human potential the latter years might bring, or what is called the "longevity bonus."

The late author Betty Friedan asserted:

> *"An accurate, realistic, active identification with one's own aging—as opposed both to resignation to the stereotype of being 'old' and denial of age changes, seems an important key to vital aging and even longevity."*

Betty nailed it when she emphasized we must live our age.

When you ask yourself, "What's my future going to look like?" And in your mind's eye, it looks like it does now, you are at risk for Hyper-habituation. Your development might be sacrificed at the altar of the illusion of stability.

In her book, *The Denial of Aging*, author and geriatrician, Muriel R. Gillick, emphasizes the social consequences of faith in an ageless old age. "If we assume that Alzheimer's disease will be cured and disability abolished in the near term," she writes, "we will have no incentive to develop long-term-care facilities that focus on enabling residents to lead satisfying lives despite their disabilities. More important, blind faith in medical solutions prevents discussion about the urgent nonmedical needs of the old. Americans need not only better long-term-care facilities for the sickest old, but community-based services to foster independence for the healthier old." The article ends by stating that only when we abandon the fantasy that "age can be defied" will we begin a conversation based on reason, and not on yearning for a fountain of youth, and figure out how to make 90 a better 90.

> ***It was formerly a terrifying view to me that I should one day be an old woman. I now find that nature has provided pleasure for every state.***
>
> —MARY WORTLEY MONTAGUE

Messaging here may seem dispiriting, especially to long-lived women, but I assure you it can be just the opposite. It is a wake-up call to view aging not solely as the absence of youth, but as a call to live fully within each age stage and make the future a part of your current philosophy. What is needed is a more empowering approach to your future self.

The future of aging into the oldest-old (>85) groups belongs mainly to women. The demographic is now trending toward an increasingly feminized gerontocracy (more in chapter 2). According to the 2018 Profile of Older Americans in 2017, among the population age 65 and over, there were 28.3 million women and 22.6 million men, or a sex ratio of 125 women for every 100 men. At age 85 and over, this ratio increased to 184 women for every 100 men. The oldest verified person ever was a French woman, Jeanne Calment, who died at 122 years, 164 days, in 1997.

Historically, the data have shown that women live longer than men. Life expectancy at birth for women in the United States dropped 0.8 years from 79.9 years in 2020 to 79.1 in 2021, while life expectancy for men dropped one full year, from 74.2 years in 2020 to 73.2 in 2021. The report shows the disparity in life expectancy between men and women grew in 2021 from 5.7 years in 2020 to 5.9 years in 2021. From 2000 to 2010, this disparity had narrowed to 4.8 years, but gradually increased from 2010 to 2019 and is now the largest gap since 1996 (cdc.gov).

The theories range from biological to behavioral to sociological and have been argued about from pool halls to academic halls. Most likely, it is a hybrid of each and some yet to be discovered X factor.

It is worth mentioning here that one study in the BMJ Open Journal (bmjopen.bmj.com) calls into question this long established female longevity advantage. The study covered 199 countries over a nearly 200-year period and found men who are married and have college degrees tend to outlive females who are unmarried or do not have a high school diploma. But the fact remains, men get old—but women get older. There is a recreating afoot of what growing older as a woman has in store for you.

The author and culture critic Margaret Morganroth Gullette once observed, "We are aged more by culture than by chromosomes." What does it mean to be aged by culture? Gullette claims that age is a socially constructed concept wrapped in a decline ideology. She suggests that our society and culture view aging in negative terms; the focus is on declines at the expense of anything remotely positive. What keeps this cultural assumption alive in the collective unconscious are the images of decay and loss associated with getting older.

Every act of ageism, such as negative comments aimed at, or media images that infantilize older people, can be considered "microaggressions" which reinforce unfavorable views. Thus, solidifying the cultural bias about aging in our western culture that privileges youth. When society embraces ageism unquestionably, this has the effect of normalizing and perpetuating stereotypes. The result is we have expectations of older adults that match negative perceptions. Eventually, we are all aged by it in subtle and not-so-subtle ways.

Gullette asserts that what is needed is push-back on the "insidious decline ideology" and the way to do it is by changing our age culture. She would like to see ageism on the cultural level of sexism or racism and have all generations behind the effort to end it by raising awareness. So, aging is more than just a biological phenomenon; it also occurs within the context of culture and the mind (self-perception).

The premium on feminine beauty means that older women often find themselves at the terrible nexus of sexism and ageism.

—OLDSCHOOL.INFO

Decades ago, social psychologist Ellen Langer made similar inquiries into the concept of cultural context with mindfulness and its relationship to physical aging, or what is now termed, "social determinants of health." Langer posed this question in her groundbreaking book in 2009, *Counter-clockwise: Mindful Health and the Power of Possibility*, "There's no way to turn back the clock or to fight the inevitable. We age and the vigor of youth becomes only a memory as we are ravaged by time. Chronic illnesses take their toll, our health and strength diminish and the best we can do is graciously accept our fate. Once sickness is upon us, we give ourselves over to modern medicine and hope for the best. We can't intervene as time marches on. Or can we?"

If we can turn back the clock psychologically, could we also turn back the clock physiologically, too? The answer to Langer's query promised to have far-reaching consequences for how we experience growing older, potentially. To find out, she and her team of researchers conducted an ambitious study way back in 1979, which became known as the "Counterclockwise" study. The study looked at older men who were immersed in an environment designed to mirror the year 1959 for one week. They listened to music, read books, viewed newspapers, and engaged in conversations as if it were the year 1959.

Langer and her team measured biomarkers like weight, eyesight, and hearing both before and after immersion week. There was a physical difference in the subjects, which suggested the biological clock had been turned back in terms of youthful biomarkers. So, the environment and culture had a measurable impact that can change physiology.

Langer's take-home message was that people were unaware of how they mindlessly reacted to cultural cues, which had consequences. Her research attempted to show that we are not passive victims if we are mindful of cultural influences. We are at choice in how we respond to getting older. Our beliefs can limit or enhance our aging experience, and the individual has more power over the process than the cultural messaging often dictates. Researchers like Gullette and Langer have been asking a more beautiful question, and we all might benefit from it.

Act Your Age

What does it mean to act your age? Historically, age differentiation has been how we have known our place in society. It dictated when we entered school, got a driver's license, voted, married, had children, started a career, and retired. Additional factors, such as social class, formal education, occupation, gender, and race, also play a role in one's experience of old age. Those additional factors aside, age identification is a product of chronological age. But age-grading has undergone some changes in the past few decades; for example, the futurist, Faith Popcorn, wrote over twenty-five years ago about a phenomenon she called "down-aging" in her brilliant book, *Clicking* (1996)."Down-aging is all about throwing out the rules and constraints that dictate how we should behave by certain points in our lives," Popcorn declared.

There are examples of this phenomenon all around us. For instance, I found myself in a shopping mall several years ago, and necessity dictated the excursion to a Mecca of shopping known as Clackamas Town Center. My wife had a list of to-dos (she is very purposeful) and I had some general notion of what I was after. We synchronized our watches like two infantry soldiers and agreed to return to a designated spot in two hours. After thirty minutes of meandering through merchandise, I thought, *Two hours! What was I thinking?*

Generally, a malaise seems to come over me as my energy level is in an inverse relationship with the time spent in malls. Feeling like the late cultural anthropologist Margaret Mead, or a stranger in a strange land, I began to have a subtle shift in my thinking. A little voice seemed to say, "observe." With a change in my interpretive filter, I noticed a reoccurring theme among the bustling masses of determined shoppers. Approaching the crowd ahead of me, I saw what appeared to be two young ladies, dressed alike, chatting. As I passed them, I noticed these were not contemporaries at all—they were mother and daughter!

Twenty years ago, there was no doubt about who was who, but that has all changed—this is known as down-aging. Ms. Popcorn predicted the rejection of the cultural construction of age and the potential for personal interpretation decades ago.

Fitness and athletics are other arenas where down-aging is prevalent. The bad news is that sports rehab clinics across the country see more geriathletes (over age sixty-five) with sports-related injuries. The good news is that these rehab clinics are seeing more geriathletes with sports-related injuries! I ran marathons with Mavis Lindgren, who began her running career in her sixties and completed her first of ninety marathons at age seventy! Go to any gym in the morning (pre-COVID-19) and you will find yourself surrounded by gray-haired regulars. I once overheard a twenty-something blonde beauty at the front desk of a well-known fitness chain share her dismay that there were too many old people at the club. It seems she was afraid of the place becoming known as an old people's gym. I laughed to myself, thinking of her disconnect with her paycheck and who comes through the door, and I envisioned her drowning in the gray tsunami (pardon the analogy).

It is becoming more commonplace for marketers who have avoided most anything to do with aging to now embrace down-aging. The return of many classics like high-top black converse sneakers (Vice President Kamala Harris will no doubt spark this trend) and the Schwinn Classic Cruiser bicycle (now supercharged with eBike batteries) play on feelings of nostalgia.

Faith Popcorn asserted:

> *"Whatever the crisis-change mechanism at work here, the underlying feeling is 'there's got to be more.' And this search for ever-more leads to down-aging. Not forgetting about your age or railing against your age, but tossing away the old ideas of what chronological age is. For down-aging is fundamentally about changing expectations, dreams, desires, visions. It is about a constant state of growing, of saying 'yes' to life and all its possibilities."*

Once aware of down-aging in our culture, one notices it everywhere as older adults time-shift life experiences and looks. Popcorn described elder moms/elder dads standing in the check-out line at the grocery with Pampers under one arm for the baby and Attends under the other arm for themselves!

The trend toward down-aging ties in with a known gerontological theory called the Continuity Theory of Aging (CTA). The theory states that, in making adaptive choices, middle-aged and older adults attempt to preserve and maintain existing psychological and social patterns by applying familiar knowledge, skills, and strategies.

George Maddox was the first researcher to use the idea of continuity to describe the behavior of aging individuals in the year 1968, when he observed people tended to engage in similar activities and to continue familiar lifestyle patterns as they aged. However, CTA was not introduced until the year 1989. Robert Atchley is credited with the development of this theory. Continuity theory takes a life course perspective in which the aging process is shaped by history, culture, and social constructs. According to this theory, continuity in aging is seen as a dynamic and evolutionary developmental process in which individuals grow, adapt, and change; however, these changes are consistent with the person's underlying ideology and past experiences (Jessica Diggs).

The central premise of CTA is that older adults will adapt to changes by employing strategies that maintain internal and external continuity in their lives. Internal continuity refers to the process of forming personal links between new experiences and memories of previous ones, and external continuity refers to interacting with familiar people and known environments. According to CTA, a person's personality, behaviors, and preferences will remain similar into old age. A pair of black Chuck Taylor high-tops can be a psychological bridge from the past to the present, and they help maintain a youthful sense of nostalgia while living in the now.

When I Grow Up

The next question is: *Do you want to be an old woman?* In the ancient traditions of western Europe, dragons were portrayed as destructive forces the gods had to battle in the pursuit of good versus evil. *"Here there be dragons"* was a phrase placed on maps of the time where the medieval English mapmakers described territories that remained unknown and unexplored. Beyond the edges of their experience were thought to be dark, freighting forces where timid souls should never go—only the gods dare venture.

The analogy of unexplored far-off frightening territory, *Here There be Dragons*, might describe old age for some. Living past the age of 65 in great numbers is a relatively recent phenomenon. For women, life expectancy at birth in 1900 was a mere 48.3 years (men = 46.3). By contrast, one in five Americans will be over the age of 65 by the year 2030. Adults over the age of 65 will then outnumber teens 2:1. For the developed world at least, longevity is the "Here There be Dragons" of modern times.

Early in my nursing career, I remember listening to the lungs of an older woman admitted with an exacerbation of congestive heart failure. She was, what we in the business call, "a frequent flyer" because of her many admissions for acute episodes of chronic conditions. As I carefully placed my stethoscope into my ears, then strategically on her chest, I requested that she take "Big breaths, big breaths," in my nurse voice. Suddenly, she said something and then chuckled with light laughter. Not being able to hear her, I pulled the ear prong out of one ear and asked, "What did you say?"

Her response has stayed with me some thirty-five years later. In a quivering Parkinson-like voice (think Katharine Hepburn in later years), "They used to be." The smirk across her face added levity to a tense situation, and I laughed out loud!

This kind of lightheartedness about aging makes me recall another woman who was quick-witted into her later years. Gypsy Rose Lee was a "stripper" (never fully undressed) and a towering intellect. She employed her craft to get men's attention as she mesmerized them into her way of thinking via political persuasion. Gypsy Rose Lee spoke about growing older and accepted herself at any age. For example, she once exclaimed, "I've got everything I always had. Only now it's six inches lower," in *A Woman's Almanac*, 1977, by Barbara McDowell and Hana Umlauf.

Through the years, I have always told this story as a highlight in my long career. It speaks to the truth about aging, and how essential it is to be accepting about growing older, and what it brings. If we are fortunate to experience old age (and not all are) hopefully, we will think about the changes like these women did.

Past research supports this positive approach to getting older. Findings from the Ohio Longitudinal Study of Aging and Retirement (OLSAR) showed older individuals with more positive self-perceptions of aging, measured up to 23 years earlier, lived 7.5 years longer than those with less positive self-perceptions of aging. This advantage remained after age, gender, socioeconomic status, loneliness, and functional health were included as covariates. Bottom line, there is evidence for the connection between how aging is viewed and how long one lives.

Kaiser Permanente, years ago, had an ad campaign:

"When I Grow Up, I Want to be an Old Woman."

It was bold and brilliant in that it flies in the face of conventional wisdom in several important ways:

1. The third rail (sure death) in marketing is to use the words *aging* or *old*. It is considered better for businesses to use euphemisms, like *living in place* instead. When selling to boomers, conventional wisdom says that alluding to getting older is the kiss of death. Gerontophobia, or the fear of aging, is the reason.
2. The traditional medical model has privileged sick-care, not healthcare, emphasizing the peak-and-decline aging model. The focus is on pathology and what goes wrong (aka biomedicalization of aging).

This campaign dared to ask straight out, "Do you want to be an old woman?" It is **not** about anti-aging—in fact, just the opposite**.** Emphasize preventive care (get a mammogram), so you can live long enough to become an old woman! And live all the unknown experiences (here there be dragons) awaiting you.

Extending life without extending health is a hollow victory—they are not the same thing. Andy Rooney once noted, "It's paradoxical that the idea of living a long life appeals to everyone, but the idea of getting old doesn't appeal to anyone." "Compressing Morbidity," or staying healthy into old age and staving off disease until the very end, is the goal (more n chapter 7). W*hen I grow up* is a message that shows a deeper understanding of human behavior and respects maturing psyches of women who embrace all ages of their human experience. Living fully within each age is a choice.

It's not how old you are, it's how you are old.

—JULES RENARD

I remember my experience as a medical escort, running multiple Portland marathons with the late, famed Mavis Lindgren (see her story). She so often exclaimed, “I’m having fun being an old lady!” And she meant it. Perhaps out in those uncharted waters of old age, she encountered a different kind of dragon, of the Asian tradition that symbolizes power, happiness, good fortune, and wealth, and has a message for those waiting on the shores of middle-age and beyond; there is pleasure at every age.

However, having described this new kind of old, there are potential perils to embracing common anti-aging sentiments uncritically. Harry Rick Moody, Ph.D., once mentioned the term “happy gerontology” and then described it as an unrealistic view of aging, ageless aging, if you will. He noted that the denying of aging could be soul eroding, in that you may miss the lessons each stage of life has to offer. My experience tells me he is right. We all love seeing those who seem to defy aging; a Betty White, or a Warren Buffett—and in my own experience, 90-year-old marathoner Mavis Lindgren, but if we define age simply as the absence of youth, we blind ourselves to the human potential and soul maturation of living longer. This is also known as the “longevity dividend.”

Baby boomers who hold on tenaciously to the values of middle age and youth (competition, ambition, looks) are potentially headed for trouble. The gerontologist, Robert Kastenbaum, suggests that “holding onto youth and denying age leads to mental and emotional stagnation.” And like with most living things, stasis is the beginning of the end.

Betty Friedan once said, “We have to live our own age.” That is, each age has something to teach, and hyper-habituation (doing what you have always done) erodes the soul and robs it of the process of becoming renewed. This essential re-framing of aging as a time dominated by decline, loss, and lack of contribution needs to be a personal, as well as national, priority.

Marvin Kaiser, Ph.D., noted, “We live in a world that will never be young again; each generation will grow older than the one before until the old outnumber the young.” His statement speaks directly to what has been called The Longevity Revolution. When Thomas Jefferson roamed the grounds of Monticello, half the population of our new United States was under the age of sixteen. Yet, by the year 2050, senior citizens over the age of sixty will outnumber children under the age of fifteen for the first time in history.

The longevity revolution is so recent and so dramatic it is estimated that two-thirds of all the human beings who have ever lived to be sixty-five years of age or older are alive today.

This is due to three main reasons:

1. Decreased infant mortality at birth.
2. Decreased morbidity from infectious diseases with antibiotic treatments.
3. Improved nutrition/sanitation.

Longevity is a global trend that I became aware of in 1999 after reading an article by Peter G. Peterson in "Foreign Affairs," published by the Council on Foreign Relations. In the piece, he described the "Floridization" (19% of the population being older than 65) of the developed world that would rapidly change the face of countries around the world.

Country/Year of Floridization
USA 2021
Canada 2023
Japan 2005
Germany 2006
Italy 2003

Source: *Gray Dawn: The Global Aging Crisis*, by Peter G. Peterson

His demographic predictions were not exactly accurate in some cases, but his concept of a global population in transition was accurate. The trends have decreased slightly since the global pandemic but will continue to go in the direction of living longer. It seems the future in the developed world belongs to maturity—but more specifically, female maturity.

Clearly, a significant success of the twentieth century has been the luxury of aging. Now is an opportune time to rewrite your personal experience with aging and society. The sheer numbers of the demographic transition to longer living humans demand that society view them as a special kind of growing resource. Peterson used the term "daunting demographics" to describe the phenomenon, fearing the numbers of elderly would cripple global economies. It does not have to play out that way. What is required is reframing older people as a cohort with age-related contributions to offer—globally, we cannot afford otherwise.

Striking a balance between who you were, who you are, and who you are becoming will serve you and society well, a continuity of self that is enduring yet malleable and allows for continued growth into later years. If you are savvy and can incorporate new sets of achievable gratifications, new sources of pride to replace old ones, and take care of yourself physically, the next phase of life will be richly rewarding for you and society.

The perceptions of aging have been in flux for some time now; much of the literature on old age focuses on facts concerning how fast, how soon, and how large the elderly population will grow. When discussed in healthcare, pensions, social security, retirement, taxes, and inter-generational relations, these statistical predictions often take on an alarmist tone. This alarmist tone has its roots in historical gerontology, which represents one school of thought in aging studies. The origins of gerontology as science emerged during the twentieth century. Before that time, pre-modern knowledge of aging was an existential mystery. The medieval mystery got replaced in the eighteenth and ninetieth centuries with scientific management of old age. From that point on, the search for senescence was on.

This re-classification of old age as a biomedical problem marked a turning point and the increasing power of modern medicine as aging's defining force. Historically, gerontology's focus on pathology and decline meant that most discussions of human development (of which creativity is but one aspect) emphasized the first half of life—especially the earliest stages. There is little refuting the magnitude of disease and disability associated with aging; geriatrician Muriel R. Gillick alluded to it eloquently. In the past, however, the potential for extending achievable vitality into advanced ages was underappreciated. Recognizing this and the dominance of the medical model into many aspects of aging, some new voices in gerontology are entering the discourse. These voices embrace human potential and growth in later years without denying aging.

Biohackers

It should be mentioned that there are researchers ("biohackers") who consider aging a disease process that may potentially be staved off for decades—if not cured entirely. One such bio-gerontologist is Andrew Steele, who authored *Ageless: The New Science of Getting Older Without Getting Old*. "The dream of anti-aging medicine," Steele writes, "is treatments that would identify the root causes of dysfunction as we get older, then slow their progression or reverse them entirely." According to Steele, aging is a problem to be fixed, and the root causes of aging are called hallmarks; treat these and you will slow down aging.

- Genomic instability: as we age, we accumulate genetic damage. Simply, over time, our DNA gets mangled. The hypothesis is that if scientists can find a way to repair that damage, they will then impact the aging process.
- Cellular senescence: the longer we live, the more chance we have of experiencing a build-up of senescent (old) cells, which tend to hang around in the body and contribute to the onset of age-related diseases.
- Mitochondrial dysfunction: mitochondria are 'organelles' that generate the energy our cells need to power necessary biochemical reactions and that mitochondrial dysfunction can accelerate aging.

If scientists can address those hallmarks, we can come up with treatments that slow down the whole aging process, deferring diseases into the future.

—ANDREW STEELE

The fact remains, many people will continue to grow older with age-related diseases.

In her seminal work, *Fountain of Age (*1993), Betty Friedan reported long ago on what she saw as a misconception with "the problem of age." Friedan noted that much of our views concerning aging centered around images of mentally incompetent, child-like, lonely, dependent, powerless, sexless, unattractive, older persons. Is it any wonder the fear of aging (gerontophobia) is rampant in our culture? Google "Successful Aging" and you get about 207 million results. The topics cover everything from the sublime to the ridiculous, not to mention the vast array of snake oil salespeople that trade on the fears of aging.

The anti-aging medicine researchers are hoping to achieve, lengthening health-spans along with lifespans, is a worthy goal. With the emerging science of precision medicine/nutrition, epigenetics, and the assistance of artificial intelligence with big data, compressing morbidity (staving off disease until the very end of life) is certainly possible. Steele thinks there is a bias toward the status quo of aging as inevitable and not preventable. He suggests that if suddenly two-thirds of the population began physically and mentally declining and succumbing to devastating diseases, the scientific community would set out to cure it. I cannot argue with his logic, but for now, postponing aging does not mean curing aging; it will continue.

The Myth of the Unending Frontier

> ***The underlying basis of ageism is the dread and fear of growing older, becoming ill and dependent, and approaching death. People are afraid, and that leads to profound ambivalence. The young dread aging, and the old envy youth. Behind ageism is corrosive narcissism, the inability to accept our fate, for indeed we are all in love with our youthful selves, as is reflected in the yearning behind the expression 'salad days.' Although undoubtedly universal, ageism in the United States is probably fueled by the worship of youth in a still-young country dominated by the myth of the unending frontier . . .***
>
> —ROBERT BUTLER, *THE LONGEVITY REVOLUTION*

Summary

Professor of Astronomy, Harriet Witt, who works in conjunction with the Pacific Whale Foundation, has a fresh take on aging that speaks eloquently to the point. "I've orbited the Sun 76 times. I could tell you I'm 76 years old, but I don't say it that way because I don't see it that way. I see it the way our Earth does."

She knows that what humans call 'one year' is one of her—and our—orbits around the sun.

"Each orbit is a journey of almost six hundred million miles. This means you can measure your age in miles. Of course, doing this results in a cumbersome number, but it's a scientific reminder that you're not just getting older; you're also becoming a more experienced traveler. We seniors can more easily crystallize ,wisdom from our experience when we are focused on the journey and not just on the number of years we've seen 'come and go.' In fact, years do not come and go; we orbit through them!"

Goodbye Myth: Aging is Not Defined as the Absence of Youth.

Step 1

Embrace each stage of life.

When Bob Dylan sang, "May you stay forever young," that sounded like sage advice, but successful aging does not mean postponing aging; every stage of the process (orbit) has something to offer if lived fully within it. Stevie Nicks, in the song "Landslide" declared, "I'm getting older too," and then asked, "Can I handle the seasons of my life?" And lately, it seems she seems to be doing it quite well. In review, the critical message again is: When (and if) you ask yourself, *what's my future going to look like?*, if in your mind's eye it looks like it does now, you are at risk for hyper-habituation and stagnation. Development could be sacrificed at the altar of the illusion of stability. Embracing each stage of life can go a long way toward loving your long life!

> ***Every age can be enchanting, provided you live within it.***
>
> —BRIGITTE BARDOT

Resources

For insightful reading on the topic of the two seemingly opposing camps in Gerontology 1) Poets 2) Pathologists, see: CMAJ. 2011 Jul 12; 183(10): E693–E694. "Grow old along with me! The best is yet to be" Reviewed by A. Mark Clarfield, MD. *Contesting Aging & Loss*. Janice E Graham, Peter H Stephenson, editors. University of Toronto Press; 2010.

The Biomedicalization of Aging: Dangers and Dilemmas

"Medicine, with its focus on individual organic pathology and interventions, has become a powerful and pervasive force in the definition and treatment of aging. The resulting 'biomedicalization of aging' socially constructs old age as a process of detrimental physical decline and places aging under the domain and control of biomedicine."

CHAPTER 2

The Feminized Gerontocracy

MYTH: Older Women are a Societal Liability

Gerontocracy; NOUN / GER·ON·TOC·RA·CY | ˌJER-ən-ˈTÄ-KRə-sē, plural gerontocracies. Definition of Gerontocracy: Rule by elders, specifically, a social organization in which a group of old men or a council of elders dominates or exercises control (merriam-webster.com/dictionary/gerontocracy).

Feminized: fem·i·nized / ˈfe-mə-ˌnīzd, Definition of Feminized: Made feminine or more feminine: notably female or feminine in quality or character (merriam-webster.com/dictionary/feminized).

Feminized Gerontocracy: A social organization in which women elders exercise control (author).

I've gathered strength behind my years; I owned them, I've earned them, I've deserved them, I have a right to have them.

—SALLY FIELD

In a recent article in the Atlantic titled, "The Invisibility of Older Women," by Akiko Busch, the author poetically describes women's aging and their place in society as a result, both real and perceived. She begins with this paragraph which draws the reader in, then with cinematic metaphor reveals her theme:

> *In Alfred Hitchcock's 1938 film, The Lady Vanishes, a young woman on a train becomes disturbed by the sudden disappearance of a kindly older woman, a governess and music teacher. The latter, a spinster, is introduced to the viewer when she writes the letters of her name in the condensation on one of the train's glass windowpanes, only to have them evaporate almost instantly. Within minutes, she is gone, and the other passengers, steward, and conductor claim to have never seen her. Asked to describe her, the young woman can only say she was 'middle-aged and ordinary,' before admitting, 'I can't remember.' Later in the film, the older woman is reduced to 'a hallucination, a subjective image, a character in a novel subconsciously remembered,' and even 'nothing but lumps of raw flesh,' all before she is revealed as a British spy, the movie's ultimate heroine in the final scene.*

Bush provides further evidence for the perceived invisibility of older women in the following paragraph:

> *Today, women appear—or disappear—in any manner of guises. In the photographer Patty Carroll's series Anonymous Women, it is household artifacts and traditions—upholstery fabric, curtains, telephones, slabs of bacon, leaves of lettuce, a braided loaf of bread, rolls of wallpaper, pillows, and plates—into which each model disappears, swallowed whole by the python of domesticity. In Whitney Otto's novel Now You See Her, the vanishing woman works in an office, present but unseen. Her cat is indifferent when she trips over it, and when she presses her palm to her forehead, it is 'only to notice her hand fading away with the motion, from fingertips to forearm.' In the more recent film Hello, My Name Is Doris, Sally Field plays an older woman who develops a crush on a*

> *younger man with whom she shares an office; at the beginning of the story, he adjusts her crooked glasses. As the film critic Manohla Dargis wrote in The New York Times, the young man's spontaneous gesture of kindness is transformative: Wrinkles, apparently, 'have a way of making women disappear one crease at a time,' and when she is noticed momentarily by a younger man, such recognition evidently 'makes her visible, most importantly to herself.'*

The author mentions antidotes to the fleeting self of age in women by another writer on the topic, Francine du Plessix Gray, in her essay, "The Third Age."

> *If the gaze of others wanes, Gray suggests, one might choose to 'acquire instead a deepened inward gaze, or intensify our observation of others, or evolve alternative means of attention-getting which transcend sexuality and depend, as the mentors of my youth taught me, upon presence, authority, and voice.'*

In the end, Bush makes a case for introspection, self-agency, and the benefits of aging:

> *Gray may be talking about the difference between being a subject and an object. It is a cliché to point out that ours is a culture in which men routinely objectify women, but according to Alison Carper, a psychologist who practices in New York, if a woman is complicit in this practice—that is, in viewing herself as an object—she cannot help but be acutely aware when that object loses its desirability. 'As humans, we all need to be recognized,' Carper adds, 'but as we grow older, the manner of recognition we search for can change. A subject is someone who experiences her own agency, who is aware of how she can have an impact on others and how she is, ultimately, the author of her own life.'*

Bush summarizes with an empowering and affirming line:

As they age, women experience less public scrutiny—and entertain a wider set of choices about when and how they are seen.

That statement is fundamentally the conceptual scaffolding for this chapter. From a life-course perspective, looking at the entire lifespan, older women make significant contributions beyond the biological imperative and social expectations of gender roles in every walk of life. This phenomenon has been called "Late Freedom" and is now being embraced by women worldwide.

For a growing number of older women, becoming invisible is not an option, and there is far too much to do. Let us unpack this by beginning with an evolutionary theory, followed by a Native American tale that embodies the value of older women to society, and explores further evidence for the rising power of older women in society.

The "Grandmother Hypothesis"

Are grandmothers an evolutionary necessity? This question has been perplexing and long debated by anthropologists. When we look at our fellow creatures in the animal world, females are often short-lived past their reproductive years. But, the human species live into their eighties and beyond—in fact, the fastest-growing segment of the western world is women over eighty-five (oldest-old).

Kristen Hawkes of the University of Utah notes, "It's the norm in the human population that women are vigorous and productive long past their fertility." Many women feel marginalized once they reach menopause, but research (and my experience and yours, I am sure) suggests that grandmothers are far from a burden on societies. The "Grandmother Hypothesis" states that grandmothers play an essential role in the evolution of human longevity. Research of modern hunter-gatherers in Tanzania, Venezuela, and Eastern Paraguay societies shows how humans evolved; they consistently show that grandmothers are doing much of the work.

Here is the theory in a nutshell; the basic idea is that menopause (end of reproductive years) allows older women to channel energy and resources into caring for their children and grandchildren—providing descendants with a survival advantage. Much of the past research argued that menopause was not natural, and that modern medicine has simply increased life expectancy beyond what nature intended. A century ago, the average life expectancy for women was around forty. Data shows that high infant mortality rates skewed the number during that period—many women lived well past four decades.

Dr. Hawkes states, "Women are strong and economically productive into their 60s; women are not being helped along by others. The flow of help is going in the other direction."

> ***Women grow radical with age. One day, an army of gray-haired women may quietly take over the Earth.***
>
> —GLORIA STEINEM

Two Old Women

In her book, *Two Old Women: An Alaska Legend of Betrayal, Courage and Survival* (1993), author Velma Wallis, in the tradition of the keepers of the stories, tells the Athabascan Indian legend passed on from mothers to daughters of the upper Yukon River. The story is about the nomadic people of the Gwich'in, who belong to the Athabaska tribes that wandered the territories of the Yukon River, the Porcupine River, and the Tanana Rivers. With the oncoming of a harsh winter and lack of food, the tribe decided to leave behind two old women in the snow-covered wilderness. Abandoned and fearful, seventy-five-year-old Sa' (star) and eighty-year-old Ch'idzigyaak (chickadee bird) were left with an elk's skin (gift of guilt) and a hatchet (gift of hope) to die.

In desperation, they were faced with a choice point and decide it was better to die by trying to survive. First, the women killed a squirrel using the hatchet, and trapped rabbits. Each night, they dug snow caves and saved embers to renew each day's fire, so it would never go out. They also hid from cannibalistic tribes.

Over time, they built up a generous supply of foods and stored them away. The following winter, the weakened tribe returned to the area, hungry and lacking, to find the old women had not only survived but thrived. The women eventually forgave their tribe for abandoning them, and the group gained a new sense of survival. From then on, the Gwich'in have never left their elderly behind.

The tale is a beautiful message about the worth of older women to society and is the "Grandmother Hypothesis" in story form. We need the cultural influences of older women's wisdom and compassion beyond mere tribalism and competition to survive.

> ***Who is The Crone? She is the most dangerous, the most radical, the most revolutionary woman in existence. Whether in fairytales or in consensual reality, the old one goes where she wants to, and she acts as she wishes; she lives as she chooses. And this is all as it should be. And no one can stop her. Nor ought they try.***
>
> —CLARISSA PINKOLA ESTÉS

The Future Belongs to Older Women

By the age of 85, there are roughly six women to every four men. At age 100, the ratio is over two to one. And by age 122—the current world record for human longevity—the score stands at one-nil in favor of women; this longevity phenomenon is known as the "sex ratio." I recently informed one of my soon-to-be-divorced-middle-aged-male friends that if he kept his "shelf-life" up, his dance card would always be filled!

One of the most influential books on aging I ever read was *The Fountain of Age* by the late author, Betty Friedan. I reference it frequently because it was so ground-breaking and thought-provoking for its time. Friedan suggested two theories of why women might age longer and better than men. These might help explain, in part, the sex ratio. Yes, the theories are dated for younger generations. However, the cultural norms of the time continue to play out for older generations of women who came of age in a different era.

The X-Over

As women age, they move into new stages of human development (not decline). Women reclaim their "male side" of assertiveness, a more commanding and adventurous nature. Men reclaim their passive, nurturing, and contemplative "feminine side." We literally X-Over and pass each other like ships in the sea of mid-life. Friedan argued that the female advantage comes as older women enjoy integrating masculine values, which our culture legitimizes. The male disadvantage of integrating feminine values in older age is that it is viewed as a crisis, illness, or disengagement that precedes death. Again, keep in mind Friedan's book was published in 1993. Things have changed—but not entirely, especially for older generations. I found her theories valid at the time and more dated today. But these remnants of past cultural norms are still relevant for many baby boomers.

Aging and Discontinuity Theory

Do changes that take place in women's roles over a lifetime account for their greater flexibility and resilience in age?

As the theory goes, women experience many more role changes in the life course than do their male counterparts, for example, student, mother, empty nester, second career, widowhood (70% more likely to lose spouse). Women spent on average 11.5 years out of the workforce as compared to men at 1.3 years. The argument was that women become more accustomed to change and the impermanence of life, and that ability is a longevity advantage for successful aging. Men had fewer role changes, and in fact, retirement for men has been called the "role-less role." They are less equipped to handle the changes brought on by the aging process. Studies have shown men's suicide rates are higher in old age (Conejero, I., Olié, E., Courtet, P., Calati, R.). Here, too, old cultural norms are changing, but for many boomers they still apply.

Regardless of whether you embrace Friedan's theories or find them outdated, the fact is, aging to advanced ages (oldest-old 85+) is mainly a women's issue because of longevity advantages. Whatever the contributing causes, this should get women thinking about their future goals and aspirations. Successful aging does not mean postponing aging, and opportunities for older women are rapidly growing. I began talking about a feminized gerontocracy in the early to mid-1990s. Others also raised the topic more recently; for example, Joseph Coughlin, director of MIT's Age Lab, was questioned in a Market Watch interview from 2017.

MarketWatch: *Can you expand on "the future is female" comment? Women have not always been considered for such a role—why now?*

Coughlin: *They were not just marginalized—they were invisible. Female consumers today have more education in all fields except engineering, and that is worldwide. That makes her a dedicated researcher. Entrepreneurialism is a new women's movement—women have startups employing Americans equal to large corporations. And while she is doing all that, she remains the caregiver, not just to her own children but to her parents. She's influencing the majority of auto decisions; she understands what the needs and wants are in the population. Women are starting companies about downsizing services to clean up houses and services to provide care in homes — they see the problems and the opportunities (found 1/10/21 at https://agelab.mit.edu/news/older-women-will-soon-rule-world-joe-coughlin-says-marketwatch-interview).*

Further, in an interview on *TODAY*, Coughlin reports:

'One of the greatest under-appreciated sources of innovation and new business may, in fact, be women over 50 with new ideas, lots of life ahead of them and with the verve to get it done.' A woman is the chief consumer officer of the house. She's the one who knows what groceries are bought, what bills are being paid, how that house actually works. Most car purchases are directly influenced or done by women. If they're luxury cars, the numbers go up even more. Home improvement is directed by the woman. Probably most striking is that 80-90 cents on the dollar of every healthcare decision is made by a woman. Because of all these factors, she is likely to be the person who is closest to understanding what the new jobs and the opportunities of living longer, better are going to be (today.com/health/older-women-will-rule-world-we-live-longer).

She believed she could, so she did.

—R.S. GREY, SCORING WILDER

Bonnie Brasure

When Joseph Coughlin talks about women over fifty who have the nerve to get it done, he is talking about women like my friend Bonnie Brasure. Bonnie, amid an **economic recession,** dared to open a small walk-up bakery. She was freshly divorced and needed to make some changes—so she took the proverbial leap of faith and became a **solo entrepreneur** (with some baking help from her mother, Sally). Stop and re-read those first three sentences.

Think about that for a moment, focus on the bold words, and imagine yourself in that scenario. She did not choose the path of least resistance. Through a breakup, recession, business takeover, remodeling a shop space, and countless other tasks, despite it all, the bakery was a success. The clientele grew so quickly it soon became evident the business space was not large enough.

Bonnie purchased a vintage clothing space next door and knocked down the common wall. The remodeling was challenging, as she kept the business open during the process. Like paving a highway in traffic without closing it down . . . the show must go on. The private victories which precede the public victories are known only to those on the field, in the trenches.

Meeting obstacle after obstacle with fierce determination, from contractors with varying senses of urgency, equipment failures, budget overruns, time delays, and setting up staffing as well as choosing décor, and dealing with city permits/red tape, Bonnie came out the other side victorious! "The Bleu Door Plus" restaurant opened, and, like the walk-up, it became an instant success.

After a period of consecutive successful years, things got even more challenging. The pandemic threw a wrench in the batter, health issues with her mother, Sally, and even her own (this kind of work takes its toll physically and mentally) but she persisted. She adjusted to a constantly changing landscape while juggling staffing challenges, public health requirements, and a home remodeling!

Bonnie's story is nothing short of heroic, and she is not alone. According to the article, "17 Women-Owned Business Stats You Need to Know," the US has 12.3 million women-owned businesses, and they generate $1.8 trillion a year. Further, 40% of U.S. businesses are women-owned, and women started 1,821 new businesses every day in 2020. It is also notable that 64% of women-owned new companies were started by women of color in the same year. The reasons vary from choice to necessity, but these are remarkable statistics and a testament to the rising power of determined women in the economy. I have been privileged to witness Bonnie's journey—and so many others like her who are creating jobs, paying taxes, and making local communities richer for their efforts.

One day, Bonnie invited me into her hollowed-out shell of a space that was soon to become her vision of a restaurant. She shared her plans as her voice echoed off the empty concrete walls and her dreams penetrated the space. She is a force of nature and inspiring to be around. I saw her vision and formulated some thoughts I wanted to share with her as I left. Below are those thoughts.

To Bonnie,

Let me begin by expressing to you that Julie (author's note: my wife) and I consider you a friend. You're one of the most courageous people we've ever met; your path is not the path of least resistance. . . . Having said this, I'd like you to consider a few points to ponder in these days of sleepless nights and overcoming Titanic obstacles to make Bleu Door+ a reality.

Point 1

Think of the jobs your efforts have created for others. Because of this, young people are getting valuable on-the-job experience, and some day, they too may become inspired to be entrepreneurs. Also, the wages earned are going to help feed families, pay for school, and fuel others' dreams.

Point 2

You have created a community space to be enjoyed by many. The new place will be an environment where people will meet on first dates, celebrate life events, de-stress from work, and feel a part of a vibrant neighborhood.

Point 3

Bleu Door is a place that you can count on for "small indulgences" that add quality to life; do not underestimate the significance of this.

Point 4

The "ripple" effect for good is something you will never fully realize when you step out of a comfort zone and do something significant, as you have done. The special-order birthday cake hand-carried to a mother in Madison, Wisconsin, the doggie treats at the end of a walk, the peanut butter cookie secretly and lovingly packed into a lunch box. All these things are made possible by your vision and determination.

Your efforts are not lost on me,

Patrick

In Her Own Words

My Journey

When I was a little girl, my mom would take me grocery shopping so I could buy boxes of cake mixes with my allowance. I loved adding things to the mix to see what effect my additions had made. Often, the center of the cake bubbled up, or the outer edges were over-baked, but I always loved seeing the smiles it put on my parent's face when they tried my latest creation. I can't express in words how proud I am of this little bakery and how appreciative I am for all the support along the way. When my mother, Sally, comes to visit, she works alongside me making all kinds of fun desserts and now asks me, "Can I lick the spoon?" Our sourdough starter is named "Mustang Sally" to remind me where it all began—with my mom, in the kitchen, with a box of yellow cake mix. *I love you, Mom!*

So how did I go from experimenting in my mom's kitchen to owning and operating my own restaurant? I decided to attend the New England Culinary Institute in Vermont to further my culinary career and, while there, rediscovered my passion for baking and pastries. After graduation, I had the opportunity to be a chef on private yachts in the Eastern U.S. and the Caribbean. This was an adventure, both personally and professionally, and I gained a new excitement for different cuisines. In 1993, I came on to the Portland restaurant scene, starting at Ron Paul Catering and Charcuterie. I spent years working in all aspects of the restaurant world, including chef, manager, and supplier. Sweet treats remained my passion, and in 2007, I created Brownies from Heaven, winning many awards for my unique creations.

In 2011, I leaped at the chance to open a small bakery and the Bleu Door Bakery was born! This gave me the opportunity to expand from just brownies to the items that I made with my mom back in her kitchen when I was a child, as well as the varied and delectable confections I experienced during my travels. I took another leap in 2015 and expanded the business to include a café, with a larger and more diverse menu. The support that I received from the local community has been incredible and humbling. I

> believe in supporting local and I am thrilled to be operating my dream business in Vancouver!
>
> —BONNIE BRASURE

Bonnie's website: bleudoorbakery.com

Bonnie is an example of a woman-owned business that has become influential in the community and is making a difference to the local economy. The evidence is mounting for the feminized gerontocracy locally, nationally, and globally.

In an article from January 2019 in The New York Times, "I Am (An Older) Woman. Hear Me Roar," author Jessica Bennett spotlights older women in the news who are in positions of newly found power. These range from Nancy Pelosi, former Speaker of the House of Representatives, actor Glenn Close, who won a Golden Globe award for best actress in 2019, Maxine Waters, the first African American woman to lead the Financial Services Committee, to Susan Zirinsky, former head of CBS News and now president of See It Now Studios.

Older women in positions of influence are trending, and the article mentions there are more women over 50 in the United States than in any other time in history. Further, they are healthier, work longer, and have more income than previous generations. Bennett reports working longer is more common among women with higher education and savings—while those not working are more likely to have poor health, low savings, and depend on Social Security.

Women who are creating the feminized gerontocracy are ubiquitous. They are transforming every aspect of human endeavor from baking to banking. I have listed just a sampling of women and their chosen fields with a quote from each. Their statements are especially telling, and they express the desire to come from a place of contribution, which is lacking in many current leadership roles.

. . .

BANKING – CHRISTINE LAGARDE

Christine Lagarde is a lawyer by background and has practiced law for twenty years with the international law firm Baker McKenzie. In 1999, she became their global chairman. In 2005, she joined the French government as a trade secretary. Two years later, she became the first woman to hold the post of Finance and Economy Minister of a G7 country. Between 2011 and 2019, she was the first woman managing director of the International Monetary Fund (IMF). Since November 2019, she is the president of the European Central Bank. July 2016, she was re-elected for a five-year term. She is also a member of the Board of Trustees, World Economic Forum.

The financial industry is a service industry. It should serve others before it serves itself.

—CHRISTINE LAGARDE

GLOBAL CRISIS MANAGEMENT – JUDY A. SMITH

Judy A. Smith is an American crisis manager, lawyer, author, and television producer. She is known as the founder, president, and CEO of the crisis management firm Smith & Company. Her work in crisis management is the inspiration for the ABC television series *Scandal*. Best known in media circles as the "Fixer," Judy Smith is a world-renowned Crisis Management Expert and entrepreneur who serves as Founder and CEO of Smith & Company, a strategic advisory firm considered one of the top crisis firms in the world (judysmith.com). She also assists in public policy work on issues like the housing crisis and education. It is well established that when a job is handed over to her, consider it handled. Her mantra is: *Trust your gut. Follow your instincts. Push your boundaries.*

I wanted to be different, and I wanted to make a difference.

—JUDY A. SMITH, AUTHOR OF *GOOD SELF, BAD SELF: HOW TO BOUNCE BACK FROM A PERSONAL CRISIS*

SCIENCE – ÖZLEM TÜRECI

Özlem Türeci is co-founder of the biotechnology company BioNTech, and not just a scientist but also a physician, an entrepreneur, and a leader in the global health sector. In 2020, her company developed the first approved RNA-based vaccine against COVID-19, which came as a much-needed moment of hope in a year of unprecedented crisis. Over 1,300 people from over sixty countries currently work at BioNTech, and more than half of them are women. Türeci says researchers should focus on the things they want to change and the problems they want to solve, thinking broader and dreaming big (unwomen.org).

Inspiring people is part of the job.

—ÖZLEM TÜRECI

LEADERSHIP – JANET YELLEN

Janet Yellen is an award-winning economist and the first woman to head the Federal Reserve of the United States. Yellen is a graduate of Yale and Brown, and President Obama once offered her high praise. "She's a proven leader, and she's tough—not just because she's from Brooklyn," he quipped, as he nominated her Federal Chair in 2013 (harpersbazaar.com). Yellen, along with Marilynn Malerba, the first Native American to serve as U.S. treasurer, now have their signatures on U.S. currency.

Yankee Stadium is a natural venue for another lesson: You won't succeed all the time. Even Ruth, Gehrig, and DiMaggio failed most of time when they stepped to the plate. Finding the right path in life, more often than not, involves some missteps.

—JANET YELLEN

POETRY – MARGE PIERCY

Marge Piercy is an American progressive activist and writer. She has written seventeen novels, including the classic *Woman on the Edge of*

Time, which won the Arthur C. Clarke Award, and *Gone to Soldiers*, a New York Times bestseller. Piercy's work is rooted in her Jewish heritage, communist social and political activism, and feminist ideals. A beautiful observation from her on living is, "Life is the first gift, love is the second, and understanding the third" (thoughtco.com/feminist-writer-marge-piercy).

> ***A strong woman is a woman determined to do something others are determined not to be done.***
>
> —MARGE PIERCY

FITNESS AND WELLNESS – WENDY IDA

Wendy Ida didn't think she'd live past age forty-three. As a domestic violence survivor, Ida escaped her abusive marriage and the East coast to start a new life in California with her two young children. Noticing that many other Californians were physically active, Ida began exercising as a way to not only cope with her struggles but to set an example for her children as well. "When I went to the gym, a whole new world opened up for me," Ida says. "I still have goosebumps thinking about it. After a few weeks, other people noticed my body changing before I did." Ida lost over eighty pounds and made fitness her new career, leaving the world of corporate accounting behind.

When Ida turned fifty-seven, she entered her first bodybuilding competition. At sixty-eight, besides being a bestselling author, life coach, and television host, she is the winner of eight national bodybuilding and figure championships and the holder of two Guinness World Records in fitness. She knows the struggles older women face to become fit because she has lived them herself (everydayhealth.com/womens-health/women-over-age-who-inspire-wellness-healthy-aging).

The first thing you need to do is jump-start your brain. The more you sit, the more you want to sit. You have to put one foot in front of the other. You don't need any special equipment or outfit. Once I started moving my body, it changed my mind.

—WENDY IDA

Author of *Take Back Your Life: My No Nonsense Approach to Health, Fitness and Looking Good Naked! (wendyida.com)*

SOCIAL MEDIA INFLUENCER – JUDITH BOYD

Judith Boyd has always had a passion and flair for fashion. In her words, she describes a lifelong love of fashion as, "I spent most of my career working as a psychiatric nurse in an emergency setting. I also spent a period of time managing the care of head and spinal cord injuries. Choosing my outfits, which always included a hat, was a way to express myself creatively and as a form of meditation as I approached my day, which usually included extreme and painful stories told by interesting, traumatized people. Because of my love for style and headwear, I co-owned a hat shop in the 80s, and I sold vintage clothing in an antique mall and on consignment in the 90s and beyond. Currently, I enjoy creating ensembles from my collections of hats and vintage, primarily discovered at estate sales, thrift stores, and consignment shops."

When her husband, Nelson, was battling a rare form of terminal cancer in 2010, Boyd started her blog, "Style Crone." "He was my photographer," she says. "It was our project. It was such a devastating and painful time, and the blog was a source of levity." After her husband's passing, Boyd continued blogging and modeling on Instagram in his memory.

At age seventy-seven, she has more than 56,000 avid followers on Instagram and connects with fashion fans around the world. For Boyd, in addition to the relationships she has created with other enthusiasts, fashion continues to be an extension of her mindfulness and personal health. Her blog states, "*Welcome to Style Crone, dedicated to the older woman, in her most creative, outrageous, authentic, powerful, adventurous, funny, and proud era. Let's take back the word crone, to its original meaning, signifying a woman of a 'certain age' who embodies all her life's wisdom, knowledge, experience, and love"* (stylecrone.com/biography).

Each outfit is its own meditation. It involves all of my senses to find something that excites me. Wherever I travel, it's really exciting to meet new friends through Instagram or the blog. As we grow older, we become invisible, and there was no way that I was going to allow myself to become invisible.

—JUDITH BOYD

ENTERTAINMENT – DOLLY PARTON

Dolly Parton was born in Sevierville, Tennessee, the fourth of twelve children. Living in a one-room cabin, Dolly learned of her musical abilities early. The now-country icon began performing all over eastern Tennessee while still a child. In 1964, at eighteen, Parton moved to Nashville shortly after graduating high school. In Music City, the artist signed to Combine Publishing House and Monument Records. She quickly found success as a songwriter, penning hits such as Bill Phillips' "Put It Off Until Tomorrow" and Skeeter Davis' "Fuel to the Flame," among others.

In 1967, Parton released her debut album, *Hello, I'm Dolly*, and became a part of Porter Wagoner's weekly TV and touring show. She remained with Wagoner until 1974, when she left to work on her solo career. In response to their "breakup" and Wagoner's reported animosity toward her decision, Parton penned her hit single, "I Will Always Love You." The singer found success at radio, but it wasn't until her seventh album, 1971's *Joshua*, that Parton scored her first No. 1 hit, the disc's title track. She has become one of the most successful artists of any genre, selling more than one hundred million albums worldwide. In addition to her music career, Parton is also a successful actress (*9 to 5* and *Steel Magnolias*, among others), runs her Imagination Library, and, since 1986, has owned the Dollywood theme park in Pigeon Forge, TN (theboot.com/tags/dolly-parton/).

I want to go and go, and then drop dead in the middle of something I'm loving to do. And if that doesn't happen, if I wind up sitting in a wheelchair, at least I'll have my high heels on.

—DOLLY PARTON

Charity for Kids reading books: imaginationlibrary.com

POLITICS – KAMALA HARRIS, VICE PRESIDENT OF THE UNITED STATES

Kamala D. Harris is the Vice President of the United States of America and the first woman in this position. She was elected Vice President after a lifetime of public service, having been elected District Attorney of San Francisco, California Attorney General, and United States Senator. Vice President Harris was born in Oakland, California, to parents who emigrated from India and Jamaica. She graduated from Howard University and the University of California, Hastings College of Law (whitehouse.gov/administration/vice-president-harris).

My mother would look at me and she'd say, 'Kamala, you may be the first to do many things, but make sure you are not the last.'

—KAMALA HARRIS

RELIGION AND FAITH – SISTER JOAN CHITTISTER

Joan Chittister is one of the most influential religious and social leaders of our time. For fifty years, she has passionately advocated on behalf of peace, human rights, women's issues, and church renewal. A much sought-after speaker, counselor, and clear voice that bridges across all religions, she is also a bestselling author of more than sixty books, hundreds of articles, and an online column for the National Catholic Reporter. She has received numerous writing awards and honors for her work and is a noted international lecturer, as well as a former fellow at

St. Edmund's College, Cambridge University, England (joanchittister.org).

In addition to being an American Benedictine nun, theologian, author, and speaker, Chittister has also served as Benedictine prioress and Benedictine federation president, president of the Leadership Conference of Women Religious, and co-chair of the Global Peace Initiative of Women, a partner organization of the UN, facilitating a worldwide network of women peace builders. In 2019, Sister Joan was the featured guest of Oprah Winfrey on "Super Soul Sunday," about her recent book, *The Time is Now* (joanchittister.org).

Find the thing that stirs your heart, and make room for it.

—JOAN D. CHITTISTER

MEDICINE – BEVERLY MALONE

Beverly Malone, Ph.D., RN, FAAN, began her nursing career with a degree in nursing from the University of Cincinnati in 1970. She combined further study with clinical practice, a master's in psychiatric nursing, and received her doctorate in clinical psychology in 1981. Her career is a mix of policy, education, administration, and clinical practice. Dr. Malone has worked as a surgical staff nurse, clinical nurse specialist, director of nursing, and assistant administrator of nursing. During the 1980s, she was Dean of the School of Nursing at North Carolina Agricultural and Technical State University. In 1996, she was elected for two terms as President of the American Nurses Association (ANA), representing 180,000 nurses in the USA.

Dr. Malone became Deputy Assistant Secretary for Health within the US Department of Health and Human Services, the highest position held by any nurse in the US government (so far). She was general secretary of the Royal College of Nursing (RCN), the United Kingdom's largest professional union of nurses with over 390,000 members, from June 2001 to January 2007. Dr. Malone was also a member of the Higher Education Funding Council for England (HEFCE). She represented the RCN, the

European Federation of Nurses Associations (EFN), the Commonwealth Nurses Federation, and the International Council of Nurses with the RCN president. In February 2007, Dr. Malone took up her appointment as CEO of the National League for Nursing in New York. Dedicated to excellence in nursing, the NLN is the premier organization for nurse faculty and leaders in nursing education, offering faculty development, networking opportunities, testing and assessment, nursing research grants, and public policy initiatives to 38,500 individuals and 1,300 institutional members (LinkedIn.com/in/beverly-malone-phd-rn-faan).

Beverly Malone is one of the most powerful nursing leaders in the country. She learned the art of healing from the ground up. As a young girl in rural Kentucky, she helped her great-grandmother, the daughter of a slave, heal the people around her. Malone recalls picking locally grown medicinal plants for her great-grandmother in the wilds of the Kentucky prairie, helping her great-grandmother mix them to create powerful herbal medicines, and using them to help return the sick to good health. Inspired by her great-grandmother and her seemingly miraculous ability to heal, Malone developed a passion for health and health care (futureofnursingscholars.org/nurse-profile/beverly-malone).

I just wanted to do that thing that I saw her do so well.

—BEVERLY MALONE, ON HER GRANDMOTHER AS A HEALER

EDUCATION – SUSAN SOLOMON

Susan Solomon, Professor of Atmospheric Science, former Director, Environmental Solutions Initiative, is internationally recognized as a leader in atmospheric science, particularly for her insights in explaining the cause of the Antarctic ozone "hole." She and her colleagues have made important contributions to understanding chemistry/climate coupling, including leading research on the irreversibility of global warming linked to anthropogenic carbon dioxide emissions and the influence of the ozone hole on the climate of the southern hemisphere. Her current focus is on issues relating to both atmospheric chemistry and climate change. She developed an early interest in science while watching such shows as *The Undersea World of Jacques Cousteau*.

Susan has written *The Coldest March: Scott's Fatal Antarctic Expedition*, Yale University Press, 2002, and *Aeronomy of the Middle Atmosphere: Chemistry and Physics of the Stratosphere and Mesosphere*, 3rd Edition, Springer, 2005 (eapsweb.mit.edu/people/solos).

ENVIRONMENT – ISATOU CEESAY

Isatou Ceesay is called the "Queen of Recycling," she is a Gambian activist who started the recycling movement called One Plastic Bag. Ceesay educates citizens about recycling and reducing the amount of waste. She saw a problem and went to work on finding a solution. She founded a project that creates plastic yarn and forms bags out of upcycled waste. The project has dramatically reduced the amount of waste in her village and employs hundreds of West African women, providing them and their families with monthly revenue.

Although forced to drop out of school at a young age, Isatou Ceesay seldom lets anything stop her from learning or acting. She has worked for the U.S. Peace Corps office in Gambia, the Swedish organization Future in Our Hands, and consulted for development organizations. Her recycling project, which began in 1998 amidst much resistance and taunting, is still thriving today. In 2012, she was awarded a TIAW "Difference Maker" award in Washington, DC. She is humbled by the fact that there is a book about her and hopes it will inspire others to join her cause or be a change-maker in their communities (oneplasticbag.com).

Isatou was born in 1972 in a small village in Gambia. As a child and teenager, she used woven baskets to carry goods to and from the market. When her basket broke, she picked up a plastic bag and began to use it. She liked how strong and light it was. Other people in Gambia saw the same benefits in plastic bags. Soon, people started using the bags by the thousands. The problem was that they didn't reuse the bags. They simply threw them on the ground. In Africa, women throw the family's trash behind their homes, so plastic bags often go there, too.

Soon, the bags caused problems. During rainy weather, the bags were filled with water, attracting mosquitoes that spread disease. Goats and other livestock ate the bags and died. The plastic bags were a hazard to small children, and they made the landscape unsightly. When families burned the plastic bags for warmth and cooking, they breathed in the toxic fumes released by the burning plastic. Isatou had an idea. What if plastic bags could be used to weave useful products, such as purses, balls, or wallets? She figured out a way to cut the plastic bags into one long strip that could be woven. At that time, women in Gambia were not allowed to work. They were expected to take care of the home and family. At first, Isatou worked in secret. Slowly, she began sharing her work with other women who joined her. The women's efforts benefitted their families in several ways. They were able to sell their products, bringing much-needed money home, and they reduced the plastic waste. Isatou started the organization, the Njau Recycling and Income Generation Group. Over 100 women take part in the organization. They gather waste and bring it to a central location to be used by everyone (easyscienceforkids.com).

> ***People thought I was too young and that women couldn't be leaders. I took these things as challenges; they gave me more power. I didn't call out the problems—I called out solutions.***
>
> —ISATOU CEESAY

Miranda Paul wrote a children's book about her. *One Plastic Bag: Isatou Ceesay and the Recycling Women of the Gambia*, 2015.

ART – ARPITA SINGH

The standard-bearer for narrative art in India

Born in West Bengal in 1937, ten years before the Partition of India, Arpita Singh is now widely considered one of her country's premier contemporary artists. Her oil paintings and watercolors are renowned for the tantalizing stories they tell, often from a female perspective. "She's the standard-bearer for narrative art in India today—a narrative tradition that dates back centuries to miniature painting," explains Nishad Avari, Indian art specialist at Christie's in New York. "She's undoubtedly the standard-bearer for women artists in India, too" (christies.com/features/5-things-to-know-about-Arpita-Singh).

She is known to be a figurative artist and a modernist; her canvases have both a storyline and a carnival of images arranged in a curiously subversive manner. Her artistic approach can be described as an expedition without a destination. Her work reflects her background. She brings her inner vision of emotions to the art inspired by her own background and what she sees around the society that mainly affects women. Her works also include traditional Indian art forms and aesthetics, like miniaturist painting and different forms of folk art, employing them in her work regularly. Early paintings were mainly watercolors on paper. She would usually paint in black and white ink. By the 80s, she began painting Bengali folk with women as the focus. She would use vibrant colors rather restrainedly, and pinks and blues usually dominated her palette. Her paintings would show women doing daily work and following simple routines in their lives. Arpita would draw objects daily like trees, flowers, flower vases, animals, teapots, pillows, festoons, and flags, and show women surrounded by them. Child Bride with Swan (1985) and Girl Smoking Cigarette (1985) are examples of her protagonists leading uncomplicated lives. In the 90s, Arpita's painting style shifted to oil on canvas, but she continued to paint women-centric art. Many women's emotions became evident in her paintings: joy, sorrow, hope, and many more. She painted a series of paintings on the subject "Women with a Girl Child" in the last decade of the 20th century. Arpita would showcase problems like hatred, social injustice, etc., faced by a contemporary woman in her art. She would also paint around the ills related to a girl child in India.

In some of her paintings, the women appear nude, but her paintings do not have sexual overtones, rather, they reflect the women's vulnerability. Arpita's paintings spoke a lot about wars and situations of turmoil at the national and international level. She would draw objects like guns, knives, cars and planes, soldiers, killers, and corpses. India's former Prime Minister Indira Gandhi's assassination, the anti-Sikh riots of 1984, communal riots, and the Gulf War are some examples. Women would continue to find the center stage in her art and are shown at the receiving end. The White Chair (1983), The series on Ayesha Kidwai, Durga (1993), My Mother (1993), and A Dead Man on the Street: is It You, Krishna (1994) are some of her paintings echoing this mood (wikipedia.org/wiki/Arpita Singh).

In 2011, Singh was awarded the Padma Bhushan, one of the highest honors bestowed on civilians by the Indian state (christies.com/features/5-things-to-know-about-Arpita-Singh).

Her book is *Arpita Singh-Vadhera Art Gallery*, 2014.

"She is bestowed with unique artistic prowess that immaculately depicts the life of real women" (indianartideas.in/artist-detail/ArpitaSingh).

ARCHITECTURE – SUSANA TORRE

Susana Torre (born 1944) is an Argentine-born American architect, critic, and educator, based in New York City (1968–2008) and in Carboneras, Almeria, Spain (since 2009). Torre has developed a career that combined "theoretical concerns with the actual practice of building" and architectural and urban design with teaching and writing. Torre is well known for things such as her plan to restore Ellis Island that is in New York Harbor in 1981, her work on the Clark House in 1982, her renovation of Schermerhorn in 1985, her fire station in 1987, and receiving the Award of Excellence of Design from the Architectural Record. Torre was the first woman invited to design a building in Columbus, IN, "a town internationally known for its collection of buildings designed by prominent architects."

In 1977, Torre organized and curated the first major exhibition of American women architects and edited the book *Women in American Architecture: A Historical and Contemporary Perspective*. The exhibition opened at the Brooklyn Museum in 1977 and traveled across the United States and to the Netherlands. The exhibition and book of the same title, in which she edited and contributed three essays, pioneered work in this field. Torre was also a co-founder of *Heresies, A Feminist Journal on Art and Politics*; was a member of the editorial collectives of *Heresies 2: Patterns of Communication and Space*; and *Heresies 11: Making Room: Women in Architecture*. She served on the editorial board of Chrysalis between 1976-1978.

Torre has devoted much of her professional life to theorizing the relationship of buildings to their physical and cultural contexts and how feminist concerns, cultural, and regional identity can be expressed in architectural form and function. One of her buildings, "Firehouse #5 (finished in 1987), was the first firehouse designed specifically to integrate women in the firefighting force. The design, which eliminated dorm-style sleeping and promoted bonding in the kitchen rather than the locker room, was adopted nationwide. "While leaving the safety assumptions of the type intact, Torre's building has created a typological invention through her challenge of program assumptions based on gender." "It is a "rare example of how a feminist perspective can alter both the spatial organization, influenced by social conventions and the form of the building" (wikipedia.org/wiki/Susana Torre).

Architecture and planning have been reshaped by these feminist agendas in many areas: the transformation of the suburbs from barren and isolating environments for women and children (as described by Betty Friedan) into more vibrant and fulfilling communities; the legitimization of identity as a design paradigm, specifically in the acknowledgement of women's difference as expressed architecturally; the redesign of public spaces to make them universally accessible; and the development of new building types and the redefinitions of old ones. My contribution in this area was the redefinition of the fire station typology with Fire Station #5 in Columbus, Indiana. It was the first to replace the dorm as the place of bonding, where women firefighters would be seen as quasi-but-not-quite males, with the kitchen and the gym as environments in which women and men could

> ***see each other as equal, powerful, and capable of conviviality.***
>
> —SUSANA TORRE

NATIVE AMERICAN STUDIES – HENRIETTA MANN, EMERITUS PROFESSOR

Dr. Henrietta Mann is a Cheyenne enrolled with the Cheyenne-Arapaho Tribes, and she is the founding President of the Cheyenne and Arapaho Tribal College. Dr. Mann was the first individual to occupy the Endowed Chair in Native American Studies at Montana State University, Bozeman, where she is Professor Emeritus and continues to serve as Special Assistant to the President. For the greater part of twenty-eight years, Mann was employed at the University of Montana, Missoula, as director/Professor of Native American Studies. She also has taught at the University of California, Berkeley; Graduate School of Education at Harvard University; and Haskell Indian Nations University, in Lawrence, Kansas. In addition, Dr. Mann has served as the Director of the Office of Indian Education Programs/Deputy to the Assistant Secretary for [the Bureau of] Indian Affairs. She also was the National Coordinator of the American Indian Religious Freedom Act Coalition for the Association on American Indian Affairs.

In 1991, Rolling Stone Magazine named Dr. Mann as one of the ten leading professors in the nation. She was one of seven recipients of the state of Montana Governor's Humanities Award in 2001. She joined chairman Earl Old Person, of the Blackfeet Nation, in delivering the Montana Tribal Nations Address to the Joint Session of the Senate and House of the Montana 57th Legislative Assembly in February 2001. In 2008, she received the Lifetime Achievements Award from the National Indian Education Association. The University of New Mexico honored her with the 2008 Bernard S. Rodey Award for her leadership, vision, and inspirational guidance in Native American education. She has published a book, *Cheyenne and Arapaho Education: 1871-1982*. She has been an interviewee and consultant for several television and movie productions, including *In the White Man's Image, How the West Was Lost, Paha Sapa:*

Struggle for the Black Hills, *The West*, and *Last of the Dogmen*. Dr. Mann has lectured throughout the United States, including Hawaii, and in Mexico, Canada, Germany, Italy, New Zealand, the United Kingdom, Spain, The Netherlands, and Belgium.

(montana.edu/nativeamerican/katz_mann)

Native women continue to live, to give, to build, to dream into existence and to always be positive about whatever it is in which they're involved.

—DR. HENRIETTA MANN

PSYCHOLOGY – ESTHER PEREL

Psychotherapist and New York Times bestselling author Esther Perel is recognized as one of today's most insightful and original voices on modern relationships. Fluent in nine languages, she helms a therapy practice in New York City and serves as an organizational consultant for Fortune 500 companies worldwide. Her celebrated TED Talks have garnered over twenty million views, and her international bestseller *Mating in Captivity: Unlocking Erotic Intelligence* became a global phenomenon translated into twenty-five languages. Her newest book is the New York Times bestseller, *The State of Affairs: Rethinking Infidelity* (HarperCollins). Esther is also an executive producer and host of the popular podcast *Where Should We Begin*.

Esther Perel learned how to embrace life from her mother and father, both the sole survivors of their families from Nazi concentration camps. In her own words, "They wanted to embrace vibrancy and vitality—in the mystical sense of the word, the erotic. I owe them much of my perspective on life, as well as my belief in the power of will, the search for meaning, and the resilience of the human spirit. To me, there is a world of difference between 'not being dead' and 'being alive.' I owe this understanding to my parents" (estherperel.com).

Couples' therapy is probably the hardest type of therapy to be in and to practice; and I have been on both sides. In my work as a therapist, I see despair, entrenched patterns, loneliness in the presence of another, contempt, violence, lack of any physical touch; so many couples come to me way beyond their due date. The great thing about being a therapist is that I don't have to worry about ageism and boredom. It's not like keeping up with technology: As long as my brain works, I can practice until I drop—and I certainly intend to.

—ESTHER PEREL

MORE EXAMPLES OF MATURE FEMALE GLOBAL LEADERSHIP

Sahle-Work Zewde, president of Ethiopia, first woman to hold office

Angela Merkel, former Chancellor of Germany

Tsai Ing-Wen, Taiwan's first female President

Sheikh Hasina Wajed, the longest-serving prime minister of Bangladesh

Erna Solberg, Norwegian Prime Minister of Norway

Beata Maria Szydło, previously served as Prime Minister of Poland, now a member of the European Parliament

Saara Kuugongelwa-Amadhila, Prime Minister of Namibia

These are just a few of the new feminized gerontocracy leaders transforming our world. These women are at the pinnacles of influence with no intention of becoming invisible or *going gentle into that good night* (thank you, Dylan Thomas). I've included books and websites so you can follow each of their inspiring journeys.

Goodbye Myth: We Are now Entering the Era of The Feminized Gerontocracy.

Step 2

Employ the spirit of the grandmother hypothesis beyond your immediate tribe.

CHAPTER 3

Bag Lady Fears, Should I be Concerned?

MYTH: Aging will Cause You to Become a Bag Lady

According to the Merriam-Webster's dictionary, a *bag lady* is a homeless woman who roams the streets of a city, carrying her possessions and shopping bags.

> ***I got my own back.***
>
> —MAYA ANGELOU

As a listener and observer during my nursing and graduate school years plus over thirty-five years in the field of nursing alongside women of all ages, ethnic groups, and economic strata, there is not much concerning women's stories I have not heard. From new immigrant-single-mothers working as certified nursing assistants to privileged-pedigreed physicians, and everyone in between, witnessing women's stories of life's aspirations, victories, challenges, and defeats, has been part of my career. Acting as a sounding board for everything from budding new romances to the aging female body is a fascinating aspect of being a male in a female-dominated profession. The topics varied depending on the cohort age group, but what turned out to be a common theme on aging in these women's stories were financial worries.

The genuine fear of becoming destitute and ending up on the streets was often laughed about—but continued to be a source of nagging anxiety in some of their lives. This fear is "Bag Lady Syndrome" (BLS) first coined in the 1970s. It describes a feeling some middle-aged women have concerning ending up on the streets without a home, carrying all their worldly possessions in shopping bags.

I cannot recall the first time I heard the term "bag lady" but it has been in my consciousness for many years. As a child, I would see homeless women wearing everything they owned layered in multiple prints and textures—lacking perspective or insight. I felt sadness for them. The presence of homeless men wandering the parks and rail lines was a familiar backdrop to small-town living, but the sight of women on the streets was even more unsettling. Did they once have families? How did they end up like this? Where do they go at night?

I have often heard women's conversations turn to finances, and inevitably the bag lady term would be mentioned, followed by pensive chuckles. Most knew what that meant, and I often felt it elicited some level of anxiety that lingered after the conversations ended. The psychology literature shows that stress over time can lead to depression and drain the joy out of living—slowly eroding like a sandcastle at high tide.

For years now, a popular refrain from motivational gurus has been to use the word 'FEAR' as an acronym for False Evidence Appearing Real. It is clever and memorable in its simplicity, but like many platitudes, it lacks in applied substance. Fear is an emotion created in the mind, not always from false evidence. Sometimes, the evidence is unknown; other times, it is quite real. For some women, bag lady fears creep into their thinking from time to time, and no amount of happy talk will diminish the anxiety-inducing thoughts. But with enough awareness, facts, and action steps, it does not have to be anxiety-producing.

The causes for women ending up destitute on the streets are multifactorial, from early sexual abuse, substance abuse, physical abuse, mental health issues, societal gender/race bias, economic and other factors. It is helpful to identify and name the "fears" and then use empowering, actionable steps to confront them.

Lance Drucker, CEO and President of Drucker Wealth Management/Park Avenue, and author of *How to Avoid Bag Lady Syndrome [B.L.S.]: A Strong Woman's Guide to Financial Peace of Mind*, says bag lady syndrome is women's number one financial fear.

I'll tell you a story. I remember meeting with a middle-aged, affluent, successful fashion executive when I was starting out. I was out of my league; she had more money than I'd ever dealt with. And I said, 'What keeps you up at night?' And she said, 'I'm terrified about becoming the best-dressed bag lady in Manhattan. I spend everything I take in; I don't have a plan. If my paycheck stops, I could have nice stuff but nothing to show for it.' That stayed with me.

—LANCE DRUCKER

Women's Bag Lady Fears by the Numbers

According to the *Women, Money & Power* study from insurer Allianz Life, nearly half of all American women fear becoming a "bag lady."

Such concerns aren't limited to people who are struggling financially. Twenty-seven percent of women earning more than $200,000 per year share that fear. The study found that anxiety about ending up broke is consistent across all types of women, though highest for single respondents (56 percent); it's also a significant concern for divorced women (54 percent), widows (47 percent), and married women (43 percent).

—CBS MONEYWATCH, "HALF OF U.S. WOMEN FEAR BECOMING 'BAG LADIES'"

. . .

When I investigated the topic of "bag lady" I encountered the image above. It is revealing; your eye is drawn first to the center where the older woman is bent over, gathering her possessions. Next, look behind the yellow pole in the upper left corner of the photo at the young woman glancing at the scene. On her face (even with only half of her profile showing) appears to reside that fear described in the Allianz Life Study.

There are numerous articles and books aimed at women concerning the issue of how to avoid being destitute in old age. Mental illness and other organic/social causes aside, becoming a bag lady will remain a vague fear of many women, even when living in one of the wealthiest countries on Earth, awash in financial information. What can help alleviate those fears is to review what the contributing factors are and learn actionable insights to counter them. Let us explore the issues and uncover some steps to tackle "bag lady fears" once-and-for-all.

Overview: Women & Aging

According to the U.S. Census, one-third of baby boomers are single, divorced (gray divorce), widowed, or never married. These singles are disproportionately women. There are twenty-five million single women over age 45 in the U.S. and having this status can, in some cases, expose boomer women to vulnerabilities.

1. Economic—Gender Pay Gap

In the United States, more women than men live in poverty. According to U.S. Census Bureau data, of the 38.1 million people living in poverty in 2018, 56 percent—or 21.4 million—were women.

After working thirty years, women can have a 25-30 percent shortfall compared to male workers with the same savings and investing patterns. Much of this can be attributed to caregiving.

Women, more often than men, take on the role of family caregiver. According to the Caregiving in the U.S. 2020 report, published by the National Alliance for Caregiving and the AARP Public Policy Institute, 61 percent are female; 39% male. The term to describe an individual who cares for a loved one with a short-term or long-term physical and/or mental disability or illness is "informal caregiver" because they are unpaid, and most do not receive compensation. The average age of an informal caregiver is 49.4 years, and the caregiver household income breakdown is: 36% have a net income less than $50,000, 64% have a net income of $50,000 or more, and the average household income is $67,500.

Informal caregiving has an opportunity cost for women in the workplace: 33% decreased hours, 29% passed up promotions, training, or assignments, 20% went part time, 16% quit jobs (Masedo-Gutiérrez A. I., Swenson N.). This translates to lost wages, lower retirement income through decreased social security, decreased defined benefit-plan payments, and decreased contributions to defined contribution plans. Bottom line, women who live longer need a more sizable nest egg to cover future expenses than their shorter-lived male counterparts.

Further, from the Economic Policy Institute/Working Economics Blog, by Nina Banks, "Black women's labor market history reveals deep-seated race and gender discrimination," the author reports:

> *Black women's labor market position is the result of employer practices and government policies that disadvantaged black women rela-*

tive to white women and men. Negative representations of black womanhood have reinforced these discriminatory practices and policies. Since the era of slavery, the dominant view of black women has been that they should be workers, a view that contributed to their devaluation as mothers with caregiving needs at home. African American women's unique labor market history and current occupational status reflect these beliefs and practices.

Compared with other women in the United States, black women have always had the highest levels of labor market participation, regardless of age, marital status, or the presence of children at home. In 1880, 35.4 percent of married black women and 73.3 percent of single black women were in the labor force compared with only 7.3 percent of married white women and 23.8 percent of single white women. Black women's higher participation rates extended over their lifetimes, even after marriage, while white women typically left the labor force after marriage.

Because of discriminatory employer and government policies against black men and women, black mothers with school-age children have always been more likely to be in the labor force compared with other moms. Today, 78 percent of black moms with children are employed compared with an average of just 66 percent of white, Asian American, and Latina moms.

Although black women have a longer history of sustained employment compared with other women, in 2017, the median annual earnings for full-time year-round black women workers was just over $36,000—an amount 21 percent lower than that of white women, reflecting black women's disproportionate employment in low-wage service and minimum and sub-minimum wage jobs. Black families, however, are more reliant on women's incomes than other families are, since 80 percent of black mothers are breadwinners in their families.

Banks' statements provide a sobering context of black women's struggles with a lifetime of discrimination resulting in wage suppression, leaving them especially vulnerable later in life.

2. Health—The Failure of Our Success Equate to The Diseases of Old Age

A Duke University study of 5,888 people over sixty-five found:

A) Women suffer two and a half times greater rates of disabilities than men of the same age.

B) Women live longer with disabilities related to obesity and arthritis.

It has been said, *your biography becomes your biology,* so how you live determines how you age. The data translates into a loss of independence in old age.

For older black women, the diseases of old age have additional layers of complexity. They must also contend with the intersectionality of gender, race, age, and its impact on health. A lifetime of racism and discrimination makes for a different experience of physical aging.

Black women are disproportionately burdened by chronic conditions like anemia, cardiovascular disease (CVD), and obesity. Health outcomes do not occur independently of the social conditions in which they exist. The higher burden of these chronic conditions reflects the structural inequities within and outside the health system that Black women experience throughout the life course and contributes to the current crisis of maternal morbidity and mortality (Chinn, JJ. et al. 2021).

3. Social—Suburbia is the Architecture of Isolation

After World War II, the soldiers returned home to start young families; they flocked from the inner-city neighborhoods to the suburbs. Developers built large communities of detached single-family homes with large lots on cheap land, made accessible by highway systems. The birth of the American dream and consumerism began here. In 2000, 70 percent of the 35-and-over population in large metropolitan areas lived in suburbs (Brookings.edu). REALTOR Magazine reports, 66 percent of U.S. adults aged 55 and older say they expect to age in place, according to a new

Freddie Mac survey. This means most boomers who grew up in the 'burbs as kids are staying right where they are as aging adults.

These are auto-dependent, designed for a 190-pound soldier returning from WWII with a young family. Designers never dreamed people would grow old there. If you lived to be 65, you moved to Sun City or a nursing home! Boomer women are caring for their parents, who are struggling with isolation accessing services and transportation—especially in the pandemic era. This type of living arrangement is known as "Peter Pan housing" for people who never grow old. Yet, this is where most female baby boomers will be living into their later years.

A Strained System "Gray Divorce"

In 2020, a larger percentage of older men (70%) than older women (48%) were married (2020 Profile of Older Americans). Women 63 and older who went through a gray divorce experience a 27% poverty rate, which is nine times the rate of married couples of the same age (farzadlaw.com/divorce-statistics).

In addition, a recent report from AARP, which studied divorce at midlife and beyond, found that as life expectancies increase—so does the divorce rate—as boomers replace their more traditional elders as seniors. The staggering number of sites devoted to finding relationships for older adults is testimony to the sheer volume of single seniors. Respondents in the AARP study ages 40s through 60s found the upside of being single to be situations like having the house, and other things, the way they want them. But, with personal freedom and independence comes the fear of being alone, named by almost half (45 percent).

Other drawbacks cited: So-called "Elder Orphan" Issues

- Being on your own financially.
- No one to care for you when illness or disability occurs.
- Lack of a sexual relationship (personal touch).
- Further, the data showed that women are more likely than men to initiate midlife divorces—reasons cited were some forms of abuse, infidelity, or drugs/alcohol on the male partner's part.

Silver separation (gray divorce) refers to separation at midlife or beyond and usually means leaving a long-term marriage. Gray divorce is a recent phenomenon, and not well understood about the impact on older people. Divorced men and women who remarried tended to rate their present quality of life higher than those who remained single, but among those who stayed single, the women were most satisfied with being unattached. Insights into why that might be are on the blog, *The New Old Age* (NYT): *With Friends Aplenty, Many Widows Choose Singlehood.* Profiled in the post is Jane Austin, who, at 69 became a widow. Her brother warned her about the "casserole brigade" of old guys looking for a nurse or an insurance settlement. Austin didn't need the advice; one husband was enough. She would miss her husband but had plans to travel, take on a part-time career, and consult—none involved managing another man's domestic life.

> ***In 2020, a larger percentage of older men (70%) than older women (48%) were married.***
>
> —2020 PROFILE OF OLDER AMERICANS

While grieving the loss of a beloved spouse and often never fully recovering from it, studies show many women, like Ms. Austin, accept and embrace their new role as single women. *The Girls with the Grandmother Faces,* by Frances Weaver, describes this eloquently. I read the book years ago and found the story life-affirming. Weaver's autobiographical description of her life after becoming a widow has been an inspiration to many women. For example, this Amazon review is typical:

> ***If your children have moved out, if you have lost a spouse, if you have had any life changes but still have a zest for living, this is the book for you! The author presents a roadmap for not just continuing to live, but for living with new freedom to do the things you have always wanted and some things you may not have thought of yet. If you are over 55, read this book!***

—DONNA, 5 OUT OF 5 STARS

Most important to all of us is attitude. The sincere desire to lead a productive, interesting life at any age depends upon our own imagination and acceptance of new ideas.

—FRANCES WEAVER, *THE GIRLS WITH THE GRANDMOTHER FACES: A CELEBRATION OF LIFE'S POTENTIAL FOR THOSE OVER 55*

Becoming widowed, Weaver quickly learned that to make the most out of her remaining years, she would have to change her life dramatically. The advice offered is primarily directed at middle-class women, but the lessons can be applied to other women as well. Weaver notes, "Boredom is 99 percent self-inflicted." She stressed the importance of making oneself, rather than family or married friends, the focus of future activities. Her advice was to get involved in education and travel as ways to develop new interests.

Men who lose their wives, on the other hand, often do not fare quite as well. Old age, particularly for white males, equates to a loss of status and physical capacity, as well as a shrinking social network. Men start with the advantages of greater financial security, fewer chronic health issues, and fewer complaints of depression. But as they age, men end up with fewer friends, reduced community involvement, and less contact with family. Women's proven abilities to accept and embrace their new roles as single women, maintain community involvement, and keep strong family ties are all longevity strategies.

In an article titled, *The Tragedy of Gray Divorce—It's Not About Finances: Some Boast That Divorce Rates Are Plummeting. Not So for The Senior Set!* by Dennis Leap, (January 6, 2020, thetrumpet.com). The author notes:

> *Within just 10 months of its September 2018 article, Bloomberg published another article by Steverman: "Divorce Is Destroying the Finances of Americans Over 50." It spoke of the high-profile divorce*

> *of Amazon founder Jeff Bezos representing millions of Americans splitting up in middle age. "The rate of divorce after age 50 has doubled in the U.S. since 1990," Steverman wrote (emphasis added throughout). This is dire news with dreadful implications.*

Leap further reports:

> *In September 2018, U.S. News & World Report featured an article titled "Divorcing After 50: How Gray Divorce Affects Your Health." It was based on the findings of Susan Brown, a Bowling Green State University professor of sociology and co-director of the National Center for Family and Marriage Research. The article's quip states, "Divorce-related stress and depression can make existing health conditions worse and set up seniors for additional risks." In other words, divorce can lead to an early death. Brown's research shows that seniors over age 50 who divorce often experience a level of depression higher than a senior who loses a partner to death. In June 2019, Psychology Today published "Divorce Is a Risk Factor for Suicide, Especially for Men," showing that divorced men were nine times likelier to die by suicide compared to divorced women.*

Note: Nationally, 53.4 percent of people in same-sex married couples were female and 46.6 percent were male (census.gov). Data on divorce rates appear to be more robust in Europe. For example, in the Netherlands, the lesbian divorce rate is much higher than the divorce rate between men. The high rate of divorce among lesbian couples has been consistent since 2016. Two years after same-sex marriage was legalized in the United Kingdom, the number of same-sex marriages increased.

Dr. Dorsey Green, PhD, a couples therapist in Seattle and the co-author of the book, *Lesbian Couples: A Guide to Creating Healthy Relationships*, reports, "Many lesbians move quickly into permanent or cohabitating relationships. As a result, they have not had time to find out what the relationship is like after the first rush in the romantic stage. What should have been a dating or going steady relationship has become a marriage. Ending marriages is called a divorce; ending a dating relationship is called breaking up. We need more breakups." Dr. Green identified this fast track as her top hypothesis as to the cause of the high lesbian divorce rate that appears in every country with marriage equality (where data is available).

The country with the most information is the Netherlands, the first country to legalize same-sex marriage in 2001. Thirty percent of female couples married there in 2005 were divorced in 2015, compared to 18 percent of straight couples and 15 percent of gay male couples (gomag.com).

In the Netherlands, lesbian women are often older on their wedding-day than heterosexual women. The average age of lesbian partners on their wedding-day (2015) is 39, versus 34 for their heterosexual counterparts.

Many women I have talked to over the years are securing their existing network of friends and family first (building "social capital"); then they may be looking for a man/woman who has done the same—or not (smile).

Aging in Place is a Woman's Financial Issue

For our discussion here, I define "aging in place" as a dynamic, self-determined process of safely living in a home environment INTER-dependently as you get older. Who lives alone in old age? Statistically, we know it is women; of those over sixty-five, 47 percent are female, and only 18 percent are male. Since 1970, that is a 96 percent increase for women, and only a 22 percent increase for men. Who ends up in skilled care facilities? According to the U.S. Bureau of the Census, slightly over 5 percent of the 65+ population are in nursing homes, assisted living, and congregate housing. Rates increase with age from 1.4 percent of the youngest-old to 24.5 percent of the oldest-old. It is usually women due to:

1. Longevity: women invariably represent a high percentage of the oldest old. For example, in the United States in 2000, some 67 percent of those above age 80 were women. Among centenarians, women accounted for 87 percent of the total.
2. Spend Down: lifetime savings are used up by caring for husbands in old age.
3. Lack of Informal Care: care provided by non-paid family members.

These vulnerabilities will strain public, private, and faith-based systems to the limits. Many boomer women do not have traditional family structures (not "well-daughter'd") and lack family support systems for their old age. These conditions will require some out-of-the-box thinking, especially for un-married boomer/gen-x women.

> ***Most elderly males have informal care; most elderly females do not.***
>
> —CYNTHIA M. TAEUBER

Women, Aging and Economics

Working in acute care for over twenty-five years, I have been on the care-giving end of older patients—mostly women, who live the longest. Women's longevity can be a mixed blessing, as there is a greater risk of an old age tempered with disability and isolation which can have economic consequences long-term. However, this does not have to be a given. Patricia Frame, a United States Air Force veteran and Wharton MBA, is an expert on the topic of economics and career planning, and she has some thoughts on the matter. Patricia authored an article, "Women and Aging: Unprepared and Unaware," that outlined the economics of being an aging female. Here are some key points:

- If you are 65 today and female, you have another 27-30 years expected life.
- If you're a married woman and both of you live to 65; you have a greater than 90 percent chance that at least one of you will live into your mid-90s.
- 27 percent of boomers have under $1,000 in retirement savings, and another quarter have less than $25,000 in all assets (excluding a house or defined benefit plan).

- The average woman has thirteen years of zero earnings under Social Security.
- Women still earn less than men on average.
- Women provide most of the caregiving.

Frame advises doing the math. She did, and in 2000, she sat down with a financial advisor and reviewed her retirement savings; she came away feeling quite good. She was on target for a sound retirement. Not the million-dollar-plus kind so many calculators say one needs, but a nice pot. But then the market tanked. And an entire decade of stagnation occurred as well as another market melt-down. And now she feels fortunate to have an account that is finally healthy again. Frame advises not to underestimate these kinds of scenarios, regardless of how unpleasant they are, realizing retirement savings can be discouraging to think about.

Did you know that most people have no idea that Medicare does not cover long-term care? And yet, on average, you can expect to need nearly 3.7 years of such assistance as a woman. This statistic is part of why so many women are providing care for elders and their children, often at the same time. Most caregivers for older people are, in fact, women. And caregivers report on average that they are spending twenty-one hours per week physically providing care. Over half of caregivers have had to give up vacations and social activities to do this. Over 40 percent have missed work, and most of these have had to take unpaid time off. And about 40 percent have had to use their savings to provide such care.

Do not give up! There are some actions you can take to create a better future for yourself and others.

Frame also mentioned that Fidelity recently released a study indicating an average retired couple, age 65 in 2022, may need approximately $315,000 saved (after tax) to cover health care expenses in retirement. Part of that is for routine costs not covered by Medicare, and part for long-term care. They also created a rule of thumb: aim to save at least 1x your salary by 30, 3x by 40, 6x by 50, 8x by 60, and 10x by 67, to help increase the odds that you will not outlive your savings in retirement.

What to do NOW

- Take care of your health. Women suffer from more chronic diseases, often because they are not caring for their health while caring for children and others. Additionally, over a third of retirees are forced to retire earlier than planned due to health problems.
- Learn about finances and do some financial planning. One resource you can use is, *Building Wealth: A Beginner's Guide* (dallasfed.org/~/media/microsites/cd/wealth/consumers). Currently, the Employee Benefit Research Institute reports that retirees draw their income from four sources. On average, retirees get 40 percent of their income from Social Security, 26 percent from continuing work, 20 percent from pensions or annuities, and 13 percent from other financial assets. What will your options be?
- Consider your family issues. What legal aspects do you need to address with parents or others who are under your care? With you and your partner?
- Consider your business issues. What impact does the need for retirement savings have? Do you offer and participate in such plans? Simple IRAs are easy for even small businesses to set up and offer. Solopreneurs can have IRAs, SEPs, and other plans, too. Can you offer any workplace or time flexibility? That appeals to many people but is also vital for caregivers.
- When moving, consideration of the services and public transportation available becomes critical. I think this has been a big driver in the rapid increase in older people buying units in my condo building—no maintenance, easy access if one has mobility issues, great hospitals in the area, and right on a bus route—in a city with some services for seniors. Many of the items critical in communities for seniors: sidewalks, good public transportation, local stores, and services, appeal to all ages. Educate yourself, pick the ones that matter to you, and voice your opinion to your elected representatives.

- Public policy issues include lack of retirement savings of many Americans, costs of health care, Medicare, community preparedness, and services for older people and caregivers. These have costs. And yet, do we want to go back to a time when so many elders were living in poverty?

Living Wills, Health Care Power of Attorney, and DNR

Knowledge about living wills, Health Care Power of Attorney, and DNR (Do Not Resuscitate) are essential for any woman's successful aging plan. Andrew M. Jaffe is an attorney at Law and a volunteer at a local hospice care center in Akron, Ohio. He limits his practice to E-Commerce and Internet Law (I am a client) and has written a handy guide about advanced health care directives. In his own words, Andrew explains why he did so:

> *Simply because every lawyer has a responsibility to perform services for the public good at no cost, I never want to give away my services in my chosen field. As I have a mother of advanced age, I decided to offer my 'pro bono' services. I volunteer at a local hospice care center to offer this same advice to families and patients at a very vulnerable moment in their lives. Therefore, please consider using this advice to create your advance health care directives before your family (or you) is in this vulnerable situation.*

Note: State laws control the form of the documents discussed below and they are sometimes called by different names. Most states have their standard acceptable forms online for you to download and fill in the blanks. These online forms also offer definitions and advice when you are filling in the forms. Finally, the forms will need to be notarized.

Living Wills

The purpose of a Living Will Declaration is to document your wish that life-sustaining treatment, including artificially or technologically supplied nutrition and hydration, be withheld, or withdrawn if you are unable to make informed medical decisions and you are in a terminal condition or a permanently unconscious state. This Living Will Declaration does not affect the responsibility of health care personnel to provide comfort care to you. Comfort care means any measure taken to diminish pain or discomfort but not to postpone death.

If you choose to limit any or all forms of life-sustaining treatment, including CPR, you have the legal right to so choose. A Living Will Declaration applies only to individuals in a terminal condition or a permanently unconscious state. If you wish to direct medical treatment in other circumstances, you should prepare a Health Care Power of Attorney. If you are in a terminal condition or a permanently unconscious state, the Living Will Declaration controls over a Health Care Power of Attorney.

Health Care Power of Attorney

The Health Care Power of Attorney allows you to appoint someone you trust, a family member or close friend, to make health care decisions for you if you lose the ability to make decisions yourself. By appointing a health care agent, you can make sure that health care providers follow your wishes. Your agent can also decide how your wishes apply as your medical condition changes. Hospitals, doctors, and other health care providers must follow your agent's decisions as if they were your own. You may give the person you select as your health care agent as little or as much authority as you want. You may allow your agent to make all health care decisions or only certain ones. You may also give your agent instructions that he or she must follow. This form or an attached form can also be used to document your wishes or instructions regarding organ and/or tissue donation.

When selecting your agent, I recommend you do three things in preparing these forms:

1. Make sure the person you have selected as your agent knows your wishes. I often suggest meeting with this person at least twice to discuss your wishes with them, and to make sure they understand what to do in any situation.

2. Further, if you are selecting someone who is out of the legal chain of command (e.g., spouse, children, or guardian) I urge you

in the strongest possible terms to tell your spouse or children that you have done this. I would suggest writing a letter or email to them to tell them you have made this choice because you do not want to burden them with the hard decisions that must sometimes be made when they are in a state of keen distress or sorrow.

For instance, what if you are unconscious, and the doctor wants to remove a limb? I, as a relative, would agonize over this decision and may not do what you would wish to have done. However, you will have discussed this situation with your agent, and they can make the decision you would have made without regard to anyone else's wishes.

3. That is why my third recommendation is so important. Be sure to choose someone of strong moral character who will not only do as you have discussed and directed but will not bow to the pressures of others present who think they know better. I have been through this process with a parent and made the decisions they wanted. While I allowed my siblings to weigh in with their opinions, in the end, it was my responsibility to look them in the eye and tell them I was doing as I was instructed to do. I had to stand up to their demands and take the actions I was instructed to do by my parent. I did as I was asked, and I never lost a moment's peace as I knew I had made the correct decision based on my conversations with my parent.

In most states, the Living Will supersedes the Health Care Power of Attorney. Why then is the Health Care Power of Attorney needed, you may ask? Because there are times when the situation at hand is not addressed in your Living Will. Expanding on the example I used above, suppose you have been in an automobile accident. You are in surgery, and the doctor comes out and says they have done everything they can to save your limb, but now the situation is either to remove the limb or you will die. Since you came into the hospital in a comma, and as you are under anesthetic, you cannot express your wishes.

Living Wills do not usually contemplate this situation and are mostly used in cases of long-term sickness (e.g., cancer.). Someone needs to make this decision immediately. Since you have discussed this possibility with your Health Care Power of Attorney agent, they will know what you want to be done, and they can decide for you. They can make this decision as you would have made it, even in the face of opposition from family members.

Do Not Resuscitate order (DNR)

> A DNR is a unique advanced directive in that you cannot make it in advance. A DNR can only be signed by your doctor after you have entered a health care situation that is terminal (e.g., cancer). If you are still awake and rational, you may tell your doctor to sign a DNR. If you are not rational or in a coma, then your Health Care Power of Attorney agent can ask the doctor to sign a DNR order. This is another reason you want both a Living Will and a Health Care Power of Attorney. If you have questions regarding Advance Directives, please contact a local attorney for guidance and advice.
>
> —ANDREW M. JAFFE, ATTORNEY AT LAW (LAWYERJAFFE.COM)

Financial Literacy

"Eighty percent of Older Women Can't Pass This Financial Literacy Quiz"

This shocking title to an article I read on cnbc.com by Rachel Cao disturbed me. Cao reports, according to Joan Ann Natola, a managing partner at Element Financial Group, when working with clients, she finds that women tend to be more risk-averse and have a more conservative portfolio when it comes to investing. Still, it does not necessarily indicate a lack of financial savviness. "When asked a question, a woman will be more likely to say, 'I don't know,' but a man will not say that," Natola said. "Women need more holistic conversations, while men will tend to make a financial decision, even without all the answers."

As for the quiz, women did show lower literacy rates in ten out of twelve knowledge categories, but they did just as well or better than men in topics of Medicare, insurance planning, and paying for long-term care expenses. You can take this quiz here:

resesarch.net/r/2020-retirement-income-survey

The article also brings up additional points about older women who are single or have lost a spouse. They rely more on social security and have higher long-term care expenses. The message was a reoccurring theme; women's longevity calls for greater financial literacy because you will be living longer in retirement.

7 Action Steps to Help Relieve Bag Lady Fears

1. Take Control

Acting can change the way you control your finances. By making a simple budget, cutting back on spending, and increasing the amount you save each month, you will *feel* as though you're back in the driver's seat of your money and your life.

If your standard of living is going to drop, you've got to pay real close attention to things like your credit rating and staying ahead of unsecured debt such as credit cards.... That will be worth its weight in gold down the road.

—KERRY HANNON

2. Take Care of Yourself

It has been said, "You can take the time to be healthy—or you will need to take the time to be sick." One is very empowering; the other is disempowering; this, too, is a choice. Your body needs to be available to you to do your mission in life, take good care of it. Small indulgences can go a long way; walk the dog mindfully (not preoccupied with the cell phone), a hot bath, return to simple pleasures like a bike ride, cut wildflowers, call on an old friend, re-read a favorite book, commit to a weekly phone-free hour strolling the weekend farmers' market, or a nature walkabout. What pleased you in the past? Revisit it.

3. Reassert Self-reliance

Christine Walsh, CPC, ACC, ELI-MP, author of *The 5 Elements of Financial Freedom,* encourages you to take responsibility for how you think and feel. Do not blame others for your thought processes.

Walsh says to take responsibility for how you think and feel. She tells her clients, "You need to hear this!" For women with bag lady fears, you most likely also think someone else is to blame for putting you in that possible thought process. Walsh reports that blaming others for our thoughts provides fear because underneath it all, your power is taken away and goes into the hands of the person(s) you are blaming. She encourages her clients to take responsibility, not to blame others, concerning their finances—which returns the power to you. This builds self-trust, which moves you forward toward your desires and away from fears. Taking responsibility will take vigilance, she warns, but imagine the payoff to your business and your income when your life is completely in your hands. Further, she confirms that you have the power to change it all—complete freedom is the next benefit after that.

During the recession of 2008, I discovered that all the financial education I had been through would have never prepared me for the financial losses I took during that time. That was when I declared one day, enough is enough. I am no longer going to allow money to control me!

—CHRISTINE WALSH

4. Avoid Regrets

Elizabeth Revenko, a senior financial planner with Mosaic Financial Partners, says everyone has a unique tolerance for risk, and exercising caution is smart. She also notes, "being overly conservative due to irrational fears of losing it all can leave you with regrets about missed opportunities. This can apply to more than just investments, and perhaps in the opposite way of what you might expect." Further, Revenko gives an example of a woman who realized her fear caused her to save more than she needed to. She finally took vacations and spent money on herself. She felt happy and confident in her new spending/saving balance.

5. Do Not Go It Alone

You may not be an expert or have an interest in finances, and it is wise to ask for help. Hire a coach or financial advisor to get you back on track, or to get you started. Having support from friends, family, and even professionals can make it easier to manage your finances and get you unstuck.

6. Cultivate Connections

It is called ***social capital,*** and women are much more adept at building relationships than men, especially as we age in the era of COVID that may look different than in the past. Supportive networks of family, friends, and professionals can cultivate a feeling of security and control in your world. Zoom is now a safe way to connect, as is socially distancing with masks outside. The key is to commit to consistent interaction with others safely and mindfully.

7. Start a Side Hustle

Starting a side hustle is yet another way to empower yourself, particularly if you are an older woman. There is a saying by Oretta Norris, from @happywoca-community, with this message: ***COMBAT AGEISM, START A BUSINESS***. An affirming message and spot on! Nick Loper is the creator of sidehustle.com (non-affiliate), and I follow his work. He gives five reasons to start a side hustle:

- Earn more money
- Pay off debt
- Learn new skills
- Use free time more productively
- Escape the rat race

This author would like to add . . .

- Hedge against bag lady fears

Summary

"It's not something either of us wants to think about, so we don't." That quote came from an article in the Wall Street Journal (September 24, 2018) written by Maddy Dychtwald, author and co-founder of Age Wave, a think tank on aging issues. The article's title was *Aging Boomers Aren't Financially Prepared for Widowhood* and is a sobering account of the widowing of America. That response came from a woman in a focus group, and my guess would be that it is quite common. Three-quarters of the surveyed married couples said they would not be financially prepared for retirement if their spouse passed away. Here is the kicker: most widows and widowers say they did not have a financial plan in place for what would happen if they became widowed.

You want to curl up in a ball and have somebody else make all the decisions for you. But this is the worst time to do that. You need to force yourself to make your own decisions.

—KERRY HANNON

Of the surveyed widows and widowers in the study, 64 percent who had not planned for their futures felt burdened by worries about supporting themselves financially while dealing with their immense grief. Their study also showed that the problem was particularly pronounced among women. According to the U.S. Census Bureau, there are twenty million widowed individuals in America today, most (78%) of whom are women. Further, the widows said one of the biggest challenges they faced was making financial decisions on their own, often for the first time or the first time in many years. A mere 14 percent say they were making financial decisions alone before their spouse died.

Maddy Dychtwald ended the article on a bright note:

Over time, most widows and widowers (77%) say they discover an

> *inner courage and resiliency they never knew they had. They are forced to jump into complex financial matters from the start of their journey and adjust to making their own financial decisions. In fact, most widows and widowers (72%) say they now consider themselves more financially savvy than other people their age. That is empowering.*

Ask any good architect and she will tell you things begin first in the mind—then in the physical. Freedom from bag lady fears (BLF) can start with controlling your thoughts and managing expectations. Taking simple steps like creating a plan, acting, remaining focused, cultivating the community you trust, committing to your wellbeing, and being honest with yourself about who oversees your money, will go a long way to relieving bag lady fears. Note all these steps are verbs (actions). Tony Robbins says, "Motion equals emotion." Taking decisive action calms the mind.

> ***We can aspire to greatness in every part of our lives simply by understanding, and using, money to pave the path.***
>
> —LYNN S. EVANS, *POWER OF THE PURSE: FEAR-FREE FINANCES FOR BABY-BOOMER WOMEN*

Final entrepreneurial thought

Working longer can be a longevity strategy for many older women, given the right circumstances and opportunities. One such growth area is to keep older adults in the homes they love and out of institutional care centers. The COVID pandemic has caused a sense of urgency in finding solutions to this societal need. If you want a *big* opportunity, find a big problem—aging in place for women is potentially both. I feel women are particularly suited to lead the way in serving this huge market trend of female longevity and living in the suburbs. The overwhelming majority of older adults prefer aging in place and remaining in their communities.

The data shows that most Americans over 55 are not in nursing homes or other institutions. The vast majority (80%) of older people receiving assistance, including many with several functional limitations, live in private homes in the community (caregiver.org/resource/selected-long-term-care-statistics).

The young children of the WWII generation who grew up in suburbia are now turning 65 at a clip of 10,000/day; and will do so for the next sixteen plus years! Most of this demographic transition, as previously mentioned in chapter 3, will occur in the suburbs. In 2016, the oldest boomers turned seventy and the youngest, fifty-two. By 2035, there will be seventy-seven million Americans aged sixty-five and over, up from about forty-eight million in 2015. Nearly two-thirds of boomers in metropolitan areas lived in the suburbs in 2014, according to a pbs.org report. Suburban living still remains the choice of most boomers, according to a recent study by National Association of Home Builders (NAHB) economists.

The bottom line is that most baby boomers will live in either small towns, rural areas, or suburbia. What was once favored for its "get-away" location from big city metropolises and hassles now can be a disaster for aging boomers. This "architecture of isolation" is auto-dependent; next is the built environment, which it is youth-dependent. Both conditions are big problems, offshore brewing, for aging boomers who, research shows, are staying put. And according to AARP, four million women 50+ live in households with at least two females 50+ and are house sharing to meet the challenges.

The aging population in general, and aging boomer women precisely (niche), will provide an unlimited opportunity for savvy-trend-aware entrepreneurs, particularly women who know what other women want and need. Goods and services will have to get to these women where they are—in the 'burbs. Who better to provide it than women starting encore careers (the X-Over) who have helped their parents with aging in place? They have earned what I call the "burden of insight" that only comes with maturity and experience. This changing landscape of domestic living will present an unprecedented opportunity for women helping women, which will have a ripple effect for future generations.

Goodbye Myth: Greater financial literacy and starting a side hustle can help end bag lady fears.

Step 3

Take initiative to become more financially literate and start a side hustle business.

Image by Oretta Norris @happywoca

Suggested Resources

Kerry Hannon is a workplace futurist and strategist on career transitions, entrepreneurship, personal finance, and retirement. She is a frequent TV, radio and podcast commentator and is a sought-after keynote speaker. Kerry is also currently a senior columnist for Yahoo Finance and an on-air expert.

(KerryHannon.com) *Great Pajama Jobs: Your Complete Guide to Working from Home, Never Too Old to Get Rich: The Entrepreneur's Guide to Starting a Business Mid-Life.*

Legal Services for Older Americans Program/found: acl.gov/programs/legal-help/legal-services-elderly-program.

Lynn Evans, *Power of the Purse: Fear-free Finances for Baby Boomer Women*.

Maddydychtwald.com for information on *Women, Aging, and Money.*

Medicare.gov and mymoney.gov.

Nerdwallet is a solid resource for small business ideas for women. See article: nerdwallet.com/article/small-business/business-ideas-for-women.

Side Hustle: sidehustlenation.com/ideas (advantage is potentially low startup costs and your identity can be kept private).

Women-Owned Businesses: Statistics and Overview (2021)

1. The US has 12.3 million women-owned businesses.
2. US women-owned businesses generate $1.8 trillion a year.
3. 40% of US businesses are women-owned.
4. Women started 1,821 net new businesses every day last year.
5. 64% of new women-owned businesses were started by women of color last year.
6. Latina women-owned businesses grew over 87% (fundera.com).

Steps to Reduce Poverty Among Women

Lifting women out of poverty requires various robust policy solutions that will ensure women's long-term economic security.

These include:

- Closing the gender wage gap
- Closing the gender and racial wealth gaps
- Raising the minimum wage and eliminating the sub-minimum wages for tipped and disabled workers
- Ensuring access to work-family policies
- Reauthorizing and expanding Violence Against Women Act
- Expanding access to unemployment insurance
- Strengthening SNAP and WIC
- Protecting and expanding Medicaid coverage
- Improving tax credits
- Fortifying and enhancing Social Security

- Reforming Temporary Assistance for Needy Families TANF
- Reforming asset limits in the Supplemental Security Income (SSI) program, which provides monthly cash assistance to nearly 8 million older and disabled people with very low incomes.

(americanprogress.org/issues/women/reports/2020/08/03/488536/basic-facts-women-poverty/)

Peer coaching service for women looking to accelerate their professional and personal growth.

I've done a lot of great stuff. Through it all, I've had one goal: A world in which women's gifts and voices are fully harnessed for the benefit of us all.

—TIFFANY DUFU, *THE FOUNDER & CEO OF THE CRU*

thecru.com
Because *Every Woman Needs One.*

CHAPTER 4

Aging in Place for The Love of Home

MYTH: Aging in Place Means Independence

> ***Home is the nicest word there is.***
>
> —LAURA INGALLS WILDER

I BELIEVE THREE THINGS ABOUT AGING IN PLACE:

1. Shelter is at the core of what it means to be human.

2. As Laura L. Carstensen, Ph.D., Founding Director of the Stanford Center on Longevity, said, "Our environments presume youth," therefore adaptation is required.

3. Aging in place is an ecosystem, a network of interactions between living beings and their environment controlled by internal factors (mind/body) and external factors (built environment, financial, support systems, and technology)—thus, to be more independent, you are going to have to be more INTER-dependent.

AARP surveyed its members, and eight out of ten favored staying at home over senior housing. Further, a study published in the Journal of the

American Geriatrics Society found that the challenges posed to older people during the COVID pandemic showed newfound resilience in some. Many seniors who were isolated in their homes increased how much trust they were able to place in themselves and their abilities; gerontologists call this "self-efficacy."

The authors of the study also noted, "Self-doubt is a part of human nature. COVID-19 restrictions forced older adults to experience the loss of in-person human interactions and overcome their self-doubt in managing social interactions. Older adults adapted to the challenges of isolated aging in place and came ahead with higher self-efficacy." The results were positive and surprising.

Aging in place is a dynamic, self-determined process of living in a home environment safely and inter-dependently as you age. Let us some of these elements can help explain why home is the favored choice of so many.

Pleasures of Home

Home is the place where not just our functional needs are met (eating, sleeping, hygiene, reproduction) but our emotional ones as well. Home is the place where family histories are created, and memories weaved from experiences shared over a lifetime—making up the very fabric of our lives. These significant lived experiences create what environmental psychologists call "Place-Attachment," or the bond between person and place. It is what makes home such a hard place to leave both physically and mentally. I have often heard dementia patients, when placed in intuitional settings, repeat over and over; they want to "go home."

Familiar Environment

Home is the vessel that contains a lifetime of meaningful objects which are cherished and define who we are. They support our identity—and delight our senses. Aging is, in part, characterized by loss and change, which can erode identity, so this is essential. A familiar environment can be stabilizing and psychologically adaptive for older adults (Continuity of Self theory).

. . .

Inter-Dependently

Aging in place is often associated with independence, which appeals to most older adults. Therefore, the polls frequently report such high numbers of seniors/boomers favoring home over custodial living environments. But aging in place is not done in isolation; without a network of support such as transportation, affordable housing, informal care/family, and increasingly technology, the prospects can be daunting. Independence occurs within the context of "inter-dependent" support.

These essential elements of aging in place are the emotional scaffolding to why the love of home is so strong. I recall hearing a story on the radio years ago of an older woman, widowed and alone. When asked about her life at this stage, she gracefully offered the interviewer a touching personal vignette. Many years ago, as a young mother, she and her husband scrimped and saved to purchase a dining room set made of the finest wood they could afford. This set was precious, something they had worked hard and saved for, and finally brought home to the new family.

One day, the young mother (now the older woman) caught her child chewing on a chair leg. She pulled her daughter from the floor and scolded her for the visible teeth marks left in the wood; a careless child had forever damaged the set. As the years passed, the husband now long gone, and the children with families of their own, the older woman deeply misses those days when her family was together. She said she still has that same dining room set and will never part with it because those teeth marks are a bittersweet reminder of the life she once knew.

Place attachment is a strong preference for home caused by a bond developed over time through experiences. The teeth-marked chair leg has become a meaningful object supporting the older woman's identity and emotional connection to her past. Home is truly where the heart is, and a lovely example of why it is often life-affirming to remain home by choice.

The term "aging in place" has quickly become an increasingly familiar concept as baby boomers and millennials (oldest now turning 40) experience what it entails to keep elderly parents buoyant at home. Yet, most do nothing for their future selves in terms of home modification. However, there are exceptions, and these savvy folks usually have what I like to call "the burden of insight."

For example, the McSweeneys were profiled in the real estate section of the Washington Post. *'Aging-in-place' Features for the Home Gain Higher Profile as Baby Boomers Get Older*. Susie and Tom, like most people, have a strong desire to remain home by choice. Tom has arthritis, so despite their active lifestyle, when the McSweeneys built their Edgewater, Maryland, house in 2013, they asked their architect to incorporate "aging-in-place" features, including an elevator, wide doorways to accommodate a wheelchair, and a flat, no-step entryway into the design. "You have to be realistic," says Susie, who has a background in nursing. "You do not know what health issues you may develop as you get older, but you try to plan for it so that you can enjoy your later years."

Denial is not an option for someone with Susie's medical background. As a nurse, she knows from experience not to deny the realities of aging, which translates to planning for aging in place. Susie McSweeney has the right idea, plan for what you do not know about the future, and yes, you can do it in style too—just do it. Robert Frost had the right idea when he touted, "The afternoon knows what the morning never suspected."

I was asked recently in a video conversation why I call aging in place a "Crisis Buy?" I first encountered the term at an American Society on Aging Conference several years ago in Chicago. The then-acting president and CEO of Home Instead Senior Care gave a keynote that mentioned the term—it stuck. Rarely do older adults prepare for aging in place remodeling; as far back as 2011, a study conducted by the Office of Policy Development and Research's Multidisciplinary Research Team suggested that most U.S. homes are not fully accessible:

> *Although approximately one-third of units have Level 1 accessibility features (see below) and are potentially modifiable, fewer than 5 percent of units have the features needed to accommodate a person with moderate mobility difficulties. The percentage of wheelchair-accessible units is even smaller; less than 1 percent of all units are equipped with features that would allow a wheelchair user to live independently. The researchers did note that some households might*

be misreporting features, which could result in underreporting some accessibility elements.

Level 1: Potentially modifiable. *Homes in this category have some essential accessibility features but would not be fully accessible without further modifications, including the following:*

Stepless entry into the dwelling from the exterior. A bathroom on the entry-level or the presence of an elevator in the unit.
A bedroom on the entry-level or the presence of an elevator in the unit.

Level 2: Livable for individuals with moderate mobility difficulties. *Homes in this category have a minimum level of accessibility that allows a person with moderate mobility difficulties to live in the home. Level 2 homes include all the features of Level 1 homes as well as additional features, including the following:*

No steps between rooms or rails/grab bars along with all steps.
An accessible bathroom with grab bars.

Level 3: Wheelchair accessible. *Homes in this category have a minimum level of accessibility sufficient for a wheelchair user to live in the home and prepare their meals. This group includes all the features in levels 1 and 2 and additional features, including the following:*

Extra-wide doors or hallways.
No steps between rooms.
Door handles instead of doorknobs.
Sink handles or levers instead of knobs.
Wheelchair-accessible electrical switches, electrical outlets, and climate controls.
Wheelchair-accessible kitchen countertops, kitchen cabinets, and other kitchen features.

(Accessibility of America's Housing Stock: Analysis of the 2011 American Housing Survey).

Understanding the Language of aging in place will go a long way toward navigating the ins/outs of the process of creating an age-friendly home.

Aging in Place Literacy

There has been much talk about "Health Literacy" in the public discourse as of late. Which begs the question: What Is Health Literacy? The Patient Protection and Affordable Care Act of 2010, Title V, defined health literacy as the degree to which an individual can obtain, communicate, process, and understand basic health information and services to make appropriate health decisions. This concept is essential because we are drowning in information, yet New Health Rankings from the article, "Stunning new report ranks U.S. dead last in health care among richest countries—despite spending the most," by Joseph Guzman, Aug. 6, 2021, showed of eleven wealthy countries show the United States is dead last. It is not a lack of knowledge—it is a lack of owning the information in a way that translates into actionable steps.

As a nation, we run into the same problem with aging in place. More and more information about the topic is in the media as the aging population drives the demand. The overwhelming majority of Americans report wanting to stay home as they age, yet few are acting on it.

According to an article by Kaitlyn Mattson, "Why Seniors Could Be Priced Out of Aging in Place Across U.S." (October 11, 2018), one out of three American households will be headed by someone over the age of 65 by 2035. And by that same year, the number of older households with someone that has a disability will increase by 76%, according to the Harvard Joint Center for Housing Studies report, "Projections and Implications for Housing a Growing Population: Older Households, 2015 – 2035," released in 2016.

The article also reports,

> *housing design features that increase accessibility or universal design elements such as zero-step entrances, electrical controls that are reach-*

able from a wheelchair, lever-style handles on faucets and doors, single-floor living, and wide halls and doorways are viewed as particularly important for older adults to stay in their home, according to the Harvard Joint Center for Housing Studies report. However, only 1% of the current housing stock in the U.S. offers all five of these features (homehealthcarenews.com).

The parallels are obvious, and there is much overlap between health and aging in place literacy. I propose an Aging-in-Place Literacy program much like the nutrition program, which began in 1916 as Food for Young Children, eventually transforming into the iconic Food Pyramid (which has had its share of critics). This public education program was successful for millions of Americans (myself included) and brought nutritional literacy into the public consciousness.

Let's take the definition of "Health Literacy" and apply it to "Aging in Place." Aging-in-Place Literacy is how individuals obtain, communicate, process, and understand basic Aging-in-Place information and services to make appropriate living at home decisions. An excellent place to start is with a review of the working definition:

To review, aging in place is defined by the Center for Disease Control as the ability to live in one's own home and community safely, independently (I prefer Inter-dependence), and comfortably, regardless of age, income, or ability level. I would like to see a national referendum to place an infographic door flyer on every doorknob in the country, not unlike the Food Pyramid, to introduce the "basic food groups" of aging in place to the masses. For example:

Aging in Place Basics (In Review)

- No-step entry: You should have at least one step-free entrance (either at the front, back, or side of the house) so everyone, including wheelchair users, can enter the home easily and safely.
- Wide doorways and hallways: A doorway that is at least 36-42 inches wide is great when you bring home a new mattress or couch, but it is even better for someone you care for or a regularly visiting friend or family member is in a wheelchair.

Including hallways that are 42 inches wide is good for multigenerational family members with varying mobilities.
- One-floor living: Access to essential rooms without the use of stairs makes life more convenient and safer for all ages.
- Easily accessible controls and switches: A person in a wheelchair can reach light switches 42-48 inches above the floor. Thermostats should be placed no higher than 48 inches off the floor and electrical outlets 18-24 inches off the floor.
- Easy-to-use handles: Consider replacing twist/turn doorknobs and faucets with lever-style handles for (painless) ease of use.

The federal government could support this campaign to educate the citizenry early on, quickly becoming a national priority. Start early, like the food pyramid, but unlike the nutritional guidelines, this campaign will be incentivized with tax credits (example H.R.7676 - Home Modification for Accessibility Act of 2022) for aging in place remodeling of existing housing stocks. Then more people (especially women) could be proactive in remaining in the community and loving their long lives—at home.

Fear of Aging

This lack of planning architecturally for the future is possibly driven by gerontophobia (fear of aging). It is the "I'll do it someday" syndrome because not everyone wants to admit they are aging. Other causes such as lack of financial means, knowledge, and resources are certainly factors. Aging-in-place remodeling is considered not as a preventative and so often ends up as a post-emergency "come-to-Jesus-moment" decision. Sadly, a fall can put a quick end to life as it once was for the older adult.

Paradoxically, the fear of aging plus lack of planning equates to "secondary agers" which speed up the aging process, and potentially, death. Certified Aging in Place Specialist (CAPS), Larry Hume, spent thirty-five years in the general remodeling and construction business when his mother and father-in-law each fell ill. The aftermath of their recovery did not just take a toll on them, it changed the direction of Hume's professional life. "My mother and father-in-law both got ill, and both went into wheelchairs," said Hume, owner of Accessible Home Remodeling in Tucson, Arizona. "There was no access throughout their house. Getting in the front door and getting in the bathroom (were the) two biggest problems."

Hume earned his CAPS accreditation, and instead of general remodeling he now focuses on helping people who are aging, in poor health, or those with special needs, to stay safely in their homes by making them more accessible. The market is enormous: seventy-six million baby boomers are approaching retirement age, and many of them have similar issues as Hume saw firsthand in his own family. In fact, according to the Center for Disease Control (CDC), about 60 percent of boomers have already been diagnosed with at least one chronic medical condition, such as arthritis, diabetes, heart disease, obesity, osteoporosis, hypertension, and depression.

According to the National Association of Home Builders, CAPS remodeling or home modifications for the aging in place is the fastest-growing segment of the residential remodeling industry. CAPS professionals evaluate a client's medical condition, look for potential fall hazards or obstructions in the home, and recommend solutions to make the home safer. Several national studies show that falls are the leading cause of death from injuries for older adults. More than half of those falls occur in the home, and research from Washington University School of Medicine in St. Louis suggests that in-home falls can be reduced by nearly 40% with a community-based program that helps older adults make modifications to their homes like adding grab bars, shower seating, slip-resistant surfaces in the bathroom, improved lighting, and handrails on staircases. Bottom line, in-home falls are preventable through home modification designs.

"My mother was a prime example," Hume said. "She fell in her bathroom, hurt her ankle, and busted her head open."

Hume says his situation is played out in virtually every aging-in-place project he has been involved with. He strongly recommends that anyone facing an accessibility issue act before remodeling is necessary.

"In 2009, I installed 98 grab bars, and 96 of them were after (the customer) had already fallen," Hume said. "The biggest thing is to be proactive. I would say all my clients should have done it ten years ago, so they could enjoy it. Baby boomers are too proud to (ask for) a grab bar.

They (would rather) step over the bathtub, squeeze through the door, or step over a curb going in the house."

The take home message is not to wait until it is a crisis. Your choices then are narrowed and hurried—never optimal. Henry David Thoreau once said, "It is a characteristic of wisdom not to do desperate things." Thoreau's quote reminds us that wisdom seldom leads to doing desperate things. When it comes to aging in place, so often, it is a "crisis buy." That is, remodeling for age-friendly living is neglected until a crisis (often a fall) forces the issue.

One of my favorite Buddhist sayings is:

When the student is ready, the teacher will appear.

—BUDDHA

The "student" in this case is you, and you must be ready before any information on home modification is sought out. For those of us in the industry, much of our efforts go into educating the public to prevent home remodeling decisions fueled by a crisis. Which, in the long run, is more expensive, stressful, and potentially too late.

Triumph of hope over experience is what aging is often all about. We are all doing it for the first time as we go; it is the uncharted territory of personal experience. Most of us precariously "age" by watching our loved ones grow old. They struggle with architecture and communities that are static, or worse, change rapidly and do not accommodate. We cannot imagine our future selves following the same path; we will somehow experience a different kind of aging.

Somehow, I always felt that growing old happened to other people.

—MARY PIPHER, *WOMEN ROWING NORTH: NAVIGATING LIFE'S CURRENTS AND FLOURISHING AS WE AGE*

Preplanning for aging in place is not for the "crisis buy" crowd but for the early adopters who see value in incremental steps toward a richer experience of remaining home as they age.

Aging in Place Truth

What is a euphemism? Definition by Rich Coffey: "A euphemism is a substitution of a delicate or inoffensive term or phrase for one that has coarse, sordid, or otherwise unpleasant associations." We are a culture awash in euphemisms. Day-in-day-out, our large flat screens spoon-feed sugarcoated "facts" that keep us insulated and disconnected from reality. For example, here are a few: certified pre-owned really means used, genuine imitation leather means cheap vinyl, partially proficient means unqualified, alternative facts are simply opinions. Some of my favorites from these professionals; a realtor says it's a "cozy home," which usually means it is too small for your big screen TV to fit inside! Politicians say "inoperative statements" which bluntly means lies.

George Orwell, author of *1984*, called this kind of re-framing "doublespeak." Call it what you like; it is deliberately deceptive language, and yet it is as ubiquitous as oxygen in our culture. When I read about a grand opening of long-term care developments euphemistically called "active communities" I understood the goal behind the marketing. Gerontophobia is driving this, and if you want to sell services or products, the smart marketers tell you to avoid the word "aging" like the plague. This advice falls into the "anti-aging" category and is a veiled form of ageism. It sounds lovely and something a marketer or politician would say to sell you what they are offering. I know the intentions are good, but whenever I read wording like "ageless design" (or ageless anything, for that matter), I cringe a bit.

George Bernard Shaw was fond of saying, "Hell is paved with good intentions, not with bad ones. All men mean well." And that is the tricky part; they mean well, but "Ageless Design" and many of these other terms widely used now are a form of dog-whistling ageism. The underlying message is that mentioning aging is somehow not acceptable, so conjure up a word around it by labeling it as something less offensive, less genuine, less authentic.

David Sinclair, Professor of Genetics, and co-director of the Paul F. Glenn Center for Biology of Aging Research at Harvard Medical School, says epigenetically, aging begins at conception. Therefore, we are all aging; it is a condition of living. We only stop aging when we die.

More inclusive terms like Universal Design, or design that works for everyone, are not trying to deny anything. It works for everyone on that conception-to-death continuum, regardless of age. It is beyond semantics, language matters. Do not get me wrong, I wish to steer clear of "Gerontological Correctness" (thanks to HR Moody for the term), but we are "aged" by the language of culture. And when I say "aged" I mean discriminated against. Language influences thinking, impacting culture, policy, and eventually, real lives. Aging is not a sin.

You can't handle the truth!

—COLONEL NATHAN JESSUP, FICTITIOUS CHARACTER FROM *A FEW GOOD MEN*

I have been around older adults my entire life, and I find most want to age well within their age. Each stage has its lessons and roles to be played out, not to be missed. Phrases like "living in place" can be thinly veiled forms of ageism. Many in the so-called "third age" live full and exciting lives at home and in their communities. Most simply want a level of independence within their communities, a space for cultivating their uniqueness, and for preserving their natural daily rituals, routines, and biorhythms. These living components define *aging in place* for so many, and I ask marketers and even some gerontology professionals not to bludgeon older adults (especially women) with euphemisms. They have earned the right not to be patronized, sell them on non-stigmatizing design and function that respects aging for what it is, a natural process of development and change. And yes, they can handle the truth.

So, in that spirit, I would like to introduce the 80/20 rule as applied to aging in place—I trust you early adopters are ready (smile).

Pareto Principle (The 80/20 Rule) "The Vital Few and Trivial Many" Applied to Aging in Place

In the early 1900s, an Italian economist named Vilfredo Pareto came up with a mathematical formula describing the unequal distribution of wealth he observed and measured in his native land. He observed, rather astutely, that roughly 20 percent of the people controlled or owned 80 percent of the wealth. Soon after Vilfredo published his 80/20 formula, others in fields such as business and science began to realize similar phenomena occurring in their endeavors.

Then in the late 1940s, an enterprising pioneer of quality management, Dr. Joseph M. Juran, recognized the universal principle of the 80/20 rule. He called it The Vital Few and Trivial Many. It became known as the "Pareto Principle." Generally, the Pareto Principle is the observation (not law) that most things in life are not distributed evenly. It can mean all of the following:

- 20% of the input creates 80% of the result
- 20% of the workers produce 80% of the result
- 20% of the customers make 80% of the revenue
- 20% of the defects cause 80% of the crashes
- 20% of the features cause 80% of the usage
- And on and on

The value of the Pareto Principle reminds us to stay focused on the 20 percent that matters and produces the most significant return (the 80 percent results). Therefore, we must identify which things/activities are The Vital Few. When considering what kind of aging in place remodeling to do and where to start, it helps to use this concept and terminology with hired professionals. For do-it-yourself projects, ask, What 20 percent of home modifications will provide 80 percent of my aging-in-place goals of remaining home as I age?

The 20 percent that matters most will be situational. Still, fundamental modifications can be vital to successful aging in place, and an excellent example of areas to focus efforts initially as a solid foundation for independence. Age should not be a limiting factor if the home is designed with aging in mind—these three design essentials will go a long way to remaining home by choice:

1. Zero step entrance into the home
2. Doors 36" clear passage
3. Full bathroom on the main floor

Ten most common aging in place adaptations to the home

1. Non-barrier thresholds into the home

2. Bathroom upgrade to accessible shower/bath/grab bars/non-slip floor on the main

3. Energy efficiency

4. Add traction strips to floors/steps

5. Brighter LED lighting (A 25-watt CFL gives you four times increased light than a 25w incandescent, where a 25w LED gives you 6-8 times increased light)

6. Alarm system

7. U-shaped pull cabinets and lever door handles

8. Risers

9. Door entry intercoms/seat

10. Personal response unit

Enabling Independence Throughout Life

Esther Greenhouse is leading a movement to enable us to thrive throughout our lives positively. Her firm's innovative initiative, *Thrive by Design: Enabling Physical & Financial Independence in Retirement,* is focused on empowering women through design. We can reduce care-giving demands and forced frailty by strategically using design features, which occurs in typically designed homes because they were not designed for the lifespan. Her approach can also prevent eviction by design, being forced to move out of your home because it was not properly designed for people of all ages. It is not just about aging in place; it is about thriving by design.

Esther has outlined the following basic concepts to enable people to choose where they live throughout their lives. From her background as a designer, built environment strategist, environmental psychologist, and gerontologist, she has distilled the essential elements:

1. THEORY

Few practitioners or policymakers are aware of the concept of Environmental Fit & Press.*

There is an optimal fit between a person and the Built Environment:

Good Fit = high functioning + independences

Poor Fit = struggle to adapt --> forced frailty --> dependence

Poor fit is a stressor called Environmental Press. The status quo of our homes and communities is unnecessarily creating press and pushing people to artificially lower levels of functioning. We must, and can, design to address this, and we can enable people to thrive by design.

*Lawton, M. P., & Nahemow, L. (1973). *Ecology and The Aging Process.*

2. FACT

The status quo is dis-abling + discriminatory. The concept that our world works for everyone is a myth. Few know that our housing and communities are optimally designed for the average height male with high physical, cognitive, and sensory abilities—requiring everyone else to adapt. As we age, this can create forced frailty, functional eviction from one's s home, care expenditures, and deplete assets. This is all unnecessary and preventable.

3. SOLUTION

The Enabling Design Approach is a solution considering design, well-being, economics, and challenges. By understanding the costly impacts of the status quo of our housing which discriminates against women and older adults, and using small, but significant design features, we can minimize caregiving demands, delay and/or prevent institutionalization, and preserve assets. Enabling Design is a vehicle for physical and financial independence as we age, enabling people to age with dignity and quality of life.

While Esther has consulted on groundbreaking projects like the design of the nation's first elder-focused emergency department, her greatest project is her mom's home. Due to the design features, Esther's 91-year-old mother is living at home, with minimal assistance from others. The design of this home has reduced caregiving demands, paid caregiving expenses, and successfully prevented her mother from moving to a facility for nearly ten years. That's enabling!

I encourage you to visit Esther Greenhouse's website for more content and contact her to request resources.

If you think hiring professionals is expensive, try hiring amateurs.

—ANONYMOUS

So, you have decided to begin the process of aging-in-place home modification. Congratulations! You are thinking ahead by making your future a part of your current strategy. But what is the next step? We are bombarded daily on radio and media about how to hire help for home remodeling projects. And then there are those horror stories you hear from friends and relatives about the remodelers from hell! Here are some steps to take so you do not feel like you are drinking from a firehose when looking for aging-in-place remodeling help:

1. Find a Professional Certified Aging-in-Place Specialist

Two trusted organizations, The National Association of Home Builders (NAHB) and AARP, have teamed up to develop the Certified Aging-In-Place Specialist (CAPS) program. This program trains building and healthcare professionals in the specifics of designing homes for an aging population. They incorporate elements from Universal Design and aging in place best practices backed by years of experience working with older adults.

There are about 3,500 CAPS graduates across the country, builders and remodelers, occupational therapists, and interior designers who retrofit homes to help people remain in them safely, said Dan Bawden, a Houston contractor. He helped develop the program in 2001. You will find the cost for CAPS home modifications can range widely from several hundred dollars to widen a doorway or install a ramp, to thousands of dollars or more to install an elevator. It will depend on the scope of your project. Find Aging-in-Place Specialist at the NAHB's CAPS online directory (located by zip code).

In addition, the National Aging in Place Council (NAIPC) organization has as its mission to bring professionals and communities together to champion Aging in Place through collaboration, education, and accountability (ageinplace.org).

2. Do Your Research (online too)

After you have found several in your area, arrange to meet each contractor in person to determine if there is a good personality fit. Here, it would help if you employed some intuition (women are good at this). Once you have a shortlist of potential home remodelers for your project, do a bit of additional background research to verify they are appropriately licensed and have a good business track record.

Look them up with your local or state office of consumer protection. Verify that the remodeler and any subcontractors have the appropriate licenses and registrations. Do they carry the proper insurance and certifications as required by law to maintain membership or accreditation in your state?

How long have they been in business in your community?

Can they provide references from customers and suppliers? Do they carry insurance that protects you from claims arising from property damage or job site injuries?

Ask for a copy of the insurance certificates. What is their working knowledge of the many types and ages of homes in the area, and what issues could arise?

Are they the ones who arrange for the building permit? The person who obtains it is the contractor of record and, therefore, liable for the work.

Check the prospective remodeler's company website and social media accounts to see photos of prior work done. Ask for referrals from friends, family, neighbors, coworkers, and others who have had remodeling work done on comparable homes under similar schedules. Also, check your local Better Business Bureau to see if complaints were filed against the contractor.

3. Do the Aging-in-place Checklist Walk Through and Estimate

They can walk the home with a checklist (see NAHB website) and see just what your specific needs might be. Have them provide a written estimate before beginning the work, and a detailed contract spells out the work that will and will not be performed. Such a contract protects both of you, provides a fair payment schedule, and complies with local, state, and federal laws. Get at least three written bids for your project, ensuring the plans, specifications, and material lists are the same.

Do not automatically choose the lowest bidder. Ask questions if there are significant price differences; there may be a good reason to pay more than the lowest offer. Contributing author to Next Avenue (AARP/Forbes), Stan Gornicz, says you need to make sure you have a detailed building contract. You will want to see specifics for the essential elements of the project, including:

- Total cost
- Begin and end dates
- Payment schedule
- Responsibility for obtaining building permits and arranging for inspections
- How project changes are handled
- Warranties for materials/workmanship; what is covered, how long it remains in effect

Typically, a small down payment (10 percent) is required when signing the contract, followed by incremental payments based on the completed stages of the project. The final installment comes upon satisfactory completion and inspection of all work.

Financing Your Aging-in-Place Home Modifications

PBS News posted an article, "Recommendation No. 1 for a secure retirement: 'age in place,'" by Lew Mandell.

Eight Reasons to Finance Aging in Place

1. Owning an age-in-place home carries many financial benefits, not the least of which is saving on exorbitant nursing home costs.

2. There are multiple benefits to owning an age-in-place home in retirement. You can plan to live out your days in a comfortable, familiar environment. You can also stay in a cherished neighborhood with beloved friends, stores, restaurants, doctors, places of worship, and perhaps relatives.

3. However, few people planning for retirement (or their advisers) recognize all the financial reasons why it is essential to living in an age-in-place home and why that home should ideally be owned free and clear.

4. These reasons are so compelling that virtually all my retired friends (who have read my book) are now trying to buy homes or modify their existing homes to enable them to age in place.

5. Owning an accessible home in which we can age in place is important to keeping our future core expenses down for many reasons. First, and most apparent, owning a home outright in retirement greatly reduces our need for income since we no longer must pay the mortgage.

6. A second major benefit of owning, outright, an age-in-place home is that it is a wonderful hedge against inflation.

7. Staying at home can also reduce the need for increasingly expensive long-term care insurance whose maximum daily benefits are often just $150 or so, a fraction of nursing home costs, leaving patients and their families to make up the huge difference.

8. A fourth advantage of owning outright an age-in-place home is that it can provide you with additional guaranteed lifetime income through a reverse mortgage while you continue to live in your own home.

*9. *Added by me:* in the time of a pandemic that has proven quite deadly for institutional settings for the care of older adults, home becomes an even more compelling choice. Potentially avoid the costs of a prolonged hospital stay/long-term disability—or the ultimate cost of death.

Affordable housing is becoming the factor that makes or breaks so many women's dreams of aging in place.

Ten ways to pay for getting your home age-friendly:

- Low-income housing (check with your local area agency on aging).
- Out-of-pocket.
- Reverse mortgage to finance home improvements.
- State and local grants: contact National Council of state housing agencies.
- Accessing your home equity.
- Assistance for energy savings; the U.S. Department of Energy helps modify homes for energy savings through its Weatherization Assistance Program and Low-Income Home Energy Assistance Program.
- Veterans the U.S. Department of Veterans Affairs offer vets grants to remove barriers and adapt to mobility devices.
- Rural homeowners, the U.S. Department of Agriculture (USDA) offers rural development loans/grants to low-income elderly/or disabled people in rural locations. Contact the local USDA office for eligibility.
- Home sharing.
- Charity home improvements like Habitat for Humanity/AARP Foundation, Rebuild Together.

Enough money for retirement?

Winston Churchill spoke many words of wisdom, including, "Let our advanced worrying become advanced thinking and planning." My friend and colleague, Scott Fulton, has been doing some advanced thinking and planning on the topic of aging in place. He is a strong advocate for his clients. He is not only a university lecturer and teaches a comprehensive course on Aging in Place, he also does built-environment design (theory + practice).

With his permission, I have included this information to get you thinking about not only your parents, but your future circumstances as well, in terms of successful aging-in-place planning. This specific example will not be relevant to all readers, but the concept has more comprehensive applications that may help many of you.

In this example, aging in place improvements protect the family from running up half a million in debt by making improvements early, allowing them to remain living at home for four more years. The result is a net benefit of over $700,000! Which situation would you choose?

Fulton asserts, "The odds do not favor waiting; they are stacked so badly you could argue it is rigged. The couple below started with $1.45 million in total equity, but a hospital visit and sudden need to move to a facility would have wiped them out, leaving their heirs with nothing but debt and regret. That is not how anyone would plan their retirement, yet we are seeing this occur more and more as people fail to make realistic plans."

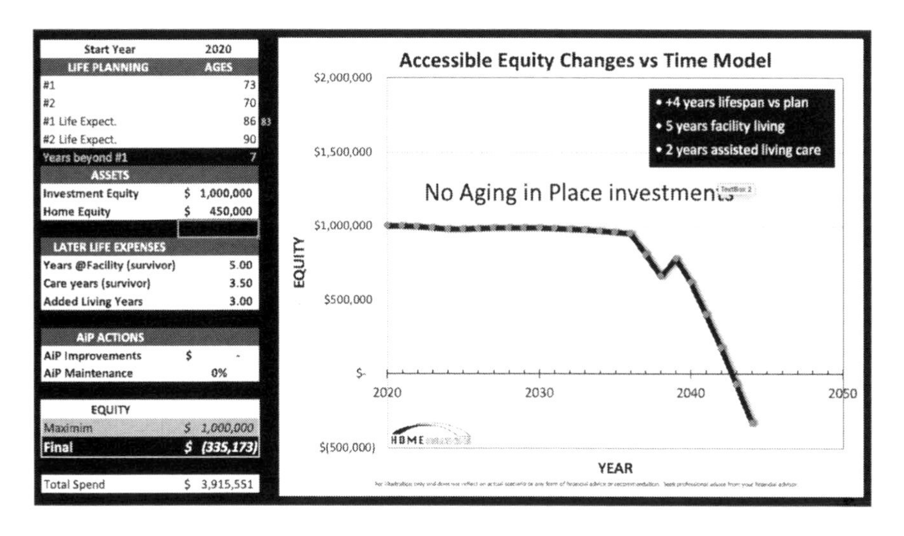

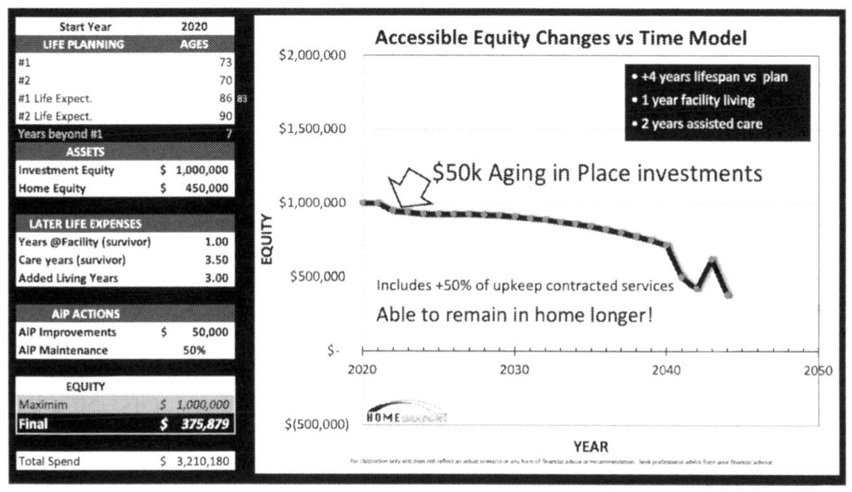

Courtesy of Scott Fulton

We know from the literature that women are more involved in caring for their aging parents. Millennials, that means you. As Fulton says, you will need to step up and get engaged early as well, as once the free fall starts, the good options are long gone, and they can be left holding the bag.

Worth noting, all relevant costs associated with aging in place versus nursing homes, such as rent/and or mortgage, utilities, insurance, taxes, upkeep, and unpaid caregiving, need to be taken fully into account. Home care may be a good thing, but round-the-clock home care is not cheap and can be more costly than a nursing home. However, in the era of COVID this, too, becomes a new element in the equation to consider.

Further Considerations— Aging in "the Right Place"

I posted this on the social media site Twitter, some time ago:

Aging in Place can preserve a sense of self as a homeowner and community member in a time of loss and change that defines aging. This is known as "Continuity of Self."

This response came in shortly after my posting: *Aging in Place is a misnomer. Aging in the Right Place more accurately represents what you describe.*

My follow-up: *It is not a misnomer for many individuals I hear from—it is their reality.*

I get it, *in a perfect world* aging in the right place would be the standard and optimal for all. But I do not live in a perfect world, and most people I know do not either. Most will be aging in place under circumstances that will be less than optimal. A term is used for the kind of housing most of us (in the real world) live in; it is called "Peter Pan Housing." Jon Pynoos, a gerontology policy and planning professor at the University of Southern California, coined Peter Pan homes for homes with stairs, inaccessible bathrooms, and inadequate lighting. They lack many of the safety features that would help people avoid falls. That describes most aging housing stocks we are inhabiting. As has been established, most baby boomers will be aging in the suburbs and rural areas. These are not "the right place," but they are where living will occur into old age.

So, "aging in place" is not a misnomer; it is a reality for most. Given this fact, some will find "the right" place, but many will not, presenting challenges for those involved. It will be daunting at times, juggling work/family/ caregiving for adult children. And for older adults themselves, this will present a mixed blessing; being at home has its upsides (the comfort and safety of home), but it also has its downsides (isolation). For entrepreneurs, the opportunities are limitless, finding creative ways to bring in home goods, services, technologies, and care to them.

Aging in place is one of the most significant societal challenges facing our nation (as well as globally) and working toward optimal outcomes is the goal. Still, we cannot bury our heads in the sand and label reality a misnomer. We must tackle the issues head-on, which means meeting people where they are, not where we would like them to be—but where they are. A practical place to begin is at the policy level, mandating that all new construction have "visitability" features (non-barrier entry, 36" doorways, and a full bathroom on the main floor). It is cheaper to do upfront and it benefits all inhabitants: young and old, male and female.

Final thoughts on aging in place and late love/sex

While working as a nurse's aide during my undergraduate days in a nursing home, we had a resident with a girlfriend who made conjugal visits. We were all aware of the scheduled times, and we pulled the curtain on his semi-private room during these encounters. Even his roommate "Sam," whose stroke left him in a wheelchair with left-sided paralysis, knew it was time to leave the confines of room #12 for the designated period. I'm ashamed to admit the staff (myself included) joked about it—because he, too, was a wheelchair user and had complicated medical issues. Like clockwork, she would show up, and the resident, let's call him "Mr. Mark," Old-Spiced up, showered and shaved, and they made love as scheduled Wednesdays at 1800 (6 p.m.).

Older people have plenty of sex when not in institutional settings. According to new findings from the National Poll on Healthy Aging, 40 percent of people ages 65 to 80 are sexually active. Nearly three-quarters of people in this age range have a romantic partner; 54 percent of those with a partner are sexually active (labblog.uofmhealth.org/rounds/sex-after-65-poll-finds-gender-differences-lack-of-communication). This reinforces the claim that older people are engaged in sexual activities, but those in institutional settings face many intimacy gauntlets such as:

- Mattress too narrow to accommodate two adults
- Culture and place-bound – lack of cultural sensitivity to customs
- Nurses and aides entering the room unannounced
- Can't lock doors
- Institutional time – nursing homes are run for efficiency, not individual schedules
- A room of my own – privacy sacrificed due to shared space
- Loss of identity – status stripped away
- Loss of meaningful objects – personal items locked up and limited room decor
- Aged not entirely human – talked about in the third person
- Exposure to constant death turn over – residents disappear without explanation
- Nursing home administrators afraid of lawsuits due to dementia in residents, being overcautious with policies on intimate contact

Source: *Limbo: A Memoir for Aging in Place Remodeling*

Sex: An Argument for Aging in Place Remodeling

Over the years, I have made arguments for the case of aging in place, suggesting taking care of yourself physically and mentally, getting a home assessment, making universal design changes in the home, considering New Urbanism, looking into aging-in-community options, or co-housing. Aging-in-place professionals often get frustrated with getting clients to consider making home modifications now, not later when it is a crisis. A few are listening and preparing, but the majority are not. Maybe sex is a compelling enough reason to plan for aging in place?

"Why is it so hard to remain sexually active in a nursing home?" asks psychologist, Ira Rosofsky. His answer is, "Because nursing homes may be denying residents the individual rights of privacy and the pursuit of happiness." Although many nursing homes are making strides, and attitudes and responses of staff and administrators appear to be shifting in a sex-positive direction (Jen, et al., 2022), sex and the nursing home are still strange bedfellows. Perhaps it is because they are institutions designed for supervision and surveillance (paternalistic), having professionals decide what is best. But will residents in nursing homes have the same rights as the rest of society to continue to mess up or enhance their lives with sex? Like most complicated issues, there will be multiple sides to consider.

"Still, in the end," says Rosofsky, "I, too, hope we continue to insist on our cherished rights of self-expression. In the meantime, does it make sense that it is easier to get a conjugal visit in jail than in a nursing home?"

With that in mind, realize that forty percent of people between ages 65 and 80 are sexually active, according to a survey from the National Poll on Healthy Aging, sponsored by AARP and the University of Michigan (healthyagingpoll.org). If you are moved by this, you may want to consider planning that aging-in-place strategy now—your future love life may depend on it—and yes, it is never too late to have one!

"Love in a Life" by Robert Browning

Room after room, I hunt the house through we inhabit together. Heart, fear nothing, for, heart, thou shalt find her, next time, herself! —not the trouble behind her left in the curtain, the couch's perfume! As she brushed it, the cornice-wreath blossomed anew, —Yon looking-glass gleamed at the wave of her feather. Yet the day wears, and door succeeds door; I try the fresh fortune —range the wide house from the wing to the center. Still the same chance! She goes out as I enter. Spend my whole day in the quest —who cares? But 'tis twilight, you see—with such suites to explore, such closets to search, such alcoves to importune!

Summary

The underlying assumption with "aging in place" is that older people can remain home by choice. This idea is that human development occurs throughout the lifespan and is not limited solely to youth. But to embrace this concept, our society must change its view of what it means to grow old. As pointed out eloquently in the thought-provoking book, *Rethinking Aging: Growing Old and Living Well In an Overtreated Society*, by Nortin M. Hadler, MD, the secret to longevity is the structure of society, not whether anyone eats bran. It is the social construction that Americans have learned, and nearly all have accepted, about aging and its issues that matter.

To better understand aging, a systems approach is essential. Thinking that a bottle of "high-tech snake oil" will reverse aging or that a magic elixir can fix low testosterone without long-term side effects is foolhardy. To achieve "successful aging" multiple conditions are required. As Dr. Hadler explains:

> *Social inequalities burden people who are in their older decades at least as much as they did earlier in life. This burden goes well beyond purchasing power. This is dramatic even in Norway, despite its egalitarian ideology and national health service. People with higher education live substantially longer than those with basic education.*
>
> *One's position on the socioeconomic gradient prior to retirement is the major determinant of one's health in later life and one's longevity.* And he further notes: *But health adverse behaviors explain only a fraction of the effect. More malevolent are the moral hazards that lurk in our neighborhood, in our self-actualization, in our wealth or lack thereof, in the stability of our income stream, in our family structure, and in our intimate relationships. This is no reason to assume that any particular influence or combination of influences pertains to a given individual. The secrets to longevity are in the fine structure of human ecology.*

> *In the mid-twentieth century, the temporal gap between traditional "retirement" and death was narrow, all the cows were undoubtedly out of the barn. It was so narrow that it drove the construction of facilities dedicated to the compassionate shepherding of the elderly through the final transitions of life soon after the ending of "productive" life, interactive living.*

Dr. Hadler's point is that "rest homes" are outdated both socially and logistically. Most older Americans will be aging in place and doing so for years to come. According to the website zippia.com only 4% of Americans over 65 live in nursing homes. In addition, 2% of Americans in this same age group live in assisted living facilities. Of those who do live in nursing homes, 18.2% are between the ages of 65 and 74, 26.7% are between the ages of 75 and 84, and 38.6% are 85 or older. Thus, successful aging in place, not unlike successful aging itself, will require a systems approach.

Universal design, aging-in-place remodeling features, and community supports are pieces of the puzzle but not the entire solution. The key line is this:

The secrets to longevity are in the fine structure of human ecology.

Our focus on longevity (and aging in place) in this country is short-sighted, piecemeal, quick-fix, and death-denying in its limited scope. Solutions will take a mature and sober eye, from technology and shared housing to village concepts. To be effective, they will all have to consider the fine structure of human ecology—aging is contextual.

Aging in Place: The Black Experience

Traditional institutions have overlooked the contextual African American experience with aging in place. Assistant professor of Gerontology at USC Davis School of Gerontology, Reginald Tucker-Seeley, reports current research on aging in place often does not include the perspectives of African American women and the issues that affect their aging and communities. He led a literature review and found a dearth of information concerning the many factors affecting older African American women. Issues from the intersecting challenges of racism and sexism to the impact of faith communities and gentrification are lacking in aging-in-place research.

African American women must manage not just race and gender-related issues but also ageism. Tucker-Seeley said, "We felt that those kinds of issues needed to be better contextualized within the aging-in-place literature to take into consideration that this group of individuals may be aging in place very different from the general description of aging in place in the research literature."

In the article, "Aging While Black: The Crisis Among black Americans as They Grow Old," author Rodney A. Brooks opens with this line that sums up the challenges facing aging African Americans, "After a lifetime of racial and health inequities, Black seniors are at risk of spending their last years with declining health, little income and virtually no savings." Brooks further cites statistical findings to support his statement from a 2016 CIGNA Health Disparities report:

- *Four in ten Black men aged 20 or older have high blood pressure, a rate 30 percent higher than that of white men. Black men's risk of a stroke is twice that of white men. For Black women, 45 percent of those aged 20 and older have high blood pressure, 60 percent higher than white women.*
- *Black women are 40 percent more likely to die of breast cancer than white women.*
- *Black men have a 40 percent higher cancer death rate than white men.*
- *Black Americans are 80 percent more likely to be diagnosed with diabetes than whites and nearly twice as likely to be hospitalized.*
- *Blacks are more than twice as likely as whites to suffer from Alzheimer's and other kinds of dementia.*

More specifically to women, the piece quotes an associate professor of sociology at Duke University, Tyson Brown. "Black women suffer from some of the highest levels of diabetes, hypertension, and other disabilities. Their health problems limit their ability to continue working. But many

Black women have to continue working because of declining income as they age."

Professor Brown notes that black women are especially vulnerable to health and wealth issues because they are more likely to outlive partners (statistics above), which means they are more likely to be isolated and alone.

As is frequently the case, they become informal caregivers for aging parents, spouses, and grandchildren, ending their formal employment. I have worked with many black women in healthcare who fit into this scenario. Sadly, this equates as an opportunity cost to pay into company-sponsored retirement plans such as pensions and 401(k) plans and reduces their payments into Social Security, which means smaller monthly checks when they retire.

The bottom line, "Many Black older Americans have endured decades of overt and subtle forms of discrimination in educational, criminal justice systems, and health care systems as well as in jobs, housing, credit, and consumer markets," said Brown, adding that "as a result of this discrimination, many older Black Americans have lower levels of education, income, and wealth than whites." The COVID public health crisis affected low-income and communities of color at more significant percentages, making the lives of older black Americans even more daunting.

After decades of discrimination in educational, criminal justice systems, and health care systems as well as in jobs, housing, credit, and consumer markets, as noted by Brown, older Black Americans, and especially women, have been hurt disproportionately to the rest of society.

Employing Negative Visualization

To summarize this section, I want to introduce an unlikely pairing, aging in place, and ancient Greek/Roman Stoicism. At first glance, it seems like a stretch—but stay with me here. Let me begin by asking the question: Do you have a philosophy of life? Moderns (you and I) seldom take the time to develop one, let alone consider the topic. We are distracted by too many shiny objects and preoccupied with keeping our heads above water in the fast-paced consumer culture. The ancient Greek and Roman philosophers not only thought a philosophy of life was worth contemplating, but it was the highest calling to develop one. And why is it worth developing one? Because, without one, there is a danger you will mis-live, that despite all the pleasant (and not so pleasant) diversions you might enjoy while alive, you will end up living a bad life.

What do you want out of life? Most will answer, a high-paying job, good health, loving partner, lovely house, plenty of toys . . . but the Ancients were not interested in daily goals; they wanted you to think about your grand goal. In other words, of the things you might pursue, which is the thing you believe to be *most* valuable? The fear is that you will look back on your deathbed and realize you wasted your one chance at living. Instead of pursuing something genuinely valuable, you squandered it by allowing yourself to be distracted. Let's say you have given it some thought and developed a Grand Goal in Living, and you can articulate why this goal is worth attaining. Even then, there is a danger you will mis-live.

Specifically, if you lack an effective strategy for achieving your Grand Goal in Living, you will unlikely attain it. So, the key to this idea of developing a philosophy of life is a strategy for achieving your Grand Goal in Living. And to help with the process, the Greek and Roman philosophers touted that to maximize your chances of gaining the thing in life that you feel is ultimately valuable, you will need a philosopher of life to guide you.

The ancient philosophers shared their wisdom (philosophy of life) through schools to improve the human condition. For example, Epicurus (Epicurean School) stated, "Vain is the word of a philosopher which does not heal any suffering of man." And the Stoic philosopher Seneca said, "He who studies with a philosopher should take away with him someone good thing every day; he should daily return home a sounder man, or on the way to becoming sounder."

They advised on how to live; of interest here is the Stoic school of philosophy of which perhaps the most famous disciple was Marcus Aurelius, the greatest of Roman emperors. When he read the Stoic Philosophers, he became filled with admiration for them. He noted they were courageous, reasonable, self-disciplined, and temperate—all traits the great man wanted to possess (and women too!).

The Stoic philosophers interested in how to live a happy life saw how unhappy humans are, in large part because of insatiability; after working hard to get the object of desire they/we quickly lose interest. Stoics called this phenomenon "Hedonic Adaptation." Think of lottery winners and how they often end up unhappy after their fortunes are squandered. Human nature is such that we take for granted what we have, and we desire things yet to be possessed. Once we start living the life we have always dreamed of, we start taking that life for granted, thanks to Hedonic Adaptation.

The Stoics desired tranquility (much as Buddhists) so a way of fixing this was to employ a technique called "negative visualization." Negative visualization (thought to be the most potent tool in the Stoic philosophy) is simply to contemplate the temporary nature of things; remember, all we have is "on loan" from Fortune, which can reclaim it without our permission. The idea is to visualize what it would be like to lose that high-paying job, good health, loving partner, beautiful house, and plenty of toys. In doing so, the Stoics believed it would make us value these things more than we might otherwise.

Epictetus provides the example to two fathers; one who is kissing his daughter good night, silently reflects on the possibility she may die tomorrow. The second father refuses to entertain such gloomy thoughts. Father #1 is most attentive in his dealings with his daughter; father#2 will postpone interactions until tomorrow. The Stoics believed by contemplating the loss, we would be less inclined to take for granted what we now have.

Marcus and Epictetus felt we would be much better off by contemplating the loss, how we would feel if we lost our material possessions, our pets, our bank balance, our ability to speak, walk, hear, or our freedom. We spend idle moments thinking about the things we want and do not have most of the time. We would be much better off, according to the Stoics, to spend this time thinking of all the things we do have and reflecting on how much we would miss them if they were not ours.

This is where aging in place and negative visualization come into play; visualize losing your independence (the unthinkable) and reflect on how much you would miss it. Visualize the loss of the daily rituals and routines that make up your day and are taken for granted. Imagine living where decisions on when you get up, what you eat, or setting the natural rhythm of the day, are not in your control. Visualize how that might look.

The Ancient Stoic philosophers saw their role as guides to the good life, and negative visualization was the most powerful tool to the goal. Thinking about loss can lead to a better life now. Take the steps necessary to secure your aging in place home.

Goodbye Myth: Aging in Place Takes Inter-dependence

Step 4

Apply negative visualization to aging in place.

The first step toward creating an improved future is developing the ability to envision it and experience what it would be like without it. Then, creating it by taking the proactive and practical steps outlined here toward achieving it. Also, remember that for minorities, aging in place has additional challenges.

Suggested Resources

Certified Aging in Place Specialists (CAPS) Larry Hume: accessibleremodel.com

Helping society create environments that enable people to thrive! (Found: https://www.esthergreenhouse.com/enabling-environments/) Esther Greenhouse is a built environment strategist consulting for municipalities, senior housing providers, and organizations to leverage the design of the built environment to enable people to thrive. She is the Strategic Director for one of the United States' first Age-Friendly Centers for Excellence. She creates and develops innovative initiatives, such as Equity by Design, collaborating with AARP International to generate a quantum leap for Age-Friendly Housing and Multigenerational Communities.

Esther Greenhouse a nationally recognized expert on Universal Design, Aging in Place, and Age-Friendly Community Planning. is the creator of the innovative Enabling Design and her work can be found at silvertogold-strategies.com.

Frederick Ryan (2021) Right Place, Right Time: The Ultimate Guide to Choosing a Home for the Second Half of Life, Johns Hopkins University Press.

Ideas for this post informed by William B. Irvine (2009) A Guide to the Good Life: The Ancient Art of Stoic Joy.

Note of caution: An article from startribune.com titled, "Aging in place could inflict a huge burden on Your Family," outlined the very real opportunity costs to keeping an older adult in the home they love too long. The piece reported, "Some households headed by seniors are delaying downsizing. Best Places to Retire lists are great conversation starters, but the vast majority of Americans have no intention of making a move in retirement." I cannot argue with any of it; I have experienced the downside myself in terms of opportunity costs: lost friendships, time away from my wife, lost wages, lost vacation time, and the unending stress caused by worrying. The key is to prepare the home to be age-friendly in advance or downsize to be more accommodating.

Author's note: *It is not always physically, mentally, or economically feasible for many older adults to be aging in place—this does not work for everyone all the time.*

CHAPTER 5

The Architecture of Happiness

MYTH: You Have to Go it Alone

> ***A dream you dream alone is only a dream. A dream you dream together is reality.***
>
> —YOKO ONO

MUCH OF THE CONVERSATION SURROUNDING THE CONCEPT OF aging in place by the professionals in remodeling and home design focuses on the physical or built environment. And for a good reason, obstacles to staying home are often environment-caused, and it is the obvious point of entry. Put a handrail on the stairs, install a raised toilet, and remodel a bathroom to accommodate a wheelchair; these are physical changes that can be marked off a checklist and seen as making tangible progress toward "independence."

As important as these accommodations are to the changing physical needs of the aging homeowner, aging in place is unlikely to be successful long-term if not done in a larger context of support. Architect Meda Ling eloquently describes the economic and social aspects of true "sustainability" and the humane quality of life factor when designing for an aging population.

Ling notes:

> *And of even greater importance to this line of thought: no matter how well an individual home may accommodate and adapt to the changing physical needs of a homeowner over time if it does not encourage social interaction or a sense of 'belonging' to a supportive community, whether intentional or serendipitous, 'aging in place' is unlikely to be an option. One must ALWAYS consider the context of a home within the greater environs of a neighborhood or community. Are the homes sited in such a way that people are encouraged to interact and know their neighbors?*
>
> *How does the location of a home or development relate to the greater community and access to transit options, shopping, healthcare, entertainment, and passive and active recreation such that it encourages a healthy lifestyle? How do the home and the neighborhood relate to the environment—does it make sense in terms of land use, water, and air quality objectives of sustainability?*
>
> *I have strong reservations about the concept of 'aging in place' as a sustainable model for a humane quality of life. From the perspective of a site architect, I consistently remind my professional colleagues to step back and see the forest for the 'kitchen cabinet' selection—and ask that we consider the quality of LIFE (QOL) as the guiding principle of how we design, how we use the land, how we build. Rather than designing/building for 'aging in place,' please consider designing/building for 'LIVING in COMMUNITY.'*

Aging-Friendly Communities

Ling's statement is a systems-thinking approach to designing communities that are sustainable and age-friendly. I have been discussing for some time now *the aging-in-place paradox,* which is to be more independent—you will need to be more inter-dependent. So, when planning your "forever home," it is critical to think in terms of community.

Aging in place has frequently been pigeonholed into meaning growing old behind four walls. This perspective limits not only the concept but any potential solutions as well. The broader outlook must include the wider multi-generational community.

Jennie Chin Hansen and Andrew Scharlach are problem solvers and part of the solution. Both have done some heavy-lifting thinking about age-friendly communities and the components that should be included. They have consolidated the essence into five C's or five areas of focus. The breakdown is the scaffolding of essential activities and services for a happier experience of living in community.

The Five Key Areas

- Continuity – Opportunities to participate in lifelong interests and activities that are self-affirming, including activities that maintain good health and prevent disease and disability.
- Compensation – Access to services, products, and structures that help to meet the basic health and social needs of people with age-related disabilities, including assisted living and technological interventions that support self-care.
- Connection – Access to sources of social interaction and social support, including built and electronic resources to overcome physical barriers to social contact.
- Contribution – Opportunities to actively contribute to the well-being of the community, of one another, and themselves.
- Challenge – Access to new sources of fulfillment, productive engagement, and interaction, including social, recreational, and educational activities designed to engage and excite older participants.

These two scholars understand the role of supportive social environments in the overall success of inter-dependence. The built environment is but one aspect of a systems approach to keeping aging adults in the homes and communities they love. Aging in place is contextual and seated squarely in the communities we all live in—no segregated "age-ghettos" (Betty Friedan term) here.

A healthy community is one in which the elderly protect, care for, love and assist the younger ones to provide continuity and hope.

—MAGGIE KUHN, FOUNDER OF THE GRAY PANTHERS

Now, having established the importance of a supportive framework, let's revisit a few issues in the context of women's aging:

1. who lives alone in old age
2. what the challenges are with female longevity
3. where the options are for creating community

The nation's first baby boomer is Kathleen Casey-Kirschling, born just a second after midnight on New Year's Day, 1946. This earned her the title, "The country's first baby boomer." Fitting the first boomer is female because although men do get old, women get older, and this presents unique challenges.

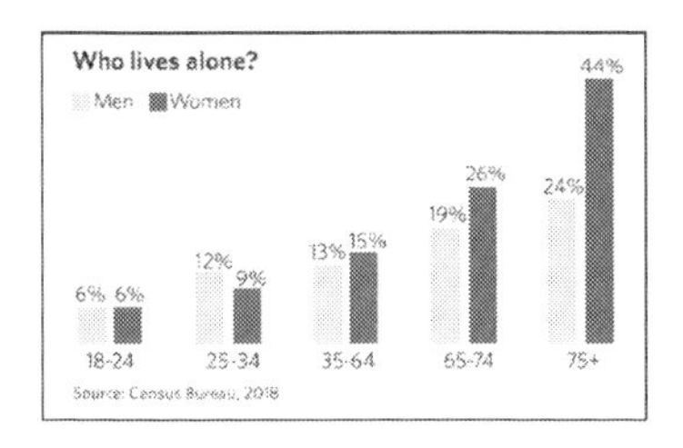

According to expert gerontologist and co-founder of AgeWave, Maddy Dychtwald (maddydychtwald.com), 44 percent of women age 75+ live alone.

Women's Longevity Challenges

1. More likely to live alone in old age
2. More likely to live in poverty than men
3. Living longer with greater morbidity (chronic disease) and decreased ability to do activities of daily living / functioning problems at a two-fold higher rate than men
4. Lack of informal caregivers
5. Aging in suburbia which is isolating (architecture of isolation)

Given these challenges associated with women's longevity, there are innovative people actively seeking solutions. Bonnie Moore was one such entrepreneurial out-of-the-box-thinker and practical problem solver. I first heard about what she was doing on National Public Radio with the intriguing program title: *Boomer House-Mates Have More Fun*. I knew she offered something very viable for boomer women. Since my first exposure to her concept, Bonnie created a media buzz nationally and internationally; taking a big problem and turning it into a big opportunity.

Golden Girls Revisited / Aging in Community

In Bonnie's words:

> *Have you ever considered living like the characters in The Golden Girls? While the show featuring those four fabulous female housemates has been off the air for years, the lifestyle inspired by the show is a growing national trend. That is right—roommates are not just for college students anymore! Many baby boomers are looking for answers because housing costs are too high, and they feel lonely when their kids grow up, and their spouse is no longer around. Or they are proud of the house they built and want to stay in the comforts of their home as they age.*
>
> *When a divorce left me living alone in a newly remodeled five-bedroom home in 2008, I found four roommates to fill the bedrooms. Now, over eight years later, my housemates have become an important part of my life. In addition to contributing rent that*

makes my mortgage affordable, we throw parties together, get to know one another's friends, and help each other out. Are you wondering if sharing a house and household duties with other like-minded people around your same age would work for you?

Do any of these situations sound like yours?

You are looking to re-invent yourself. Perhaps you are questioning the circumstances, meaning, and direction of your life, and resolving to do things differently. Wouldn't it be wonderful to surround yourself with other people seeking change? Sharing your home and life with others who are "reinventing" provides laughter, companionship, and financial and emotional support as we go down that crooked path called life.

You have an extra room where you live. That home with all those wonderful memories can begin feeling a little haunted when you are the only one roaming around in it. Sharing a room in your home, townhouse, or apartment with a housemate will give you someone to say "hello" to at the end of the day, someone to talk about your children with, and someone to call when your car breaks down.

You enjoy home-based activities. You enjoy cooking a meal and doing some gardening and getting some exercise. Now imagine how much more fun meal planning, dirt-digging, and taking a walk could be with another person. Shared living allows you to find like-minded people who can help transform household duties into household delights.

You are healthy and not ready for assisted living or moving in with your children. The momentum we had as younger adults can feel like it is stalling as we age. The end of a marriage, child rearing, or a career can leave us wondering what is next. Shared living is not a retirement home. In fact, finding the right shared living situation can open doors that allow you to take an exciting next step in your life.

You would like to make new friends. Perhaps that one person who received all your unconditional love—a spouse, a child, a parent, a best friend—is no longer around. But we all deserve lives filled with laughter, joy, and companionship. Shared living can connect you with people who share your interests and value the unique qualities you bring to a friendship.

You can no longer afford to stay in your home by yourself. All kinds of circumstances—job loss, a divorce, an economic downturn—can make keeping that home you love difficult. By inviting a housemate to live with you, you can gain the confidence of financial stability while creating a welcoming environment for someone who might become a lifelong friend.

You are feeling a lack of community. Shared living can help you build your own "community" using the resource of your home. Find individuals interested in the same passions you have, like cooking, the environment, or spirituality. Or, if you are new to an area, you can quickly integrate into a community by becoming a member of a group household.

You feel you have become too focused on your job. If your job or volunteer position or hobby feels like the only activity you must occupy your time with; your housemates can bring new energy to your life. Inspiration from others keeps us from stagnating.

You like activity in your home. If you are the kind of person who likes to have a friend over for dinner, host a committee meeting, or invite a crowd at Thanksgiving, then you are a perfect housemate. All housing situations are different, but the best ones thrive on the energy of like-minded people living and having fun together.

Golden Girls Network was featured in a CBS news segment, PBS, and on a French TV network. It was also mentioned in the Christian Science Monitor, Kiplinger's Retirement Report, The Huffington Report, and other retirement blogs as well as the Golden Girls Network blog.

Bonnie Moore was the original founder of Golden Girls Network, a nationwide network that helped adults ages 50+ find roommates and access the resources they need to make a shared living work. She taught classes about shared living and is the author of *How to Start a Golden Girls Home,* which is still in print and available. The website is no longer active, but the spirit in which it was created is.

Bonnie has moved on to a 55+ community to be near her children, and her newest adventure is writing mystery novels. I recently received an email message from her: *My protagonist is a modernized version of Jessica Fletcher. If you ever want to say anything about me, you can always say that I strongly believe in staying active and starting new careers! I now call myself a writer.*

Similar innovative home-sharing programs are developing worldwide; in Queensland, Australia, sharingwithfriends.org is designed to help older women overcome this demographic's housing crisis. The issues are housing struggles, financial insecurity, and loneliness. The program pairs up five older women to live together and share expenses. It also gives them a sense of community and combats loneliness. They come together with the assistance of workshops to decide on things such as:

- Rules and responsibilities
- How they will share expenses
- Having visitors
- Pets
- How their investment will be recouped if/when they leave the group
- Budget and financial management strategies

They have a consultation with the organization's architect to help them design their home and gardens. Each person invests $120,000 for a house constructed for each woman to have her own private space while sharing common gardens and spaces where they can be social together.

Lesbian co-housing and retirement communities are also available across the country, as are social media sites supporting them. These groups discuss what kind of community housing they can create that will best meet the needs of lesbian and feminist elders. Also discussed are concepts such as how to create women-centered housing in which women's culture and community can be enjoyed year-round.

For example, here are two women-only retirement living options:

- The Resort on Carefree Boulevard in Fort Myers, Florida, is a women-only community of manufactured homes and recreational vehicles.

- Discovery Bay Resort is a small women-only development featuring small, manufactured homes of about 400 square feet and RVs. It is on the North Olympic Peninsula, about halfway between Sequim and Port Townsend, Washington.

Building Social Capital

My sister has a close network of boomer women friends who are divorced or never married. They take trips and vacations, go to the movies, attend parties and family functions, and provide support in times of need, together. They are like spouse stand-ins, but not exactly. Many of these women are successful in careers, have investments and savings, live in comfortable homes, and have no kids or husbands. They have this funny line about *women either aging gracefully—or becoming real-estate agents.* There is often truth in jest. Betty Friedan, as mentioned, talked about heterosexual couples that often pass each other in role reversals (hence the X-Over) where males turn domestic and relational—while their female partners take on new careers like real estate sales. The data Friedan found would be dated for younger generations with less traditional gender roles, but it is still relevant for older generations.

My sister and her friends now fix flat tires and gutters, tasks they once would have delegated to husbands. They are going to get T-shirts made saying,

"I'M BECOMING THE MAN I ALWAYS WANTED TO MARRY."

During their "white wine sessions," they talk about the future, pooling their resources (social security checks), getting a big home together, and a single man (the sex ratio) to have around to help out, and to provide male company.

Women all around the country are not only discussing the concept—but have been doing it (maybe not the man part). According to an article in AARP, back in 2007, 500,000 women fifty years of age and older lived with nonromantic housemates. This trend of home-sharing promises to increase as projections from the Joint Center for Housing Studies report the number of people over seventy-five years of age will grow from the 2015 figure of 6.9 million to 13.4 million in 2035. Many of this age cohort will have limited financial resources for housing, and women will comprise nearly 75 percent of this group.

The concept of women pooling resources makes sense on so many levels. Teaming up to spend retirement years together can be a winning solution to many challenges facing older women, like aging in place alone, finding caregivers, needing rides, providing meals, friendship, and sharing chores. There are many things to consider, from sharing the simple activities of daily living tasks, to the more complex legal issues such as homeownership and tenant relations or inheritance. But the benefits may well be worth the effort. As with many ideas and concepts facing baby boomers, this is all new.

We're just making this up as we go along.

—INDIANA JONES

As for the guy who plans to take on that role for my sister and her housemates, I hope he eats his Wheaties (boomer reference); he will need it!

Peter Pan Housing

Peter Pan is a character who never grows up. Some urban planners use this dream of eternal youth to describe the Never-Never Land of the nation's endless sprawl of suburbs designed for people who never grow old. Today, that same end-user is a boomer (and increasingly, Millenials) who grew up in suburbia and will face many of the same issues their parents are living with now. And the challenge with the new developments is much like the ones facing the old developments, miles from any commerce, expansive lawns with steep yards, gates for privacy, hill-top settings with lots of stairs, wide cul-de-sacs, limited sidewalks, and no bus stops. These amenities have been selling points for young families—but they do not serve aging populations so well.

"New urbanism" is a reaction to this suburban sprawl, creating human-scale, walkable communities (so-called 20-minute neighborhoods because you can get anywhere in 20 minutes), transit-oriented, with mixed-use, much along the lines of old European cities. Also known as traditional neighborhood developments (TNDs), these communities are showing up all around the country. For example, Fairview Village in Portland, Oregon, is a TND that boasts community living that is multigenerational, pedestrian-oriented, near bus/light-rail, with shops and a civic center just minutes away. The homes are traditional craftsmen, and some have Universal Design elements, along with porches and sidewalks, for neighbors to keep in touch with each other—like they once did.

If you live in Peter Pan Housing and it is not working for you, consider looking into one of these TNDs or the many neo-traditional neighborhoods around the country. If you are planning on buying, selling, staying put, or looking for other types of housing such as rental, vacation, or investment property, there are ten elements to consider.

10 Elements of a Home in High Demand for an Aging Population

John Lennon once asked a generation to, "Imagine living life in peace." Now, imagine living life in old age. Imagine yourself at eighty years of age; where do you see yourself living? Have you thought about it? Try to visualize for a moment. Aging baby boomers, some seventy-six million, will live longer than previous generations and many with chronic conditions. They will also be more spread out in suburban areas. Now, this should get you thinking about the relationship between aging and geography.

1. One-level housing
2. Near a bus stop or light-rail station
3. Markets within walking distance (aka "20-minuteneighborhoood" because it takes that long to walk to services)
4. Mixed-use housing
5. Sidewalks & nearby park/green space
6. Homes with a porch (maintain connections with the community)
7. Universal design in the home

8. Civic center, entertainment, church, exercise outlets minutes away
9. Home office
10. Smart home technology

These ten elements will be in high demand as the population ages and desires to create an optimal experience of living into the future.

Caring Communities

Another exciting possibility is the Caring Community web-based model, which is popping up around the country. I read about Dorian Mintzer, a Boston retirement authority who supports joining one of a growing number of web-based and community-based models for caring communities. She notes, "People help others, knowing that they can also count on being helped when the need arises. This is particularly helpful for women living alone."

Recommended:

- Lotsahelpinghands.com
- ttnwomen.org
- caringcommunity.org

Accessory Dwelling Unit (ADU)

The big trend in senior housing, especially in the west, is Accessory Dwelling Units (ADUs). They go by many names like Granny flats or mother-in-law suites. An ADU is a legal and regulatory term for a secondary house or apartment that shares the building lot of a larger primary house, secondary dwelling unit, or carriage house.

- An ADU is an additional residential building that occupies the same lot as a primary residence.

- Examples of an ADU could be a guest house or a detached garage with a rented apartment above.
- The establishment and use of an ADU will fall under different zoning rules and regulations depending on where you live (Investopedia.com).

Go to buildinganadu.com for more information.

One morning, I was out walking my dog and we encountered a lovely woman named "Joan." We had a stimulating conversation that eventually got around to my work with aging in place. She informed me that her family built an ADU in their backyard for her. She was a grandmother, active, held a Ph.D., and was loving life and her family, but still wanted some level of inter-dependence that suited all parties involved. When I queried further, Joan conveyed some of her rules for living in an accessory dwelling unit near her family. She said she had made a schedule that included two movie nights a week with the family, at a specific time and day. "They stick to it as best they can."

Her boundaries were:

- Movie night scheduled 2x/week with the family (at the big house)
- Always knock first (both ways)
- Lights out at 10 p.m. each night at the ADU
- Respect privacy (both ways)
- Give the family a schedule of what her week looks like

These speculations were negotiated before moving in and are still negotiable. Of course, she told me, but it was essential to her to manage expectations with all parties involved.

ADU Types

- Detached new construction
- Garage conversion
- Above a garage or workshop
- An addition or bump-out

- Basement conversion
- Internal

Common Traits

- ADUs are an accessory and adjacent to a primary housing unit.
- ADUs are significantly smaller than the average US house.
- ADUs tend to be one of two units owned by one owner on a single-family residential lot.
- ADUs tend to be primarily developed asynchronously from the primary house by homeowner developers.

A range of municipal land use and zoning regulations differentiate ADU types and styles and affect their allowed uses.

The critical consideration is always building ADUs with accessible design (consult an occupational therapist or Certified Aging in Place Specialist from the National Association of Home Builders, or National Aging in Place Council).

Joan is living her best life in an ADU, connected to family, yet enjoying a negotiated level of independence. She is a model example of successful inter-dependence and designed happiness at home.

The New Life Plan for Happiness

My colleague, Rama Ramasubramanian, sent several articles on happiness he encountered online one day. Happiness is a topic we often discuss in one form or another, and reading what others have to say on the subject interests us. There is a robust body of research on getting older and happiness, confirming yet another paradox of aging. Studies show that happiness peaks in your 20s, dips at middle age, and then ascends once again after 50. It appears in a "U" shape and is thus dubbed the "U-Curve" of Happiness when graphed.

In an informative article by Meg Selig, "Older but Happier? 5 Amazing Findings from Recent Research: Whoever dubbed old age 'the golden years' was right," the author unpacks several vital elements to happiness in old age:

1. Older adults no longer require extraordinary experiences to be happy; instead, they find happiness in ordinary things.
2. Meaningful relationships (authentic) are another source of happiness.
3. Volunteering seems to be a common meme in the development of happy old age.
4. Purpose beyond the self is another.

Happiness can be a problem, and its pursuit is written into our very constitution, making it an obsession in our country. Like most things in our capitalist society, happiness has been poisoned by subjugating it to commodity status (yes, there is an app to find it). Happiness, to me, seems to be a byproduct of serving, loving, kindness, self-expression, and contribution; again, all acts.

As many spiritual teachers have noted, it is a choice. What leads to your happiness as you age? It is a subject worth contemplating and discussing with valued others; the late psychologist Dr. Wayne Dyer once noted, "There is no way to happiness. Happiness is the way." I think he was onto something.

"Gerontophobia" is defined as the fear of aging or growing old. "Age ghettos" describe age-segregated living. These terms, and many more, have become part of my professional vocabulary and everyday speech. The individuals featured in this book have been on the front lines, reimagining aging, so we will have a richer experience of growing older. Before social change around aging became a thing, the late Betty Friedan was in the media boldly demanding change. She proclaimed gerontophobia was the denial of age by the society at large, and the cause of "leisure-world ghettos." She argued that our fear of older people causes society to sequester elders away from the community, not to remind us of our aging selves.

Wake up and live in Sun City
for an active new way of life.

Wake up and live in Sun City
Mr. Senior Citizen and wife.
Don't let retirement get you
down! Be happy in Sun City;
it's a paradise-town.

—RADIO ADVERTISING JINGLE DEL WEBB CORPORATION, 1960

It was not always like this. Elders were once the keepers of the stories! In agrarian societies, the elders had ensured roles and status as landowners and workers. The industrial revolution of the 1800s ushered in an era of aging as a scientific problem and the body-as-machine (peak and decline model) viewpoint. Older workers could not keep pace with the industrial revolution's work mode, and many ended up as casualties on the scrap pile of social perceptions as no longer beneficial to society.

Late-nineteenth-century physician, I. L. Nascher (who coined the term "geriatrics" for the study of aging) said, "The old man does not know what is best for him . . . he cannot accommodate himself to new conditions brought about by the progress of civilization (Prime Time, 2002)." The problem with Dr. Nascher's statement is professional prescriptions end up as public policy—among them, old-aged homes and mandatory retirement. In turn, popular perceptions (rather than reality) shape social expectations and cause a fear of aging!

I once heard of a study done to determine which society of elders has the best memory retention. Researchers determined it was the Chinese, and when they returned to the data a second time to see what other factors may have been influential, guess what? Chinese society *expected* the elderly to retain memory into old age, so they did. To my point, the conditions of some older adults are changing because of social expectations. The old linear life plan where education is for the young, work is for the middle-aged, and leisure is for the old, gives way to new plans. Many baby boomers live cyclic life plans of alternating education, work, and leisure, which are full-time activities for periods throughout life. Further, the more likely scenario is the blended life plan where work, education, and leisure are concurrent throughout life–often in the same week!

The new life plan for the 21st-century favors various new options for aging in place and staying plugged into the vibrant nature of the community with mixed generation environments. In addition, most older adults prefer staying where they have situated their lives for years. According to author Marc Freedman, the model for success in later life was the emergence of a mass leisure class and Sun City-like retirement. Age-segregated and leisure-oriented living are fine for some (Ken Dychthwald called it Twilight Zoneish) but for others, it is outdated. What is good is that society's expectations are changing, especially for aging women.

> ***They recognize that ageism will not be defeated by a retreat to age-segregated corners but only by engagement, collaboration and dialogue across age, race, and class divides.***
>
> —PAUL IRVING

Summary on Home and Happiness

Over the years working in Intensive Care Units as a nurse, I have witnessed the most tender moments between families. When the life of a loved one is threatened, it brings out the deepest emotions of what it means to be human. Many times, I have watched bedside vigils that only love could explain. I write on the topic of aging in place and living in environments of choice as we all get older because it is essential; shelter is at the core of what it means to be human. We all need a safe physical dwelling in which to situate our lives and cultivate meaning, and there is no higher human undertaking than to love and be loved in return. The home is often the setting in which this meaning-making occurs. In my experience, most patients had two desires; first, for healing and restored wellness, without exception, to go *home.*

Advocating for aging in place, I have always promoted the positive aspects of remaining home by choice. Yet, there are two nagging issues in search of solutions—these are isolation and money.

The dangers of social isolation in older populations are well documented; from increased risk of dementia to a shortened lifespan, it is a barrier to aging well. The solutions to isolation and money issues for aging in place are multiple and becoming more mainstream as the demographic shift makes it a national priority. Here are just a few to review:

- Co-housing
- Golden girls' home sharing
- Aging-in-place technologies
- Age-friendly cities designed for social encounters
- Contact the Elderly (UK) social groups
- Freebirdclub.com (Travel club for 50+)
- Airbnb Win-Win for aging in place

Money has always been an issue when considering affordable housing for aging in place. As we hear every day in the media, most Americans have not saved enough for their retirement years. According to Yahoo!money (yahoo.com), one in four Americans have no retirement savings—and those who do aren't saving enough. With women living longer, this is a fundamental quality of life issue.

Along comes Airbnb, with a potential solution to both the isolation and money issues related to aging in place. "Airbnb's mission is to create a world where all 7 billion people can belong anywhere. At least a billion of those people are over 60 years old, and their decades of stories and experiences make them some of the best Airbnb hosts in our worldwide community."

What is Airbnb? It is a community built on sharing that began in 2008, when two designers who had space to share hosted three travelers, looking for a place to stay. Today, millions of hosts and travelers choose to create a free Airbnb account to list their space and book unique accommodations anywhere in the world. Airbnb helps make sharing easy, enjoyable, and safe. The business verifies personal profiles and listings, maintains an innovative messaging system so hosts and guests can communicate with certainty, and manages a trusted platform to collect and transfer payments. Worldwide, there are almost one million Airbnb users who are over 60. Among hosts, 10 percent of them are over 60; these hosts come from all walks of life (aarp.org).

The benefits for the 60+ hosts:

1. Social interaction that is multi-generational and global
2. The mental stimulation that is so essential to the aging brain (Novelty and Complexity = Dendrite growth)
3. Environmental press (the physical, interpersonal, or social demands that environments put on people) of having to host guests
4. Income generation to supplement retirement
5. Purpose

Airbnb seems to be one creative solution to overcome the social isolation and money challenges older adults face. It is out-of-the-box thinking and one of the most innovative ideas to facilitate aging in place in recent years. It might be a solution for you if you are 60+ and are willing to experience the potential upside or downside risks.

I was listening to Dr. Bill Thomas (Eden Alternative founder) describe the danger of creating "too safe" of an environment where individuals are not allowed the opportunity to take risks that would permit them to grow and thrive. He notes that the term "risk" means an outcome that differs from the expected.

In defining risk this way, there are two sides; the familiar downside to risk, which is the probability that things will turn out worse than expected, and the lesser-known upside to risk, where things turn out better than anticipated.

Upside of Risk

This upside to risk seems to be lacking in long-term care settings, which, according to Dr. Thomas, are obsessed with the downside—I agree. This is a byproduct of the *"biomedicalization"* of aging, where elderly are treated as a disease category to be cared for by experts. One aspect of this paradigm is infantilizing older people and turning them into "patients" subject to over-protection. Elderly people are not viewed as capable of human development and growth. The unstated here is that the end of the lifecycle is not worth risking for potential upside benefits. Thomas makes the point that in no other part of the life cycle is risk aversion allowed.

I guess every form of refuge has its price.

—EAGLES

The Upside Risk of Environmental Press

Aging in place is risky. Older adults are called upon to rise to the occasion, daily, to meet the demands of living at home: drive to the market, mow the lawn, tend the garden, care for pets, and deal with home upkeep, repairs, security, activities of daily living (ADLs), laundry, bills, cleaning, cooking, and many other related responsibilities that could, in some cases, be done for them.

These traditional *burdens of homeownership* that many seek to avoid are forms of Environmental Press (EP) *or forces in the environment that evoke a response together with individual need.* It is in meeting the demands and needs of EP, older adults remain not just physically challenged—but mentally as well. For example, it has been established for decades that older men lose muscle mass at twice the rate of older women (Goodpaster, et al.). The reason is in retirement, women traditionally continue to do chores around the house—and "the life of leisure" may not be neuro-protective (stimulate the brain).

Perhaps it is time we equate aging in place with the upside of risk. As Bill Thomas states, "Lives should include a balance of downside and upside; risks are part of a normal healthy life."

Grandma always made you feel like she had been waiting to see just you all day, and now the day was complete.

—MARCY DEMAREE

I will close out this chapter with a poem I wrote about visiting Grandma's house. For so many of us, memories of our grandmother's home conjure up happiness, whether the occasional holiday events or drop-in visits. Please enjoy; I hope it stirs up some warm memories for you.

A visit to Grandma's house

Amber lights glow through windows, damp from the inside out; plastic-covered couch, yellowed and opaquely transparent, exposing floral prints too dear for mere human contact. A hard-candy dish, whose sticky contents have clung to each other like lovers, vowing 'until death do they part'. And a chipped Harrah's Hotel casino ashtray sits, lonesome from benign neglect on the end-table, a relic from vices long since abandoned.

The air is heavy with the lingering scent of bacon and eggs, BenGay, old dog, and a pervasive musty kind of love that for years has baked into every corner of this modest dwelling. Delicate lace doilies lounge on worn mohair armrests, like aging beauties in the waning soft light of the late afternoon. Hallway wooden floors creak in old familiar places as you pass over them; they announce your presence like stepping onto an aching back, on cue, with the predictability of the arrival of spring.

And these walls adorned with framed records in chronological order of the passing of time; the first baby, off to war, the 1946 Dodge, the trip to Hawaii, a bowling league team, and the retirement party. This is not the contrived aesthetic of Architectural Digest—no, things here have frayed edges from love like the Velveteen Rabbit. They are meaningful, have a shared history like family archaeology, and are the poetry of aging in place.

Goodbye Myth: You Do Not Have to Go It Alone— You Have Options!

Step 5
Consider co-housing, home sharing, ADUs, and caring communities.

Suggested Resources

Co-housing and Aging Women

Co-housing is a form of aging in place, in that people live in non-institutional settings of one's own choosing with shared living spaces and interdependence. In this sense, environments embedded in vibrant communities provide mutual support for an optimal aging experience. Is co-housing for you? Visit cohousingco.com for more information.

Dorian Mintzer, MSW, Ph.D., BCC, CSA. Email: dorian@dorianmintzer.com. Website: revolutionizeretirement.com.

Eden Alternative: edenalt.org / Dr. Bill Thomas MINKA, Homes and Communities.

FREE guide for building an ADU, buildinganadu.com/adu-resource-packet.

Watch the film, *The Older Women's Co-housing Project*, imdb.com/video/vi1475979033.

NAHB Aging-In-Place Remodeling Checklist.

Nationalsharedhousing.org.

Old Lesbians Organizing for Change (OLOC): oloc.org.

Silvernest.com: A Home Sharing Network.

The ABCs of ADUs, aarp.org. *A Guide to Accessory Dwelling Units and How They Expand Housing Options for People of All Ages.*

The Village Movement: *Has been described as an innovative type of grass-roots organization emerging in the last decade from the organizational field of support services for community-dwelling older adults.*

WomenforLivinginCommunity.com

Purpose Statement

Women for Living in Community brings together women, as natural leaders and nurturers, to create communities for growing older with grace and dignity.

Definition of Environmental Press Theory (EP)

Lawton (Lawton, Brody, and Turner-Massey 1978, and Lawton 1983, Lawton 1985) presented to the gerontology field a theoretical framework for understanding adaptation to the environment in older persons. The environmental press theory is a theory of adaptation that focuses on person variables (competencies), environmental variables (environmental press), and the interaction between the two variables. Competencies include physical and functional health, cognitive and affective functioning, and quality of life, including a sense of efficacy or mastery. Environmental press variables include the person's home environment, their social environment, and even their neighborhood environment. The fit between a person's level of competencies and the demands from their environment affects how well an individual is functioning (https://academic.oup.com/gerontologist/article/40/5/549/586997).

CHAPTER 6

A Legacy of Less and The Meaning of Things

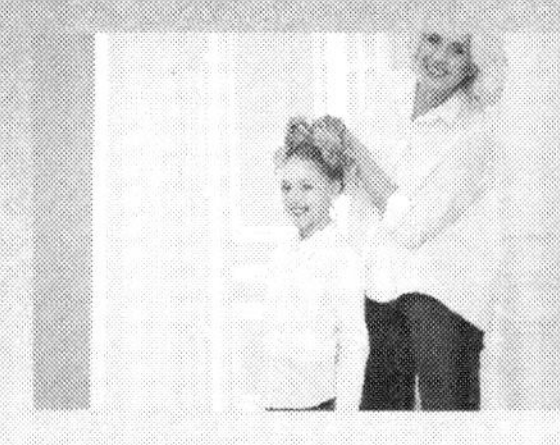

MYTH: The More Things I Leave for Others, the Greater my Legacy of Love

All my possessions for a moment of time.

—ELIZABETH I

It was a sunny Saturday morning in Portland (a rare event), and I found myself in the parking lot of the mega home-furnishings store, IKEA. If you have never been to the store, it is an enchanting experience. The design is European, unique, affordable, and the layout is like a giant maze of visual delights. Enticed by one of those IKEA flyers which landed on our front doorstep, and having succumbed to the manufactured need to buy something I did not need but wanted, I now waited in line out front to buy some new flatware. It seemed I was not the only one as a line of fellow shoppers formed before the store formally opened. Like Catholic grade school kids on their way to recess (filled with the anticipation of getting a deal) we marched single file to the back of the store. Soon, we were rewarded for our early arrival with shiny Euro-design silverware.

Next, I made my way to the register to pay for my newfound treasure. In no time, I headed for the exit with that bit of dopamine lift that comes from buying something (and the perception of getting a deal). Nearing the egress, I glanced over and noticed a display of irresistible IKEA catalogs; I picked one up, tucked it under my arm, and left for home.

IKEA Knows IKEA is thriving because they understand three fundamental things:

1. Home is the most important place in the world.
2. The Aesthetic Imperative.
3. Affordable small indulgences.

What immediately caught my eye on the IKEA catalog cover was this text:

Home is the most important place in the world.

They not only get it, but they also state it on the cover. They have built an enormously successful business on this emotional appeal. Home, for younger people, acts as a kind of psychic anchor, reminding one of where they started. For older adults, attachment to home serves to preserve a sense of personal identity; it is a "fulcrum" to the rest of the world. Graham D. Rowles, PhD, Chair of the Department of Gerontology, University of Kentucky, coined the term "insideness" to describe a physical sense of attachment to home along with being psychologically melded into the environment, that stems from years of rhythm and routine, using the space over many years. The IKEA business model understands this innately.

The Aesthetic Imperative

We live in the age of aesthetics, meaning items need to work well and must also dazzle the eye. Products cannot compete solely on function anymore; most things made today will do the job nicely. To gain an advantage, products must now be aesthetically pleasing. Target has traded on this idea for years, hiring the late Michael Graves to design simple everyday products with aesthetic appeal that gives an edge (competitive advantage) if you sell trash cans or fly swatters that function equally well. IKEA is delivering multi-sensory aesthetic experiences, or what author Virginia Postrel calls "immersive environments." The concept brings the home experience into an almost intangible realm—which is vital for boomers, as the spirit will come to dominate matter in later years.

Futurist Faith Popcorn nailed this decades ago, and she is still spot-on. Small indulgences, or the trend of thinking highly enough about you as a person to treat yourself, are alive and well in boomers. When the economy is doing well, one might splurge on a bottle of Veuve Clicquot champagne, but as things tighten up, the small reward might be a set of two LACK nesting tables in white from the IKEA catalog. Popcorn says this has to do with some deep sense of deprivation as we grow up thinking each generation will have it better than before; it is a perceived quality of life issue. For a reasonable price, IKEA can scratch that deep psychological itch.

The home not only has a supportive function of shelter, cooking, rest, storage, etc., but it has a psychological function of meeting emotional needs, like the desire for beauty and sensory stimulation. IKEA also knows this too well, and I would add a fourth to the list . . . they would be wise to tap into the aging in place and universal design market. For aging baby boomers around the globe, home is the most important place in the world, as they will spend more time and money in and around their domestic spaces in later years.

Many years ago, I sat in a statistics class, listening to Professor Ann Wax have the unenviable task of explaining the difference between reliability and validity to undergraduates. Her brilliant treatment of the topic came as a story, which I still recall with admiration to this day. Professor Wax began her narrative by telling us about a death in the family. Her aunt, who lived back east, had passed away. Being prudent before she died, she had labeled various personal items to be dispersed among surviving relatives.

Because Professor Wax had been a favorite of her aunt's, she received her share of meaningful things in the mail from the estate. However, one sizable slender package stuck out because it was wrapped with the care offered to a newborn baby. When she carefully unveiled the object, to her surprise, it was a closet mirror, the cheap kind you adhere to the back of a door. Why on Earth had she taken the time and effort to wrap an item that could be bought at any Target or Walmart for several dollars, and mail it across the country?

It soon became apparent why this was one of her aunt's precious objects—when Professor Wax casually looked at her image in the mirror; she appeared fifteen pounds slimmer! For many years, the mirror had made her aunt appear fifteen pounds lighter every time she gazed into it (reliable), but the weight remained (validity). So, the mirror was reliable, but not valid; lesson learned. Things have meaning for personal reasons, regardless of reliability or validity—we create the significance.

Things embody goals, make skills manifest, and shape the identities of their users. Man is not only homo sapiens or homo ludens, he is also homo faber, the maker and user of objects, his self to a large extent a reflection of things with which he interacts.

—MIHALY CSIKSZENTMIHALYI & EUGENE ROCHBERG-HALTON

Psychologists Mihaly Csikszentmihalyi and Eugene Rochberg-Halton (*The Meaning of Things: Domestic Symbols and the Self)* asked respondents in a survey, "Is there one personal possession you value above all others?" Over four of every five could readily identify such an object. Gender differences appeared as men identified more consumer items and women more symbolic items like photographs and jewelry. For adults over 75, more of them (30 percent) could identify no cherished object compared to only 8 percent of the younger respondents. The researchers found this was because many of the older participants lived in nursing homes, and lack of cherished things was associated with the absence of one's own home.

The authors' findings showed that moving into institutional settings often means living in environments devoid of meaningful things typically found at home. That almost symbiotic bond between home and objects is then severed.

Dr. Bill Thomas, a Geriatrician and advocate for senior housing built on humanity, not efficiency, once commented about some corporate chain long-term care facilities by saying, "Brass and glass have no soul."

From glass roses I gave my friend in the nursing home that lasted two weeks before being broken by a nurse-aide, to the antique Santa that required labeling with a black marker (nursing home necessity), meaningful things lose meaning in institutions. I was moved deeply by a haunting response after writing about the meaning of things in the home environment and how they support our identity and delight our senses. I was lamenting how institutions for older adults that are run on efficiency can neglect the mindful care that meaningful objects are subject to at home.

A response from a reader evoked a heartbreaking story about her father:

> *What a beautiful and powerful article. I have had experience with cherished things belonging to cherished people (my parents) in nursing homes. The loss of my dad's glasses still haunts me. How could someone have taken his glasses? How could we have prevented their loss? In his final days, he could not clearly see the faces of the people he loved. His mind was totally sharp it was his body that was sick.*
>
> *After the morning that we discovered that they had disappeared overnight, he never mentioned them again. We could not get a new prescription fast enough. He never again saw us or the smile of his beloved grandchildren. Cherished objects become cherished because they connect us to the world and to ourselves. We cannot dismiss them as unimportant—they are part of what helps us to live and eventually to let go, at peace.*
>
> *—Roberta*

Being able to remain home as one ages can maintain that essential bond between the person and their things. It is a reliable and valid way for us to continue interacting with meaningful objects that contribute to what environmental psychologists call "place attachment." The message is beyond materialism.

I like how the late Csikszentmihalyi and co-author, Rochberg-Halton, describe it:

> *Objects affect what a person can do, either by expanding or restricting the scope of that person's actions and thoughts. And because what a person does is largely what he or she is, objects have a determining effect on the development of the self, which is why understanding the type of relationship that exists between people and things is so crucial.*

In Praise of Empty Spaces

Now, having described the essential role of meaningful objects in our domestic lives, there is also much to be said for downsizing as we age. Dr. Bill Thomas of the Eden Alternative calls it "lightening our load." Most likely, you are dealing with your accumulation of stuff and/or that of older family members. George Carlin famously said, "A house is just a place to keep your stuff while you go out and get more stuff." Was he ever right!

On a personal note, I spent years de-cluttering the home I grew up in, and it took years because I could only do it part time around work and other responsibilities. Because my folks never threw anything out, the dwelling was crammed with sixty years of family accumulations. I can hear the refrain reverberating in my ears, "I may need that someday." The family joke was that I would inherit the garage (which was a floor-to-ceiling jam-packed mess) for my entire life. That time did eventually come along with every room in the house, and several storage units as well.

It is difficult to explain to someone who has not gone through the experience of sorting out the material lives of our elderly loved ones, and to do it in a brief window of time. The task is daunting in that the physical aspects of laying hands on a lifetime of accumulation can seem like stringing beads without a knot on the other end. That would be enough, but layers of emotional sentiment infused with meaning add to the complexity. And there is the who-gets-what aspect to toss into the mix, as well.

Perhaps it matters less that people cannot park in their garages or close their closet doors earlier in life. But when hoarding researcher Dr. Ekerdt asked respondents how reluctant they felt about moving, considering the effort required to transfer or dispose of their belongings, he found that 48 percent felt "very reluctant" to move, another 30 percent were "somewhat reluctant." That adds up to over three-quarters of people over 60 with the feeling of being trapped, to some degree, by stuff. New York Times author of the New Old Age blog, Paula Span exclaimed, "I found myself wondering whether some of the widespread insistence on aging in place reflects a weary assessment of how hard it would be to pack up and age anywhere else."

Dante's Inferno

The 14th-century epic poem *The Divine Comedy* by Dante Alighieri is 14,000 lines of allegory describing the author's philosophical journey through hell, purgatory, and beyond. In the story, Dante one-night dreams of a beautiful hillside, and at the top is a paradise in waiting. All he must do is climb to the peak to reach it. As he embarks on the journey, it is interrupted by a monster who tells him that before he climbs to the top of the hill, he must first descend through nine circles of hell, down to the pit, and back again. Only then can he ascend to the top.

The ancient poet Virgil is his guide and when the two enter the fourth circle of hell, they encounter dueling armies at war with each other, each rolling huge stones with their chests and crashing about.

One army shouts out, "Why do you hoard?"

The other army shouts back, "Why do you waste?"

Virgil describes them as the hoarders and the wasters in life. They have spent so much time worrying about their wealth and possessions "that they lost the light of God and were forever doomed to this joint punishment." These heavy stones represent the material objects they clung to so tightly in life, and the metaphor for "hell" is the opportunity cost of possession obsession.

A colleague called me about an elderly gentleman he was helping. The older fellow had several issues threatening his ability to remain home independently. My friend asked me if I had any resources that may assist the man in maintaining his aging in place status. After listening to the scenario, I wanted to assess the situation and see how I could help. As it turns out, the older man is a compulsive hoarder. He lived alone as a bachelor in one of Portland, Oregon's most desirable neighborhoods; yet, he was a prisoner buried in his treasures.

The definition of hoarding is the acquisition of an inability to discard items, even though they appear to others to have no value. People with Compulsive Hoarding Syndrome (CHS) have immense difficultly throwing things away, even objects of little or no value, such as old newspapers, bits of string, worn-out clothes, and junk mail. Most people with compulsive hoarding disorder are also thought to have obsessive-compulsive disorder (OCD). A third of people diagnosed with OCD have hoarding behaviors. The challenge with hoarding people is they are usually oblivious to the problem and resist any intervention.

Randy Frost, Ph.D., one of the country's leading authorities on this, describes the definition of compulsive hoarding as a three-fold process:

- The acquisition and failure to discard possessions that appear to be useless or of limited value.
- Living spaces so cluttered that using the room as intended is impossible.
- Significant distress or impairment in the ability to function.

Frost says, "Our research indicates that they save things for the same reasons we all save things. The difference seems to be that people who suffer from compulsive hoarding apply these reasons to a wider variety of things."

That wider variety of things presents a wider variety of dangers, including:

- Beds and bathtubs were so filled with belongings there was no room for sleeping or bathing.
- Kitchens that were unsafe and unusable due to cluttered stoves, sinks, and tabletops.
- Large amounts of combustible materials blocking walking paths, radiators, and fire exits.
- No working toilets, sinks, heating, and cooling appliances - fearing eviction, they do not get repairs.
- Mounds of trash, rotten food, human and animal waste.
- Insect and rodent infestation.
- Many unkempt pets in need of care.

With the aging population, hoarding is increasingly recognized as a mental health problem that threatens older adults' health, safety, and dignity. Compulsive hoarding (which often begins in young adulthood) becomes more challenging for older people with multiple chronic health conditions. According to Frost, mobility is an issue in homes filled with clutter. The elderly will often form "goat-paths" among the clutter to move from room to room. This clutter increases the risks of tripping and falling and is hazardous to emergency personnel should a rescue be needed. These unsafe conditions in the dwelling affect the health of the occupant, and they put the community and neighborhood at risk.

The irony is that CHS sufferers are perfectionists in constant fear of making a mistake. To avoid errors, they take longer to make decisions; they spend time "churning," moving one pile to another instead of getting rid of anything for fear of making a "bad choice." They are also in need of control, and to throw something out is to surrender control of the items over to others. Family members are collateral damage as feelings of embarrassment, frustration, or resentment toward the hoarding behavior can lead to stress.

The clutter also causes social isolation and few social contacts because of the lack of visitors to the home. Ashamed of the clutter, family members may attempt to clean up and organize, leading to further chaos and fights. In my case, growing up, we never had visitors over to the house—there was nowhere to sit. And as a visiting adult, I could not stay overnight because the cluttered home afforded no space to lie down.

I read a disturbing story by elder law attorney Geoff Bernhardt about a couple married for over fifty years. The wife was a compulsive hoarder, and the husband was meticulously clean. The difference was so pronounced they had separate rooms in their home; one jam-packed with stuff, the other meticulously organized. When the wife's health declined over time, the husband took on the caretaker role. At the end of her life, as she lay dying, her last message to her lifelong mate was not "I love you," it was, "Please don't touch my stuff." This heartbreaking story is evidence of a compulsive hoarder.

Compulsive Hoarding Syndrome is a threat to aging in place. Home health services will be denied unless the hoarding is addressed and resolved. As I witnessed in this case, medicines under mounds of clutter and lung conditions were made worse by dust and mold (to mention only a few health hazards). The home was not livable in its current state, and the hoarding spiraled out of control.

The importance of understanding the psychosocial issues and reasons for hoarding is essential for successful interventions. Forced clean-outs, which can be costly, are reported to be unsuccessful as homes revert to an uninhabitable level within a relatively short period. Further, older adults may suffer acute emotional responses during forced clean-outs requiring emergency psychiatric care. Insights into the reasons older people hoard can help facilitate effective and compassionate interventions, including ongoing support and maintenance. The goal is to support successful aging in place and true quality of life.

With the many loads to the dumpster and runs to Goodwill we made; he pleaded his case to keep various items. As gut-wrenching as that was to watch, my colleague reminded him gently that the overall goal was to keep him safely in his dwelling. We all hope, on some level, the message hit home.

Note: We saved him from seeing the items as they were removed from the home. Eventually, he was taken to a family member's house to stay during the cleanup.

Have nothing in your homes that you do not know to be useful or believe to be beautiful.

—WILLIAM MORRIS

Or in more contemporary terms . . .

Does it spark joy?

—MARIE KONDO

As for my journey in de-cluttering my childhood home, it was all-consuming for years. Like most senior care, there are mixed emotions. I want to be there for them, as they were there for me. The limited-time allocation I had as a working adult meant there was a significant opportunity cost to dealing with my parents' vast amount of stuff. Time moving, sorting, selling, donating, recycling, negotiating with siblings (additional stressors here) was precious time away from the people with whom I had limited time left to spend. The lessons here are hard won, and I pray you do not have the same experience. It will be one of your greatest gifts to leave a legacy of *less* for your loved ones. Because in the limited time we have with the people we cherish, it becomes crystal clear that there are no ordinary moments.

Final Thoughts

One morning, on a serendipitous run for coffee, I stumbled on an interior design, crafts, and coffee shop. My adventurous wonderings got rewarded with a hot, steaming mug of strong coffee and some visual delights. I love old things; they have a presence and a character earned over time not found in new things (not unlike people). The shop was a "shabby chic" establishment graced with vintage lace and whitewashed French farm décor. My aesthetic appeal is less calculating, but I can appreciate beautiful objects.

> ***Beauty is eternity gazing at itself in a mirror.***
>
> —KHALIL GIBRAN

I will admit I pondered the frivolous nature of such places—after all, these items are not "essential" (coffee is, however). Or are they? The shop is a portal to material objects that allow folks (who can afford it) to obtain things that create meaning in their domestic spaces. This meaning—aesthetic meaning—has the potential to renew one's energy and feed the depleted soul. Visually delightful objects must not be overlooked as a source of power. They can infuse a dwelling with contagious energy to its inhabitants—enough so that they can go back out into the world and accomplish their heroic missions in life.

My argument is that it is not just family and friends, but "beautiful" (eye of the beholder) objects that can bring vital energy to the home. Aesthetic input infuses the material, physical, and spiritual alike, and can replenish what living in the modern world extracts. Beautiful things in the domestic space are vital to successful aging in place and should be a part of your strategy. Dante Alighieri said beauty awakens the soul to act. The act is to keep a few things that "spark joy" and cull out the rest.

My plea is to women who are Gen-Xers, Boomers, or older seniors. If you are "over-provisioned," please self-downsize, before it is a crisis and left to loved ones. It will be one of your greatest gifts to leave a legacy of *less*. I have heard countless times from Millennials and younger generations, they do not want your stuff!

> Working with my mother as she has progressed through four home environments of decreasing size, I can attest to her comfort at being surrounded by furniture, photos, art, and other objects that are important to her. As she downsizes each time, she feels better that many items she no longer has room for are going to family members. Now she is down to a tiny fraction of her original household items . . . and she has found yet another equilibrium in those items.
>
> —RICHARD DUNCAN, UNIVERSAL DESIGN INSTITUTE, EXECUTIVE DIRECTOR

Goodbye Myth: Your family will be better off with a legacy of less and more time with you.

Step 6

Begin de-cluttering today with a simple napkin exercise.

Suggested Resources

While hoarder personality traits and demographics vary widely, people who live with a hoarding disorder often share a set of characteristics. On average, individuals who exhibit hoarding behavior:

- Live alone
- Are three times more likely to be obese than the average person
- Are perfectionistic
- Have at least one family member who is also a hoarder

Currently, researchers believe compulsive hoarding affects one in fifty people, but it may impact one in twenty. According to the National Alliance on Mental Illness (NAMI), up to 5 percent of the world's population displays symptoms of clinically diagnosable hoarding (therecoveryvillage.com).

Thanks to R. Frost for *The Divine Comedy* story.

Resource

The National Association of Specialty & Senior Move Managers® is the leading membership organization for Move Managers in the United States, Canada, and abroad. Recognizing and managing the stress of relocating older adults, individuals and families is the hallmark of the National Association of Specialty & Senior Move Managers® (NASMM). Additionally, NASMM members will help you downsize, organize, and simplify your current home through our NASMM@Home program.

Contact: nasmm.org

CHAPTER 7

Compressing Morbidity

MYTH: Aging is a Disease That Can be Cured

You can take the time to be healthy—or you will have to take the time to be sick.

—UNKNOWN

THE COMPRESSION OF MORBIDITY IN PUBLIC HEALTH IS A hypothesis put forth by James Fries, professor of medicine at Stanford University School of Medicine. It means to reduce the length of time a person spends sick or disabled, and the goal is to maximize a healthy lifespan and minimize the time being unhealthy.

Many of our disease states, especially in the elderly, have gone from acute, such as pneumonia (the "old man's friend") which once killed in a matter of weeks—to chronic, not cured but managed, over long periods. Health professionals tend to see acute exacerbations of chronic conditions such as congestive heart failure, diabetes, or chronic obstructed pulmonary disease repeatedly. The illnesses that drastically shortened lifespans in the past are now the cause of multiple hospitalizations and caregiver burnout. In the parlance of medical slang, they are called "frequent flyers" and they get to be well known by staff as they come in for periodic "tune-ups."

Dr. Vonda Wright is an orthopedic surgeon and internationally recognized authority on active aging and mobility. She reports we can harness our power to control 70 percent of our health and aging with mobility, smart nutrition, and building relationships. Dr. Wright is also an advocate for women's healthy aging on her podcast, speaking engagements, and multiple books on healthy aging, including *Fitness After 40: Your Strong Body at 40, 50, 60, and Beyond*. She says, "As we age, our bodies change—but that doesn't have to impact our fitness level. We may not be teenagers anymore, but if we exercise smarter, we can remain youthful, energetic, and strong."

Dr. Wright talks about optimal mobility, which is defined simply as being able to safely and reliably go where you want to go, when you want to go, and how you want to get there—a key component of healthy aging and one she emphasizes. She notes,

> *People believe that at some arbitrary age, you get old, and you start dying. But the fact is, researchers in the area of pure longevity and active aging have shown that no matter what your age or your skill level, you can reverse the hands of time. And knowledge of science can help us make this change. This body that we're given is a dynamic and changing organ. One thing that we were led to believe a few decades ago is that we were given one brain, one body and we should not waste it. But actually, we know that is not true. We know that our bones replace themselves every 10 years through tissue regeneration. Our body takes out minerals, puts back minerals. Our brains also regenerate. She reports that even 90-year-old people in nursing homes can increase their function by 150 percent by sitting in chairs and doing a little bit of mobility or exercise therapy.*

Dr. Wright shares another example of how powerful the body can be, especially with a strong purpose behind it, with a story about the oldest Pearl Harbor veteran, U.S. Navy veteran Ray Chavez, who passed away in 2018 at age 106. At the age of 101, he decided to be a part of Pearl

Harbor's 75th-anniversary celebration. For three years, he worked with a trainer to build up twenty pounds of muscle so he could sit on a six-hour plane ride and attend the ceremony. Dr. Wright said, "Now, don't tell me that if the World War II vet who is 104 years old can decide to improve his strength and mobility, that the rest of us can't invest a little time in ourselves."

From her website (drvondawright.com) she posted a headline: *33 DISEASES . . . known as Sedentary Death Syndrome, are the #1 killer in the U.S.* The message is attention-grabbing. A related article from the National Institute of Health suggests similar evidence supporting her statement. Many of the chronic conditions we blame on aging have nothing to do with getting older. Conditions, such as being sedentary, fall under the category of "secondary agers" or the things we do to ourselves to speed up the aging process. As the saying goes, our biography becomes our biology—how we live will largely determine how we age.

Two such inter-related conditions often caused by lack of movement are obesity and arthritis. Researchers at Duke University Medical School found that obesity and arthritis begin for women in the childbearing and perimenopause years caused by weight gain. In addition, the study showed the women were more likely than men to experience fractures, vision problems, and bronchitis.

Women have a natural tendency to gain more weight than men over the lifespan but may be more motivated to maintain a healthy weight if they realize that those extra pounds make it more likely that they will be disabled in later years - potentially becoming a burden to their children or requiring a nursing home. This is important because it suggests that women's tendency to pack on extra pounds in their child-bearing and perimenopause years translates into a loss of independence in their old age.

—HEATHER WHITSON, M.D. (ASSISTANT PROFESSOR OF MEDICINE)

Women's Chronic Diseases Translates to Loss of Independence

Using the Kaiser Family Foundation definition (kff.org) of an adult who has a BMI of 30 or higher is considered obese:

2007-2008, the prevalence of obesity

32.2% among adult men
35.5% among adult women
(JAMA: Obesity Trends)

In 2017-2018 (according to the CDC), the prevalence was:

40.0% among younger adults aged 20–39
44.8% among middle-aged adults aged 40–59
42.8% among older adults aged 60 and over.
There were no significant differences in prevalence by age group.

Among men, the prevalence of obesity

40.3% among those aged 20–39
46.4% among those aged 40–59
42.2% among those aged 60 and over

Among women, the prevalence of obesity

39.7% among those aged 20–39
43.3% among those aged 40–59
43.3% among those aged 60 and over

(Source: *Prevalence of Obesity and Severe Obesity Among Adults: The United States*, 2017–2018).

The association between obesity and older adults is complex. It can depend on multiple factors, including income or educational level, and differs by sex, race, ethnicity, social influences, and medical conditions, so weight viewed in context is essential. With that acknowledged, consider this: at forty-two pounds "overweight," you are negotiating stairs, bathtubs, kitchens, and chores like yard work . . . carrying the equivalent of three average size bowling balls! Imagine, if you will, what that does to

- your energy level
- your cardiovascular system (extra vessels to feed the adipose tissue are an extra workload on your heart)
- your skeletal system (knees, hips, back)
- your psychological wellbeing

What is misuse or disuse, and what is normal biological aging? Losing forty-two pounds means not being burdened by three bowling balls. How might that improve your odds of aging in place (remaining independent at home) successfully? There are all kinds of home modifications, high-tech gadgets, and excellent universal design products available on the market to facilitate independence. Some are reasonably priced, some expensive, and some even priceless, but none are as effective as mindful living and making choices that will honor your future independence.

I recall giving a talk to the Kaiser Permanente Silver Sneakers group and asking them, "Why do you participate?" From the back of the room, one senior woman raised her hand and gave an answer I will never forget. She said, "I joined Silver Sneakers because I want my body to be available to me to do whatever it is I want to do in life." Hands down, the single best answer on successful aging I have ever heard.

On the other end of the spectrum is frailty. Linda P. Fried, MD, MPH, Dean of Columbia University's Mailman School of Public Health, has focused her life's work on creating a health span that matches an increased life span. Dr. Fried's focus has been on prevention of frailty, disability, and cardiovascular disease, and defining how to transition to a world where greater longevity benefits people of all ages. She has identified the five traits of frailty syndrome:

1. Weight Loss >10 pounds over a year
2. Frequent Exhaustion
3. Lower Levels of Activity
4. Slow Gait

5. Poor Grip Strength

Further, there are fundamental additional problems with frailty. For example, it is age-related, four out of ten identified as "frail" are over the age of 85. In addition, there is a lack of a physiological safety-net to bounce back from infectious diseases and injuries. Tragically, the medical system, for the most part, has been historically designed to be reactive and not well equipped to deal with frailty. Loved one also often become collateral damage with the loss of "independence" associated with being frail. The good news is that with advanced age, frailty is not necessarily a given.

Jack was right . . .

Many in the WWII and baby boom generation turned on their black and white TVs to view images of a handsome, sincere, high-energy, buffed guy in a tight-fitting jumpsuit, giving motivational chats, leading invigorating workouts.

He encouraged viewers to breathe deeply, and live healthy while being accompanied by lively organ music. His name was Jack LaLanne, and he pioneered the fitness industry before it was cool. His audience was stay-at-home wives of the 1960s as their baby boomer kids looked on. The sets were simple (a steel office chair and a poster board) but the concepts were not, and they still ring true today.

Jack LaLanne was right; he knew that many people's lives were just suicide on the installment plan. Jack recognized our changing disease states, which went from acute to chronic, and many were due simply to misuse or neglect.

His message was about functional aging, which, incidentally, is the critical element of remaining home by choice. Essential to staying active and engaging at home, and in the community, is walking, which depends on muscle strength. Sarcopenia, or the loss of skeletal muscle mass, or muscle function, increases the risk of losing physical independence and death in older adults. LaLanne described "functional aging" in his *The Hands of Time* episode. The goal was to die "young" as late in life as possible, which is the difference between extending life versus extending health—they are not the same thing (optimally you want both).

Further, much attention has been paid lately to the biomarkers of aging and how they can be affected by lifestyle. One key biomarker (measurable physiological factor related to aging) is aerobic capacity. Aerobic capacity (age and weight-specific) is how exercise physiologists measure the body's uptake and oxygen utilization; the term used is VO2max. Oxygen uptake is an essential factor for "independence." If you have a VO2max of less than 10ml/kg/min, you can't live independently at home because of the inability to do activities of daily living (ADLs).

The bad news is, as we age, under normal conditions (meaning no underlying diseases like lung cancer), VO2max after age 30 decreases by 1 percent each year. A 70-year-old has a 40 percent decrease in VO2max. The good news is exercise can decrease that 1 percent yearly decline in VO2max after age 30 by half. A 70-year-old may only experience a 20 percent decrease in VO2max.

While you are doing that elder-friendly home evaluation, embracing the concept of universal design, emphasizing fall prevention, comparison shopping for Certified Aging in Place Specialists remodelers (more on this in the following chapters), do not overlook taking care of yourself physically. I am sure Jack would have agreed; your body needs to be available to you.

Practical Suggestions to Combat Frailty:

1. Cultivate resilience by building relationships with supportive others and a grateful attitude.
2. Find a purpose beyond the self (meaning-making).
3. Simple, basic, good nutrition of a well-balanced, varied diet that includes adequate amounts of calories and protein, and adequate deep sleep.
4. Body movement or *Awareness Through Body Movement,* view Feldenkrais.com.

5. Exercise with weight resistance for older adults (consult professional trainers here, like Fitness Over 50 or Silver Sneakers).
6. Build social capital by nurturing community and joining groups or places of worship (safely in the era of COVID).

(Source: *The Challenge of Treating 'Frailty'* by Richard Gunderman)

Summary

Most older adults do not want to burden others with the opportunity cost of frailty. This often means time off work or away from other commitments for 'informal' caregivers. Time spent in caregiving could have been invested in different activities with parents, like travel or time with friends and family, if frailty could be postponed or avoided altogether. Avoid the path of frailty; it is the road to premature institutionalization.

Falls Steal Dreams

Some time ago, I heard one of the most impactful statements ever made on the topic of older adults and falling. Louis Tenenbaum, an expert in aging in place, delivered it during a webinar. He said, "falls steal dreams." Here is the obvious point: I could list scary fall statistics, the annual costs of falls and then provide a list of action items to prevent falls around the house for aging in place. Instead, I want to elaborate on the aftermath of a fall—and those lost dreams.

Imagine, if you will, a vibrant, healthy 73-year-old successfully aging in community. The woman is active in her church, does exercise three mornings a week at the YMCA, volunteers with the grade school teaching kids to read, and meets with a book club at Starbucks once a week. She has an active family life and is a grandmother of three. She recently started dating a retired man she met at her evening painting class, as it has been two years since her beloved husband died. Life is good.

One morning, the doorbell rings. It is the mailman, and she rushes downstairs to catch him before he drives away. She trips on a pile of clean laundry placed on the steps the night before, and she falls. In the emergency room, she waits (in excruciating pain) with her anxious family. After what seems like forever, the doctor sees her, does the workup, and orders a series of blood tests, x-rays, and pain medications, then she is finally admitted with the diagnosis of a broken left hip. She will need an operation. After several hours, the pain is intolerable, and they will not let her get up to go to the bathroom—so they place a Foley catheter in her bladder and administer more IV pain killers.

Her surgery is a success, but her recovery is not. With her immune system now weakened from the physiological and physical stress, she develops a urinary tract infection (UTI) from the Foley catheter, and the bed rest leads to pneumonia. The pain is not allowing her to sleep, and her appetite has dwindled. She is now confused by the pain medications, sleep deprivation, lack of proper nutrition, and the low-grade fever from the undiagnosed staph infection from bedsores (caused by decreased movement in bed). Her overall condition is deteriorating from comorbidities that compromise the healing of the initial problem—her hip.

After three weeks in the hospital and exhaustive treatments, including admission to ICU for sepsis caused by a nosocomial infection (from being in the hospital, likely due to the unwashed hands of a caregiver or equipment), she transfers to the rehabilitation center for follow-up care. Losing weight and getting weaker, her family sees her decline and pleads with the staff to help, and they wonder if she will ever return to her home again.

Dreams Denied by Fractured Hips

This scenario may seem extreme to the reader but ask any nurse who has been in the business for a while, and they will affirm the all-to-common nature of this sad scenario. This once vibrant 73-year-old with total health is now clinging to life and may never recover. What will come of the children at the grade school? What about the budding romance? What about the people at the church, the YMCA, her book club, and her family? They have all lost the gift of her presence, not to mention her dreams. The loss is not in isolation; we live within the context of others.

According to the American Geriatrics Society Foundation for Health in Aging, the risk of death for seniors the year following a hip fracture is as high as 20–25 percent. The rate can vary depending on age, gender, race, physical condition, and medical history. Further, women are more prone to hip fractures (two to three times more often than men) and the risks of breaking a hip double every five years or so after 50.

The American Academy of Orthopedic Surgeons reports that white, post-menopausal women have a 1-in-7 chance of fracturing a hip. Almost half of women who reach the age of 90 years will experience a broken hip. Your story (or someone you love) does not have to end that way; rewrite it with proactive-preventive measures taken now.

Ten Steps for Preparing Home for Surgical Recovery (should you need to)

1. Prepare Your Home in Advance

Since patients are likely to spend most post-surgery time at home, it is essential to prepare the living area better to accommodate the process. Preparing the house in advance will make things easier and more comfortable. In the weeks before surgery, patients will want to evaluate their living environment and make the necessary modifications and adjustments for a successful recovery.

2. **Clear the Hallways**

First, make sure they have a clear path to navigate hallways and rooms. Patients may need to move furniture and objects to make it easier to move around.

3. **Stay Downstairs**

If patients have a multi-story house, consider creating a temporary bedroom on the first floor. Avoiding the stairs will reduce the chances of strain or injury. If you are fortunate enough to have a bathroom on the first floor (this goes for a bathroom on any floor), consider installing a handrail or grab bar in your shower and next to your toilet. You might also want to place a bench in your shower and an elevated toilet seat or a riser. These devices will make it easier and more comfortable to move around in the bathroom. They also reduce the risk of a fall.

4. **Remove Rugs**

Remove throw rugs and area rugs that could cause patients to slip and fall if they catch the tip of a cane, crutch, or walker on them. Make sure the carpeting is secure and that no ripples or ridges exist.

5. **Clear Cords**

Ensure patients know about securing all power and phone cords so they do not pose a tripping hazard.

6. **Secure Handrails**

Verify that the patient's handrails on stairs and showers are in good condition and secured to the walls or posts for safety. Patients can install handrails wherever needed before surgery so that when home, they will have assistance when moving about.

7. **Nightlights**

Patients might be used to getting around their house in the middle of the night, but they cannot take too many precautions during recovery. Add nightlights that plug into outlets in the wall, particularly in their bedroom and bathrooms.

8. **Organize**

Clutter and disorganized areas can present unneeded stress and make it hard to move around smoothly. Eliminate clutter and clear floors, table-tops, counters, and other areas. Make sure the patient's clothes and necessities are reachable from closets and cabinets.

9. **Infections Avoided at Home**

All visitors to the home must wash their hands and use gloves and/or wear masks before any contact with the elderly patient (COVID-19 Precautions).

10. **Pet Care**

Secure a trusted informal caregiver to help with the pet's needs before the surgical date; that may include walking and feeding.

Prepare in advance; since you are likely to spend most post-surgery time at home, it is vital to prepare the living area to accommodate the process. Preparing the house in advance will make things easier and more comfortable. In the weeks before surgery, you will want to evaluate your living environment and make the necessary modifications and adjustments for a successful recovery.

Systems Approach to Aging Well

Ramiah Ramasubramanian, MD., wrote eloquently on a systems approach to aging well within one's age. I requested to add his thoughts in this chapter on healthy aging and compressing morbidity because it is relevant and comprehensive from a deep thinker, and it is a beautiful summary on optimal aging.

Aging Well Within Ones' Age and Living an Exemplary Life

By Ramiah Ramasubramanian

We live in an age of infinite possibilities and exponential change. Human life span has lengthened and will continue to do so in the future. Progress in science and technology has contributed to striking improvements in our living standards. The pace of change in many areas of contemporary life continues at a rate that can only be described as dizzying, relentless, and, to many, disorienting and threatening. Despite our material progress, the fundamental questions that we face in our spiritual lives have remained unchanged since the early days of Roman and Greek civilizations. How do we live an exemplary life—a meaningful, regret-free, ethical life—with happiness, wellness, and mental tranquility? Unique to our digital age is the question of how to incorporate rapid advances in science into our daily routines to improve and enhance the quality of our daily lives.

The unchanging nature of our spiritual quest highlights one of the most important challenges of our age: the ever-widening gap between the rapidly changing material world and the gradually evolving spiritual world. This gap has created some profound moral and ethical dilemmas. Rev. Martin Luther King Jr. once said, "Our scientific power has overrun our spiritual power. We have guided missiles and misguided men." Search for meaning in human existence is a recurring theme whose powerful manifestation can be found in works of great thinkers of the past and the present. Through the character of dying, Ivan Ilych Tolstoy brings to life some of the eternal questions about life. One of them was the ultimate question that Ivan Ilych faced on his deathbed: What if my whole life has been wrong?

Bonnie Ware's writing on the Regrets of the Dying (see chapter 10 for more on Bonnie Ware) vividly documents the emotions, thoughts, and transformative processes experienced by terminally ill patients during the final weeks of their lives. Viktor Frankl's extraordinary physical and mental resilience in the face of unimaginable and unspeakable evil is a shining example of the importance of a code of ethical and moral values in defining a virtuous life. In trying to live an exemplary life, we face some critical questions and challenges. Foremost among them is defining a set of core values that form the foundations of an ethical and moral framework that guides our daily practices and lifelong pursuit of long-term goals. In this task, asking the right questions is critical to achieving lasting success.

Building a Framework of Moral and Ethical Values

What values define you and the life you lead? As is often the case, it is the simplest questions that are most often the difficult ones to answer. In reflecting on this question while trying to find enduring answers, it is worth remembering the fact that there are plenty of time-tested sources of help—from the very ancient to the most modern and science-based — available. Writings of Stoics like Seneca and Marcus Aurelius have as much relevance to us as the thoughtful observations and suggestions of Mr. Greg McKeown, a digital age writer who has studied our current way of living more closely. While Stoics deal with existential questions of life like cultivating tranquility of mind and leading a life of virtue, Mr. McKeown offers some practical solutions based on sound philosophical thinking, particularly on problems of our digital age: distractions, disruptions, and wasting precious time on non-essential activities and trivial pursuits of life. Mr. McKeown's central idea is deceptively simple yet carries a deep and profound message: Define what the essential elements of your life are and eliminate the rest.

Achieving and maintaining wellness

The natural state of the human body is good health, and the natural state of the human mind is happiness. Yet, in our digital age, ill health and chronic mental and physical stress are rampant. Here are some science-based practices that help restore health and preventing diseases.

Rethinking Age and Aging

We will need to rethink our ideas about the connection between age (measurement based on time/calendar) and aging (a process of structural and functional changes in the human body). Findings from the world of science highlight two key facts:

An individual's chronological age and biological age are two distinct entities that have a variable relationship. An individual with a chronological age of 70 may have a biological (physiologic/functional) age of 55. It is possible to slow the aging process and stimulate the body's built-in regenerative cells and repair processes by fasting, a simple, ancient practice that can be adapted by most individuals. There are multiple methods of fasting. Some are quite simple, and others may require medical supervision.

Meditation: Fewer aspects of living in the modern age characterize it more acutely and vividly than the sense of overwhelming stress, particularly chronic mental stress, experienced by many. The incidence of stress-related illnesses and the huge human and economic tolls extracted by these illnesses are well known. Recent scientific studies of mind-body interaction offer strong support to the regular practice of mindful meditation in alleviating the corrosive effects of chronic stress on our mental and physical well-being. Beneficial effects of meditation — after a short and long time of practice — documented in these studies include changes in the structure of the brain, alleviation of depression and chronic pain, and genetic changes.

Nutrition: Some of the most spectacular progress in our efforts to gain a deeper understanding of wellness has taken place in the field of nutrition. Despite the never-ending debates and conflicting and, most often, confusing advice and suggestions published in the popular media and the scientific literature on the food we eat, or we should eat, certain helpful trends are apparent in this field. One of the most critical factors that determine the status of our health is the type, the quality, and the quantity of the food we consume daily. It is interesting to note that the link between health and food was well known to Hippocrates, who was one of the earliest scholars to recognize the importance of this link.

Sleep: In addition to sleep's restorative role, studies from the emerging science of Sleep and Circadian Rhythm Disruption (SCRD) have highlighted the far-reaching effects and hence the importance of regular and adequate sleep in several areas, including but not limited to immunity, genetics, mental health, and workplace performance.

Physical Activity: In addressing the challenges of physical fitness at any age, we can rely on a variety of rigorously tested options. Ranging from the regular practice of brisk walking to yoga with a spiritual foundation, these options enable us to achieve a state of physical well-being that is vital to our existence.

We live in a golden age of human achievement and individual empowerment. Living an exemplary life in this age is certainly possible if we are guided by a framework of spirituality built on timeless ethical and moral values.

Dr. Ramiah Ramasubramanian MD, FRCA (England) is a practicing, board-certified anesthesiologist with a fellowship in critical surgical care. He lives and works near Portland, Oregon.

Author's note: Dr. Ramiah Ramasubramanian believes aging is a disease, therefore he supports the scientific inquiry for treatment/prevention of aging and related diseases that will extend lifespan along with health-span.

Is aging a disease?

Should aging be considered a disease? This is a hotly debated issue and has been going on for longer than you might imagine. In an article from SLATE, "Is Aging a Disease?" author Joelle Renstrom begins the piece describing humanity's obsession with curing death. The Epic of Gilgamesh, which dates to at least 1800BC, is an epic poem from ancient Mesopotamia and regarded as the earliest surviving notable literature and the second oldest religious text, after the Pyramid Texts. This tale is about how the death of a friend sends Gilgamesh on a long and perilous journey to discover the secret of eternal life. He eventually learns that "Life, which you look for, you will never find. For when the gods created man, they let death be his share, and life withheld in their own hands" (wikipedia.org/wiki/Epic_of_Gilgamesh). Renstrom goes on to write, centuries later, the ancient Roman playwright Terentius declared, "Old age itself is a sickness," and Cicero argued, "we must struggle against [old age], as against a disease."

The search for eternal youth and immortality is the stuff of legends and myths. In the 5th century BC, the Greek historian Herodotus wrote of a fountain of youth in the land of Macrobians, claiming it bestowed on the humans of the region exceptionally long-life spans. None other than Alexander the Great in the 4th century BC got in on the quest, searching for eternal youth and was said to have come across a healing "river of paradise.' And there is the most famous of all seekers of the fountain of youth, 16th century Spanish explorer Ponce de León, who allegedly 'discovered' Florida instead.

> *Ponce, of course, never found the Fountain of Youth. If he had, he'd still be here to tell us about it. Instead, he died in 1521, on the Gulf Coast, he was shot in the thigh with an arrowhead carved out of a fishbone. The wound festered and eventually killed him in Cuba. Ponce's actual Fountain of Youth, it turns out, is probably the legend of the Fountain of Youth itself—the Spaniard and his insatiable thirst for eternity—which has outlived him now, in spite of most historians' objections, by almost 500 years.*
>
> —SAM ANDERSON, "Searching for the Foutain of Youth," The New York Magazine/The Health Issue

Not only was Ponce de Leon's fountain of youth a myth, so was his search for it—as it turns out. But hope springs eternal, as the saying goes, and today the search still is on. The current version of eternal youth explores are called Biohacker-scientists. These modern-day longevity adventures consider aging a disease process that may potentially be staved off for decades—if not cured entirely. One such biogerontologist mentioned earlier is Andrew Steele, and there are many others joining the search from the Silicon Valley to the halls of the finest research universities around the world. For example, Professor Juan Carlos Izpisua Belmonte of the Salk Institute for Biological Studies. Armed with rapidly advancing technologies like stem cell treatments, cell restoration and genetic editing to name a few, this new breed of biohacker-scientists is hoping to extend healthy lifespans well beyond current levels. Izpisua Belmonte says there is no reason why we cannot extend the human lifespan by at least another thirty to fifty years.

I think the kid that will be living to 130 is already with us. He has already been born. I'm convinced.

—DR. JUAN CARLOS IZPISUA BELMONTE

Izpisúa Belmonte believes epigenetic reprogramming may prove to be an "elixir of life" that will extend human life span significantly by "reprogramming" cells and resetting the body's so-called epigenetic marks: chemical switches in a cell that determine which of its genes are turned on and which are off. These marks can be erased, and a cell can forget if it was ever a skin or a bone cell, and revert to a much more primitive, embryonic state. In other words, reversing the epigenetic changes (wear and tear on cells) that occur with aging through reprogramming individual cells may enable scientists to turn back aging itself. The goal is to go from repairing at the cellular level to eventually the entire body—further, Izpisúa Belmonte is proposing to go one better, and reverse aging-related aberrations without having to create a new individual. He cautions that epigenetic tweaks won't "make you live forever," but they might delay your expiration date (technologyreview.com/2019/08/08/65461/scientist-fountain-of-youth-epigenome).

Some of these longevity scientists begin with the premise that aging is a disease to be cured. Another such prominent voice is Harvard Professor David Sinclair PhD, who feels aging in the mother of all diseases. Sinclair's theory is, instead of trying to treat all the various age-related diseases like dementia and cancer, just cure the principal cause—aging. He calls the way it is currently done "whack-a-mole" medicine, and advocates for labeling aging as a disease, so research funding will be supported. He is searching for one disease mechanism (the cause of aging) and one cure.

The aging-as-disease theory is rapidly gaining supporters in sectors such as large academic research centers, biotech companies, and Silicon Valley, which see economic opportunity. But viewing aging as a disease (tragedy) is not shared by all aging experts. The argument goes, that if growing old is a chronic disease, then is a cancer diagnosis the same as an aging diagnosis? What about older people who aren't sick, active, engaged in community, mentally sharp, have no apparent limiting pathology and die in their sleep?

This is a question asked in an opinion piece by Connie Mason Michaelis, author of the book, Daily Cures: Wisdom for Healthy Aging (cjonline). Michaelis poses another interesting point. Is a child maturing from 10 to 11 years old and growing an inch, suffering from an aging pathology? Further, when does aging become pathology? This makes me wonder about puberty and menopause—both age-related. Are these disease conditions too?

Sharona Hoffman, JD, Professor of Law and Bioethics at Case Western Reserve University and author of the book, *Aging With a Plan: How a Little Thought Today Can Vastly Improve Your Tomorrow*, says, "Aging is a natural part of life for those who are lucky enough to live a long time." Barr views aging not as a disease but rather a continuum we are all on. This camp views aging as a universal human condition. It is not abnormal so why would it be considered pathological? Further, The National Institute on Aging (NIA) agrees, and currently has as the official scientific stance: *Aging is not, in and of itself, a disease. However, aging is the major risk factor for developing many major chronic diseases. Furthermore, many diseases appear to accelerate the aging process-which is manifested as declines in functionality and reduced quality of life* (Robert Roy Britt).

The World Health Organization (WHO) in 2018 did not outright label aging as a disease, instead adding to its disease classification "aging-related diseases" defined as "caused by biological processes which persistently lead to the loss of organism's adaptation and progress in older ages." Cited were sarcopenia (muscle loss), dementia, and osteoporosis, for example (Robert Roy Britt).

These organizational stances are subject to change as more scientific information becomes available, but for now, aging is not officially labeled a disease by the NIA or the WHO.

> *Viewing aging as pathological is both accurate and flawed, constructive and problematic. The possibility of maintaining physical function as we age has obvious appeal. Rather than targeting ailments one at a time, as we do now, researchers are developing agents that lower the risk of many diseases as well as age-related conditions, including frailty. Although that may sound like progress, it brings us to the ways in which viewing aging as a disease is problematic. Aging is a universal phenomenon that gives life shape, direction, urgency, and meaning. Perhaps the most immediately worrisome consequence of the age-as-disease perspective is that it turns us all into disorders by our 50s.*
>
> —LOUISE ARONSON, MD MFA, geriatrician, writer, educator, professor of medicine at UCSF

Aronson wrote the New York Times bestseller and Pulitzer Prize finalist, *Elderhood: Redefining Aging, Transforming Medicine, and Reimagining Life* (publishersweekly.com).

Proponents of classifying aging as a disease argue two main points:

1. Being called a disease would lead to more individuals adopting healthy habits and taking medications to slow a "disease process" rather than a "natural condition."

2. Stronger support in terms of funding for treating disease would come from government agencies like the Food and Drug Administration.

Opponents fear labeling aging as a disease could in fact do just the opposite by: 1. Normalizing physical and mental decline fostering compliancy downplaying the role of lifestyle choices, diet, sleep, exercise, retirement, loss, and social interaction (*what's the use I have a terminal disease called aging*).

2. Further stigmatizing and adding to ageism in society.

Time will tell which side of this long-standing debate will prevail; whether aging is a disease, or a natural process is unresolved in the minds of many in the fields of gerontology and geriatrics.

Primary versus Secondary Aging

For years, I have used a basic binary framework to describe two types of aging. The first is "primary aging" which is a multifactorial process of physiological changes causing functional decline over time. What has been called "normal aging." The second is "secondary aging" which is the things we do to ourselves to speed up the process (i.e., smoking, excessive drinking, morbid stress, insomnia, drug abuse, poor dietary choices, routine behavior). It is the secondary agers where we can exercise a level of choice and control in our daily living. I call it "self-induced aging."

The excessive use of alcohol falls under the "secondary agers" category and a growing concern for women. I recently read a piece on the aarp.org website concerning women and alcohol that describes the increasing rates of alcohol use in older women (especially since COVID).

> *'My career was very fulfilling but also very stressful,' says Debra Henning, 67, recently retired from a high-powered job as a pharmaceutical company executive. Upon returning home in the evening, Debra would turn to alcohol to relax. 'It was difficult shifting gears —transitioning from 100 miles an hour to a more sedate home life,' she says. 'A glass or two of wine helped put the stress of the day behind me to chill out a little.'*
>
> *Henning isn't alone: A growing number of women seem to be falling into a pattern of heavier drinking. A study published in 2017 in JAMA Psychiatry, examining drinking habits among adults in the U.S. between 2001 and 2013, found that high-risk alcohol use—specifically women consuming four or more drinks in a day, on a weekly basis—rose about 58 percent. And while men drink more than women, research indicates that the gap between the genders is narrowing.*
>
> —Barbara Stepko

I can report from my experience working with healthcare colleagues, nurses, and friends (females), who report increasing their alcohol consumption within the past few years. While women's drinking has increased, the aaarp.org article suggests that so have the options for treatment. More women-centric approaches have emerged to confront the increasing need for treatment. For example, all-women support networks at sites such as Sexy Sobriety, run by the Australian Rebecca Weller (author of the 2016 book *A Happier Hour*), Soberistas, and Hip Sobriety. The article also offers helpful suggestions to get in touch with the nonprofit Women for Sobriety, which offers online and in-person support groups; and the Substance Abuse and Mental Health Services Administration's National Helpline – 800-662-HELP (4357), and treatment locator - FindTreatment.gov.

You take your pension in loneliness and alcohol . . .

—BILLY SQUIER, *EVERYBODY WANTS YOU*

A post on the social media site Twitter a couple years ago from Joseph Coughlin (MIT AgeLab) caught my attention one morning: *Boomers reaching older age? 2.8 M older adults in the US meet the criteria for alcohol abuse, and this number is expected to reach 5.7 million by 2020.*

My first thought was how tragic this is on so many levels; my second thought was that this happens when alcohol replaces purpose. A concept that requires unpacking because I have taken care of many alcohol-caused diseases that eventually lead to brain damage and early institutionalization (a real threat to longevity and aging in place).

These numbers are most likely under-reported; my guess is they are much more significant. And the problem with alcohol is it does not kill you acutely (unless you are in a car accident). It chips away a little at a time until there is an accumulative effect. From cancer to early dementia and many other chronic diseases, alcohol abuse is essentially suicide on the installment plan.

Not to mention the heavy drinker's relationship damage of the "present-absence" (the body is there, but personality, soul, mind is absent), which puts a toll on the others in the alcohol-dependent person's life. Excessive drinking can affect the spouse, making the so-called Golden Years a living hell. The retired alcohol-abusing person will soon find themselves a regular, not at their favorite watering hole, but rather at the doctor's office or emergency room. Heavy drinking leads to chronic diseases, meaning we do not cure them. We only manage acute episodes over and over until the tragic, prolonged end.

A course of self-destruction is sad, but burning up limited inter-generational resources as you go is unconscionable. The potential opportunity cost in dealing with the co-morbidity factors associated with chronic alcohol abuse in such staggering numbers represented by the baby boomer generation is cause for alarm. I have seen, for example, how a single case of esophageal varices (enlarged veins in the esophagus caused by alcohol) case can deplete an entire community of a particular type of blood throughout an evening. That means possibly no blood for the accident victim later that night or the gunshot wound sustained by the police officer on duty.

With 76 million baby boomers aging into retirement, as a society we cannot afford millions of cases of "sick careers" (finding purpose and meaning through involvement in the medical system, aka "biomedicalization of aging"). The sheer volume will put a devastating burden on the healthcare industry. When alcohol replaces purpose in older adults' lives, society's cost is too high a price to pay.

I think this Nobel Prize Winner says it all:

> We should ask ourselves this question: Since we are here-and no one asked us if we wanted to be-what should we do about it? We should make the most of this difficult but extraordinary experience and strive to live in harmony with ourselves and our fellow travelers. We should realize that most unhappiness stems from excessive apprehension and concern about ourselves when we would greatly benefit instead by investing all our thought and effort in confronting far more crucial problems. Most of the human population lives in tremendous misery and starvation, while a small minority enjoys not merely excessive comfort,

> but luxury. It is my hope that people will realize that it is not through the possession of material goods that one can find happiness in this world. Only by a deep involvement in the problems of the greater society can one achieve happiness or, at least, harmony with oneself.
>
> —RITA LEVI-MONTALCINI, ITALIAN BIOLOGIST AND NOBEL PRIZE WINNER

Summary

The topic of aging as a preventable disease and the lifespan having no limits is an urgent one. This will require more long-term studies to see if biotechnologies are applicable and can actually work in humans. In the meantime, there is plenty of evidence that controlling secondary aging to extend lifespan and health-span is possible. Evidence-based actions like eating a nutritious diet, exercising, not smoking, controlling weight, and social supports, are well known—not as sexy as biotech, but proven. A motivator to do so might be to keep your shelf life up long enough to take advantage of the evolving science.

The promise of immortality is alluring. We cannot imagine a world without us in it, let alone a world where 100 million Americans will be 65 or older by 2060 (The Population Reference Bureau/prb.org). That is 16 percent of the world's population who will be senior citizens by mid-century. How will they be cared for? Financed? Who gets to benefit from the longevity technology? What to do with the extra years? If science can add twenty to thirty years of extended life with extended health, that seems like a positive thing. However, an open-ended lifespan is hard to imagine. When can you claim you have cured aging? Many unanswered questions remain.

The reality is, "curing" aging is a myth—it will go on even if researchers find a way to stave off age-related diseases for several additional decades, aging will go on. Do not count on the technological foundation of youth just yet—do what you can now to compress morbidity.

Goodbye Myth: Many of the things we blame on aging have nothing to do with getting older.

Step 7

Take a systems approach to healthy aging.

Primary aging is less controllable than secondary aging, which is highly modifiable and within our sphere of influence (one does affect the other). A systems approach includes consulting an occupational therapist (see aota.org) and an aging-in-place professional (nahb.org) for age-friendly home modifications, adding a bit of de-cluttering, then educating yourself on fall prevention, as well as incorporating weight-bearing physical activity, nutrition, sleep, and a framework of moral and ethical values that support your optimal aging, and find a compelling purpose.

Note: Having said goodbye to the myth and stated the case for *many of the things we blame on aging have nothing to do with getting older*; for African Americans generally, and black women specifically, this needs to be considered in context.

Aging While Black

In the article, "Aging While Black: The Crisis Among black Americans as They Grow Old," author Rodney A. Brooks opens with this line that sums up the challenges facing aging African Americans. "After a lifetime of racial and health inequities, Black seniors are at risk of spending their last years with declining health, little income and virtually no savings." Brooks further cites statistical findings to support his statement from a 2016 CIGNA Health Disparities report:

- Four in 10 Black men aged 20 or older have high blood pressure, a rate 30 percent higher than that of white men. Black men's risk of a stroke is twice that of white men. For Black women, 45 percent of those aged 20 and older have high blood pressure, a rate 60 percent higher than white women.

- Black women are 40 percent more likely to die of breast cancer than white women.
- Black men have a 40 percent higher cancer death rate than white men.
- Black Americans are 80 percent more likely to be diagnosed with diabetes than whites, and nearly twice as likely to be hospitalized.
- Blacks are more than twice as likely as whites to suffer from Alzheimer's and other kinds of dementia.

More directly to black women, the piece quotes an associate professor of sociology at Duke University, Tyson Brown. He says, "Black women suffer from some of the highest levels of diabetes, hypertension, and other disabilities. Their health problems limit their ability to continue working. But many Black women have to continue working because of declining income as they age."

Professor Brown notes that black women are especially vulnerable to health and wealth issues because they are more likely to outlive partners (statistics above), which means they are more likely to be isolated and alone. As is frequently the case, they become informal caregivers for aging parents, spouses, and grandchildren, ending their formal employment. I have worked with many black women in healthcare who fit into this scenario.

Sadly, this equates to an opportunity cost to pay into company-sponsored retirement plans such as pensions and 401(k) plans and reduces their payments into Social Security, which means smaller monthly checks when they retire. The bottom line, "Many Black older Americans have endured decades of overt and subtle forms of discrimination in educational, criminal justice systems, and health care systems as well as in jobs, housing, credit, and consumer markets," said Brown, adding that as a result of this discrimination, many older Black Americans have lower levels of education, income, and wealth than whites.

The COVID-19 public health crisis has only exasperated the ongoing challenges specifically for older black women, and the pandemic affected low-income and communities of color at more significant percentages. The causal factors stem from decades of discrimination in educational, criminal justice systems, health care systems, jobs, housing, credit, and consumer markets; as noted by Brown, older Black Americans, and especially women, have suffered disproportionately to the rest of society. Again, we are aged by culture, and for African Americans, especially women, this has additional meaning.

What is social prescribing? Get to know it.

Social prescribing, also sometimes known as community referral, enables health professionals to refer people to a range of local, non-clinical services. The referrals generally, but not exclusively, come from primary care professionals, such as General Practitioners or nurses. Social prescribing seeks to address people's needs holistically and recognize that people's health and well-being are determined mainly by a range of social, economic, and environmental factors. It also aims to support individuals in taking greater control of their health. Schemes delivering social prescribing can involve a range of activities typically provided by voluntary and community sector organizations. Examples include volunteering, art activities, group learning, gardening, befriending, cooking, healthy eating advice, and a range of sports (kingsfund.org.uk/publications/social prescribing).

My Longevity Equation to help prevent Secondary Agers:

EAT < MOVE + PURPOSE + GROWTH MINDSET + DEEP SLEEP x COMMUNITY - SMOKING = LONGEVITY

I have found over the years, when caring for older women, that longevity is often a byproduct of following this simple longevity equation.

Here are a few quote components of the Longevity Equation (LE) by some notables.

EAT

The only way you get that fat off is to eat less and exercise more.

—JACK LALANNE

. . .

MOVE

> *I thought, you know the food and the diet thing is one way to start yourself onto a healthy lifestyle, but if you don't move, if you don't start exercising, you're gonna deteriorate.*

—WARREN CUCCURULLO

PURPOSE

> *The purpose of life is to contribute in some way to making things better.*

—ROBERT F. KENNEDY

GROWTH MINDSET

> *When studying human physiology generally, and the brain in particular, it is essential to keep in mind that development and aging are a continuum. From the moment you are born, you begin to age. So, too, your brain does not simply 'develop' in the first part of your life and 'age' in the last part of your life.*

—MARIAN DIAMOND

SLEEP

> *Having peace, happiness, and healthiness is my definition of beauty. And you can't have any of that without sleep.*

—BEYONCE

. . .

COMMUNITY

> *Diet and supplements and exercise programs aren't what is achieving longevity. Having a faith-based community can add 4 to 14 years.*
>
> —DAN BUETTNER

LONGEVITY

> *If you ask what the single most important key to longevity is, I would have to say it is avoiding worry, stress, and tension. And if you didn't ask me, I'd still have to say it.*
>
> —GEORGE BURNS

SMOKING

> *When I don't smoke, I scarcely feel as if I'm living. I don't feel as if I'm living unless I'm killing myself.*
>
> —RUSSELL HOBAN

Remember, the goal is to make sure your body is available to you in this long life!

Resources

Remember when discussing age, there are three:

- Chronological Age: On your birth certificate
- Physiological Age: Of your biology and biomarkers
- Psychological Age: How you think

Psychological age (how you think) is key to aging well within your age (not talking about anti-aging). Successful aging begins first in the mind—then in the physical. And for our purposes here, I define successful aging as expanded healthy and functional years in the life span.

An excellent resource for the Center For Health and Wellness is:

davidlynchfoundation.org

Vonda Wright, M.D., is an orthopedic surgeon and director of PRIMA, a pioneering program for athletes over 40. A prominent authority on sports medicine and active aging, she has appeared on Dr. Oz, The Doctors, and CNN. She is quoted in The New York Times, USA Today, Prevention, Fitness, and other major media.

For an insightful and scholarly exploration of the cultural and sociological influences on the racialization of black female bodies over the past 200 years, see sociologist Sabrina Strings' award-winning book, *Fearing the Black Body: The Racial Origins of Fat Phobia* (NYU Press, 2019).

womenshealthconversations.com

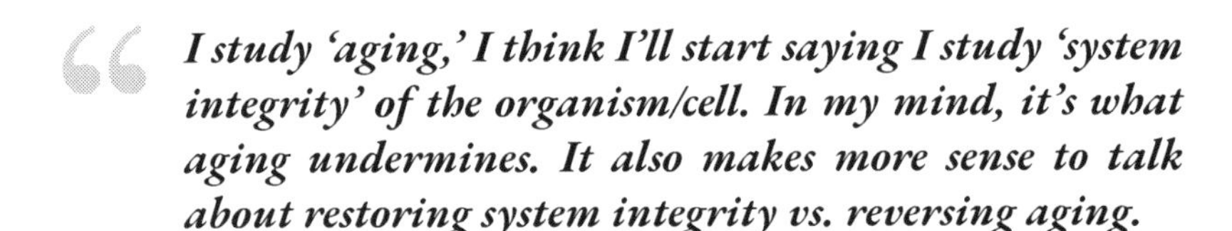

> ***I study 'aging,' I think I'll start saying I study 'system integrity' of the organism/cell. In my mind, it's what aging undermines. It also makes more sense to talk about restoring system integrity vs. reversing aging.***
>
> —MORGAN LEVINE, PH.D., YALE SCHOOL OF MEDICINE ASSIST. PROFESSOR

Wrote, *True Age: Cutting-Edge Research to Help Turn Back the Clock*

For more cutting-edge research on the science of aging, follow the work of Morgan Levine, PhD. Her website: Laboratory for Aging in Living Systems / morganlevinelab.com. On YouTube she explains in understandable terms the evolving science of longevity—check it out.

CHAPTER 8

The Long Goodbye

MYTH: I have Alzheimer's in my family, so there is nothing I can do to escape it

> *Her purse was a weight, ballast; it tethered her to the earth as her mind floated away.*
>
> —ANNE LAMOTT, *PLAN B: FURTHER THOUGHTS ON FAITH*

According to the Alzheimer's Association, more than five million Americans are living with the disease. In 2020, Alzheimer's and other dementias cost the nation $305 billion. By 2050, these costs could rise as high as $1.1 trillion. 72 percent are age seventy-five or older, and one in nine people aged sixty-five and older (11.3%) has Alzheimer's dementia. Almost two-thirds of Americans with Alzheimer's are women. Older Black Americans are about twice as likely to have Alzheimer's or other forms of dementia as older whites (alz.org).

The present-absence and the long-good-bye of Alzheimer's disease is heartbreaking. I sat with my once brilliant friend, Frances Gabe, famed inventor of the self-cleaning house, holding her hand and longing for the excursions into the deep end of ideas that we once shared. But that was in the past. To quote Chuck Heston, quoting Shakespeare in his statement, ***"they bade farewell and 'melted into air, into thin air.'"***

The unraveling of life in the mind of a person with Alzheimer's disease has been described as "the great unlearning," the "demise of consciousness." Just what does the condition uncover about the nature of being human? What is left when memory dissolves "into thin air?" What role does the disease play in our fears of growing older and ageism?

Granny Dumping by Anton Christian

Some years ago, an older man with Alzheimer's disease was abandoned by a relative at a dog racing track in Idaho. The New York Times ran an Opinion piece about the story. Here are a few selective lines from that post:

> *It was a sad and troubling story. John Kingery, 82, suffering from Alzheimer's disease and wearing a sweatshirt inscribed 'Proud To Be An American,' was abandoned outside the men's room at a dog racing track in Post Falls, Idaho. His wheelchair had been stripped*

> *of identification and his clothing labels ripped out; he couldn't remember his own name.*
>
> *Pictures of him clutching his teddy bear as attendants prepared to send him home to Oregon provoked a national wince. But what turns a wince into an ache is the sudden awareness that John Kingery is no isolated case. Social workers call this phenomenon 'granny dumping'. But they are reluctant to condemn those who do the dumping. Instead, they paint a harrowing portrait of millions of Americans who are near the breaking point with the burden of caring for their ill and elderly parents.*

"Granny Dumping" was something I experienced every holiday season as a critical care RN in the hospital, a sad situation the public has little awareness of happening. As the holidays come and go, it is essential to remember that so many of our friends and neighbors (and many of us) are not cheery and bright. As we look to the future with anticipation, my wish is to be closer to solutions to this devastating disease which is, in part, a failure of our longevity success. Women are living longer, but with that come the morbidities associated with old age. I do not want young nurses working the holidays to have to encounter "Granny Dumping" as I did, and I do not wish to have anyone's season of cheer be tainted by having to make that kind of decision for a loved one.

> ***Like the wind crying endlessly through the universe, Time carries away the names and the deeds of conquerors and commoners alike. And all that we are, all that remains, is in the memories of those who cared we came this way for a brief moment.***
>
> —HARLAN ELLISON

The Visitor

It was 6 a.m. on Christmas morning when a strange woman tapped at the door. She was dressed only in her nightclothes. The lady was cold and dazed, and Brian invited her in for tea. Brian, a retired 84-year-old doctor, rang his son to announce a rather good-looking older woman in a nightgown having tea in his kitchen. Brian's son, who lived two hours away, thought his father had finally lost his grip on reality, so he rang the police to check him out. The police went to Brian's house, and sure enough, there was a scantily dressed woman, now with a blanket wrapped around her, sitting by the fire sipping tea. Unable to give them her name or address, the police decided to go around the village, knocking on doors to see if people could help with their inquiries.

A local shop owner suggested a house where he knew an old lady was staying for Christmas. The police, when they arrived at the house, asked whether the lady was home? The old lady's friend said she was, but there was little point in checking as her friend could not walk far. The police asked if she would check anyway, and sure enough, the bed was empty. Far from being in bed, the old lady had left the house in complete darkness, dressed only in her nightclothes, and wandered for around a mile in freezing weather. On seeing Brian's Christmas tree lights, she simply turned up on the doorstep!

After finishing a cup of tea, cereal, toast, and some Christmas cake, the lady was finally collected by her flustered friend.

—Christine Kinnard, *A True Story About Christmas*

The holidays are so much about memories. Dr. Bill Thomas noted:

Once past the age of 30, we become custodians of a past that has vanished from the world. This is especially true at holiday time.

Being a keeper of the holiday stories and traditions requires memory of the past. But what if there comes a time when memory vanishes?

For many, Christmas and New Year's will not be spent where memories were once created, in the family home—but in care facilities where meaning-making is moment-to-moment and melts away like icicles in the midday sun. Reading an account of a woman (anonymous) whose mother had advanced-stage Alzheimer's and was living in a care center reminded me of a different holiday scenario. She warns,

residents have lost the concept of mine and yours. They wander into other rooms and take things. So—do not give anything of value—it disappears quickly. Things like books or magazines are fine to carry around, but not to read. And 'favorite' anything is erased from memory.

Things do not count anymore.

Forgetting past memories doesn't mean that you were not a part of it. You build those memories, and your loved ones know it well.

—CAROLINE LEE

The person with advanced Alzheimer's is there in body yet lacking in memory, a "present-absence" that is heartbreaking for loved ones. What counts is a mindful presence, a hug, "I love you," a walk together, reminding them that they are a part of a loving family. Talk of good times, how they made a difference in the lives of others, and to listen. Nothing to unwrap, no receipts to keep or take back, only moments shared in the spirit of the season. In time, the disease carries away names and deeds of the past; what remains is an opportunity to show kindness and remember for them.

She is leaving him, not all at once, which would be painful enough, but in a wrenching succession of separations. One moment she is here, and then she is gone again, and each journey takes her a little farther from his reach. He cannot follow her, and he wonders where she goes when she leaves.

—DEBRA DEAN, *THE MADONNAS OF LENINGRAD*

Some years ago, I developed a theory about gender differences in appreciating environmental aesthetics and the aging brain, which I will not burden the reader with here. Confident that I was onto something, I decided to contact some leaders in the field of aging and neuroscience. Top on my list was the distinguished professor of anatomy at U.C. Berkeley, Dr. Marian C. Diamond. I organized my thoughts in a concise email and cast it out to the cyber gods like a message in a bottle, hoping to reach some distant shore.

The next day, as I went through the usual email suspects, I saw a reply from Marian Diamond—*THE MARIAN C. DIAMOND!* My pulse quickened as I fumbled to open this email:

Dear Patrick,
I think you have caught the essence of aging in every sense of the word ... the constant flow of new experiences. I don't know if you have come in contact with my Five Basic "Ingredients" for a healthy brain

> *at ANY age. These particular five items were confirmed by experiments in our laboratory.*
>
> **I. Diet**
> **II. Exercise**
> **III. Challenge**
> **IV. Newness**
> **V. Love**
>
> She graciously went on to briefly elaborate on gender differences in the aging brains of rats in her studies. She ended with:
>
> *. . . Just continue to grow your dendrites until well over your 100 years.*
>
> *Warm regards,*
>
> *Marian Diamond*

I still have that email and cherish it. Dr. Diamond had contributed significantly to our understanding of how the brain works and, in turn, debunked culturally constructed myths about aging. At the time, she was in her 80s and continued to lead by example every day, incorporating her five ingredients for a healthy aging brain. I encourage you to investigate her work; it is a knowledge journey worth taking.

> ***The brain is a three-pound mass you can hold in your hand that can conceive of a universe a hundred billion light-years across.***
>
> —DR. MARIAN DIAMOND

Further supporting Marian Diamond's first two (diet and exercise) of her five items, was an article from CNN Health (Ryan Prior). According to a study published in the International Journal of Epidemiology, the paper reported that women in later adulthood with above-average belly fat could lead to a 39% increased risk of dementia within fifteen years compared with those who have a normal waist circumference.

Dr. Richard Isaacson, head of the Alzheimer's Prevention Clinic at Weill Cornell Medicine and New York-Presbyterian Hospital, put it this way:

> *As belly size gets larger, the memory center in the brain gets smaller, based on prior studies. This new study is important since it supports these findings and relates a larger waist size to increased dementia risk, especially in women. Based on emerging data from studies like this, we are now able to clarify sex differences in dementia risk. Combining these findings with my clinical experience, I have seen greater impact on visceral fat on memory function in women, likely mediated by metabolic pathways.*

The bottom-line message from the CNN Health report was this: to avoid dementia, pay attention to your waist size.

Jean at the front desk

A while back, I was a regular at what one could only call an "iron gym." This place was old school with vintage equipment. The regulars in the morning were mainly middle-aged or better, the atmosphere was classic, dingy, moist, and cold in the winter, stifling hot in the summer, and loaded with characters. Loud grunts, slamming weights, old westerns on TV, and no spandex—anywhere. I loved the place. I worked out mornings for two reasons: to get a workout in early—victory over self—and to be greeted by Jean at the front desk.

Every year around early January, the same phenomenon occurs at the gym; all of us long-time gym regulars or "gym rats" know the scenario. There would be an influx of fresh-enthusiastic New Year's resolution makers. They are the ones with the new gear and the personal trainers. I was always silently pulling for them but a bit reluctant to invest any emotion. Like foxhole relationships, you do not want to get too friendly because there is a high probability they will be gone soon. My point is, the difference between an interest and a commitment; if you are interested and there is something more exciting than doing sit-ups, you will choose the more compelling and put off the workout. When committed, you will do the sit-ups and consider the "more compelling" if time permits (again, take the time to be healthy or take the time to be sick).

Jean was a part of my wellness strategy. She was always there at the front desk to greet us with a smile and eye contact that only someone who likes humanity can provide (grandma-like). Before I even touched a dumbbell, I got an infusion of energy from Jean's smile. She was a tonic, and I did not pay extra for the perk!

What is more remarkable is she was nearly 90 years old, and a reminder of the longevity power of purpose. Researchers have shown that smiling, saying something pleasant, and being generous with your thoughts and actions can increase serotonin levels. Further, the person receiving the gift of kindness also has a measured increase in their serotonin—even those watching or passing by benefit by increased levels. Serotonin is an important neurotransmitter in the brain, and it has been proven that mild increases in the levels of this neurotransmitter will help bolster the immune system.

The physical and psychological benefits of laughter and smiling are plentiful. Research shows that those who consciously or subconsciously smile more live better and longer.

—PSYCHOLOGY AND COUNSELING NEWS,
PSYCHOLOGY TO GRIN ABOUT: THE BENEFITS OF SMILING AND LAUGHTER

The groundbreaking book back in the day by John Rowe, M.D., and Robert Kahn, Ph.D., *Successful Aging* (1989), provided two factors that predict 80 percent of longevity survivors (those who live past 65). The first seems obvious; it is whether you smoke or not. The second, however, is more surprising; the degree of complexity in one's daily behavior. It turns out daily behavior that requires choice-making and continual social connectedness is good for the brain and a longevity factor. The researchers cite the examples of artists and Supreme Court justices who live long lives.

People who retire early are significantly more prone to dementia. One study found that with diminished opportunities for cognitive and social stimulation, new retirees lose about 3 IQ points in the first 2 years.

—LISA MARSHAL, *THE END OF ALZHEIMER'S: HOW NEW TREATMENTS MIGHT REWRITE 'THE LONG GOODBYE'*

Jean was known as "grandma" to middle-aged women, tattoo-clad iron pumpers, and everything in between. Her daily duties included a light workout between morning tasks, greeting members at the front desk, babysitting, consoling moody teens, answering phones, problem-solving (soap is out in the women's locker room again), chatting with hipsters, pet sitting for members, giving tours, signing up new members, and on-and-on. This brings me full circle to the issue of interest and commitment in our New Year resolution makers; Rowe & Kahn noted that how we live determines how we age (a familiar theme of this book). To be committed to a purpose may be the ultimate "anti-aging" plan.

The evidence for this has been around for decades and can be found in works such as *The Healing Power of Doing Good: The Health and Spiritual Benefits of Helping Others,* by Allan Luks with Peggy Payne. They proved decades ago, those who volunteered to help others change their blood chemistry (biomarkers) in favor of longevity. The evidence for 'doing good-does you good' is robust and has been compiling for years (Arbor, A.). Having a purpose beyond the self seems to favor longevity—this makes intuitive sense to me. Smiling more at the gym might just buy you more years on the treadmill.

Aging and Solitude

Blaise Pascal once said, "All of humanity's problems stem from man's inability to sit quietly in a room alone." Preliterate societies thought persons who liked to be alone were witches because "normals" would not choose to be alone. In Dobu, if a person had to relieve themselves, they always took someone with them into the bush—fearing harm from a witch if caught alone. The origins of this thinking stem from safety in numbers; a solitary baboon soon will fall prey to leopards or hyenas. Our ancestors realized long ago we are social beings.

In our society, the average person spends about one-third of their waking time alone. According to the late psychologist Mihaly Csikszentmihalyi, people who spend much more or much less time by themselves often have problems. Left on our own, we tend to go negative into thoughts of depression and isolation, feeling less happy, less cheerful, less strong, and more passive—and seniors can be even more vulnerable.

I am unusual in choosing solitude, but that is the key; I am at choice. I do not feel lonely because, at any time, I can commune with others. For older adults, the choice to be alone may be imposed by socially isolating factors outside of their control. As we get older, we have deteriorating social networks caused by family members moving away, retiring from work, the death of friends and spouses, and limiting health or financial resources. The most recent annual data from the Census Bureau reports that 7.5 million senior women and 2.6 million senior men live alone. Aging in place can be a lonely proposition, and as a recent study found, loneliness may cause mental decline. The Centers for Disease Control and Prevention report recent studies found:

- Social isolation significantly increases a person's risk of premature death from all causes, a risk that may rival those of smoking, obesity, and physical inactivity.
- Social isolation was associated with about a 50 percent increased risk of dementia (Source: cdc.gov/aging/publications/features/lonely-older-adults).

"People who described themselves as lonely were twice as likely to develop dementia," says researcher Robert Wilson of the Rush University Medical Center in Chicago.

"Other studies have found that people who are unmarried and socially isolated are at higher risk for dementia, including Alzheimer's. But this study is one of the first to show a link between loneliness—or the feelings of disconnection from other people—and a higher risk of developing dementia late in life," says Laurel Coleman, a spokeswoman for the Alzheimer's Association and a geriatrician in Portland, Maine.

Increasing numbers of older adults are now turning to online social networks like Facebook, twitter, reddit, and others to combat loneliness and boredom. Online networks provide the kind of benefits past social outlets once did—only now they are easier to assemble and maintain, some experts report. Pioneering sites like SeniorNet (which grew out of a research project funded by the Markle Foundation in 1986 to determine if computers and telecommunications could enhance the lives of older adults) have paved the way for newer sites such as The GREAT COURSES PLUS and Master Class. Individuals can take online courses taught by accomplished people like Carlos Santana, teaching how he approaches guitar, for example.

This is a booming era for self-directed adult education on your schedule. These digital outlets provide avenues for human development, creativity, and the primal need to connect with others. More research needs to be done on whether online social connections can help delay the onset of dementia, but one thing is sure, many boomers will only be able to sit quietly in a room alone if they have their smartphones!

I often hear people say that a person suffering from Alzheimer's is not the person they knew. I wonder to myself—Who are they then?

—BOB DEMARCO

Review of Key Points

- There is currently no cure for Alzheimer's disease.
- Two-thirds of Americans with Alzheimer's disease are women.
- The disease process is underway years or decades before symptoms appear.
- The causes of Alzheimer's disease are thought to be multifactorial but not yet fully understood, and probably include a combination of the following:

1. Age-related changes in the brain, like shrinking, inflammation, blood vessel damage, abnormal tau and beta-amyloid proteins build up in the hippocampus (area of the brain stores long term memories), and breakdown of energy within cells, which may harm neurons and affect other brain cells.
2. Common health, environmental, and lifestyle factors that may play a role such as, high blood pressure, heart disease, stroke, diabetes, exposure to pollutants, processed meats, high sodium, lack of greens in diet, insomnia, obesity, smoking, and early retirement.
3. During sleep, research shows a cleansing channel of fluids passes through the spaces between our brain cells, providing a midnight wash cycle that ferries away the toxic plaques and tangles that can promote Alzheimer's. Sleep is also the time when the hippocampus gets to work making memories last. Insomnia is a risk factor for dementia and Alzheimer's disease. Acute insomnia leads to Alzheimer's disease pathology (β-Amyloid accumulation) in the human brain. (Source: Lisa Marshall, "The End of Alzheimer's: How New Treatments Might Rewrite 'The Long Goodbye,'" webmd.com).
4. Changes or differences in genes, which may be passed down by a family member. Both types of Alzheimer's—the very rare early-onset type occurring between age 30 and mid-60s, and the most common, late-onset type occurring after a person's mid-60s—can be related to a person's genes in some way. Many people with Down syndrome, a genetic condition, will develop Alzheimer's

as they age and may begin to show symptoms in their 40s. A person's chance of having the disease may be higher if he or she has certain genes passed down from a parent. However, having a parent with Alzheimer's does not always mean that someone will develop it.

5. From the HARVARD HEALTH BLOG, "What to eat to reduce your risk of Alzheimer's disease," author Andrew E. Budson, MD, reported on researchers from around the world who had been studying a variety of different factors that might reduce these risks of cognitive impairment, Alzheimer's disease, and dementia, thus keeping the brain healthy. Dr Budson jokingly writes, "Old news: The Mediterranean diet is beneficial. The diet includes fish (emphasis on fish consumption), olive oil, avocados, fruits, vegetables, nuts, beans, whole grains, red wine in moderation." And what is "moderation" you might be wondering?

U.S. Department of Health and Human Services and the U.S. Department of Agriculture recommends one drink or less per day for women or two drinks or less per day for men. The lower recommendation for women isn't just because they are, on average, smaller than men. It turns out alcohol affects women differently. They produce less of the enzyme called alcohol dehydrogenase, or ADH that breaks down alcohol. In addition, women tend to have more body fat, which tends to retain alcohol.

Key Take Aways

Enriched environment (EE) can not only promote normal neural development through enhancing neuroplasticity but also play a nerve repair role in restoring functional activities during CNS injury by morphological and cellular and molecular adaptations in the brain (Han, et. al., 2022).

Daily novelty and complexity involving problem solving and choice can build up "cognitive reserves" that may for a time buffer you from the ravages of Alzheimer's. Each new lesson or experience strengthens our neural network and protects it from fraying. Reconsider retiring early (best if you enjoy your career).

According to the National Institute on Aging, it is essential to know the three family factors to access Alzheimer's in family histories.

- A family's health conditions.
- Lifestyle habits like smoking and exercise.
- Where and how family members grew up.

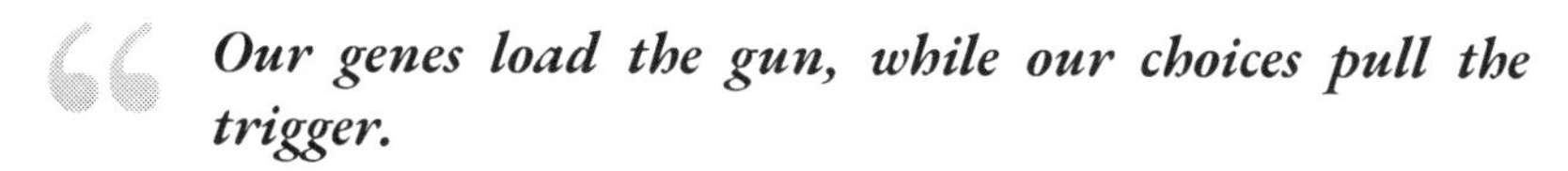

> ***Our genes load the gun, while our choices pull the trigger.***
>
> —DR. FRANCIS COLLINS

You are more likely to have a genetic vulnerability than someone with a single occurrence in their family. But that does not mean Alzheimer's disease is in your future; it is a risk but not a guarantee. And there are things within your control to decrease the risk.

An increasing amount of research supports the increased probability of dementia risk with physical inactivity, hearing loss, depression, obesity, hypertension, smoking, social isolation, diabetes, and low education levels. The good news is these are factors are modifiable (khn.org).

Steps to Maintain Cognitive Health

The National Institute on Aging reports your doctor may suggest the following steps to stay healthy and watch for changes in memory and thinking.

- Exercise regularly (consult your doctor before starting an exercise program).
- Eat a healthy diet that is rich in fruits and vegetables.
- Spend time with family and friends.
- Keep one's mind active.
- Control type 2 diabetes.

- Keep blood pressure and cholesterol at healthy levels (less than 120/80 for adults, consult your doctor).
- Maintain a healthy body weight (metabolism slows with age, as does body composition of fat and muscle, consult your doctor for ideal body weight profile specific for you).
- Stop smoking.
- Get help for depression.
- Avoid drinking a lot of alcohol.
- Get plenty of sleep.

. . .

Goodbye Myth: Because you have family members with Alzheimer's disease does not necessarily mean you will get the disease. There are strategies within your power to decrease your risk.

Step 8

Build novelty and complexity into each day and control modifiable risks.

Resources

Alzheimer's Common Symptoms

- Vagueness in everyday conversation
- Repeatedly saying the same thing over and over
- Taking longer to do routine tasks such as ADLs
- Forgetting people or places that are known and familiar
- Changes in ability to plan, problem solve, organize, and think logically
- Difficulty processing questions and instructions
- A decline in social skills and avoiding people
- Symptoms vary from person to person.

How Alzheimer's Is Diagnosed

A diagnosis is made after careful clinical consultation.

This assessment might include:

- A comprehensive medical history
- Neuropsychological tests
- A physical examination
- Blood and urine tests
- A psychiatric assessment
- Medical imaging MRI scan

How to Setup an Alzheimer's Home

How to set up a safe Alzheimer's Home is covered so thoroughly by the National Institute on Aging; Home Safety and Alzheimer's Disease website that I am reprinting here and crediting them with the great content. Please visit their website (nia.nih.org) for further help.

Over time, people with Alzheimer's disease become less able to manage around the house. For example, they may forget to turn off the oven or the water, how to use the phone during an emergency, which things around the house are dangerous, and where things are in their own home. As a caregiver, you can do many things to make the person's home a safer place. Think prevention—help avoid accidents by controlling possible problems.

Dementia does not rob someone of their dignity; it's our reaction to them that does.

—TEEPA SNOW

While some Alzheimer's behaviors are managed medically, many cannot be, such as wandering and agitation. It is more effective to change the person's surroundings—for example, to remove dangerous items—than to change behaviors. Changing the home environment can give the person more freedom to move around independently and safely.

. . .

Create an Alzheimer's-Safe Home

Add the following items to the person's home if they are not already in place:

- Smoke and carbon monoxide detectors in or near the kitchen and in all bedrooms.
- Emergency phone numbers (ambulance, poison control, doctors, hospital, etc.) and the person's address near all phones.
- Safety knobs and an automatic shut-off switch on the stove.
- Childproof plugs for unused electrical outlets and childproof latches on cabinet doors.

You can buy home safety products at stores carrying hardware, electronics, medical supplies, and children's items.

Lock up or remove these potentially dangerous items from the home

- Prescription and over-the-counter medicines
- Alcohol
- Cleaning and household products, such as paint thinner and matches
- Poisonous plants—contact the National Poison Control Center at 1-800-222-1222 or www.poison.org to find out which houseplants are poisonous
- Guns and other weapons, scissors, knives, power tools, and machinery
- Gasoline cans and other dangerous items in the garage

Moving Around the House

Try these tips to prevent falls and injuries:

- Simple the home Too much furniture can make it hard to move around freely.
- Get rid of clutter, such as piles of newspapers and magazines.
- Have a sturdy handrail on stairways.

- Put carpet on stairs or mark the edges of steps with brightly colored tape so the person can see them more easily.
- Put a gate across the stairs if the person has balance problems.
- Remove small throw rugs. Use rugs with nonskid backing instead.
- Make sure cords to electrical outlets are out of the way or tacked to baseboards.
- Clean up spills right away.

Make sure the person with Alzheimer's has good floor traction for walking. To make floors less slippery, leave floors unpolished or install nonskid strips. Shoes and slippers with good traction also help the person move around safely.

Minimize Danger

People with Alzheimer's disease may not see, smell, touch, hear, or taste things as they used to. You can do things around the house to make life safer and easier for the person.

Seeing

Although there may be nothing physically wrong with their eyes, people with Alzheimer's may no longer be able to interpret accurately what they see. Their sense of perception and depth may be altered, too. These changes can cause safety concerns.

- Make floors and walls different colors. This creates contrast and makes it easier for the person to see.
- Remove curtains and rugs with busy patterns that may confuse the person.
- Mark the edges of steps with brightly colored tape so people can see the steps as they go up or downstairs.
- Use brightly colored signs or simple pictures to label the bathroom, bedroom, and kitchen.
- Be careful about small pets. The person with Alzheimer's may not see the pet and trip over it.

- Limit the size and number of mirrors in your home and think about where to put them. Mirror images may confuse the person with Alzheimer's disease.
- Use dishes and placemats in contrasting colors for easier identification.

Use Signs

People with Alzheimer's disease can read until the late stage of the disease. Use signs with simple written instructions to remind them of danger or show them where to go.

Touching

People with Alzheimer's may experience loss of sensation or may no longer be able to interpret feelings of heat, cold, or discomfort.

- Reset your water heater to 120°F to prevent burns.
- Label hot-water faucets red and cold-water faucets blue or write the words "hot" and "cold" near them.
- Put signs near the oven, toaster, iron, and other things that get hot. The sign could say, "Stop!" or "Don't Touch—Very Hot!" Be sure the sign is not so close that it could catch on fire. A person with Alzheimer's should not use appliances without supervision. Unplug appliances when not in use.
- Pad any sharp corners on your furniture or replace or remove furniture with sharp corners.
- Test the water to make sure it is at a comfortable temperature before the person gets into the bath or shower.

Smelling

A loss of or decrease in smell is common in people with Alzheimer's disease.

- Use good smoke detectors. People with Alzheimer's may not be able to smell smoke.

- Check foods in your refrigerator often. Throw out any that have gone bad.

Tasting

People with Alzheimer's may not taste as well as before. They also may place dangerous or inappropriate things in their mouths.

- Keep foods like salt, sugar, and spices away from the person if you see him or her using too much.
- Put away or lock up things like toothpaste, lotions, shampoos, rubbing alcohol, soap, perfume, or laundry detergent pods. They may look and smell like food to a person with Alzheimer's disease.
- Keep the poison control number (1-800-222-1222) by phone.
- Learn what to do if the person chokes on something. Check with your local Red Cross chapter about health or safety classes.

Hearing

People with Alzheimer's disease may have normal hearing, but they may lose their ability to interpret what they hear accurately. This loss may result in confusion or overstimulation.

- Do not play the TV, CD player, or radio too loudly, and do not play them at the same time. Loud music or too many different sounds may be too much for the person with Alzheimer's to handle.
- Limit the number of people who visit at any one time. If there is a party, settle the person with Alzheimer's in an area with fewer people.
- Shut the windows if it is very noisy outside.
- If the person wears a hearing aid, check the batteries and settings often.

It may not be necessary to make all these changes; however, you may want to re-evaluate the safety of the person's home as behavior and abilities change.

Films to See

Away from Her , a Canadian independent drama film written and directed by Sarah Polley, based on *The Bear Came Over the Mountain*, by Alice Munro.

On Being with Krista Tippett, a podcast; Alan Dienstag – *Alzheimer's and the Spiritual Terrain of Memory,* On Being Studios.

I remember better when I paint: irememberbetterwhenipaint.com

CHAPTER 9

Someone to Watch Over Me

MYTH: You Will Always Be The One Giving Care

> ***Embracing a healing presence requires you to just be in the moment together.***
>
> —NANCY L. KRISEMAN, *THE MINDFUL CAREGIVER: FINDING EASE IN THE CAREGIVING JOURNEY*

"Informal Caregiving" Profile

The average caregiver is a 49-year-old woman providing 20 hours of unpaid care a week to a parent. These "working daughters" are employed and in the sandwich generation. Twenty-six percent of them are parents of a minor, and more than 50 percent financially support an adult child.

The majority of family caregivers remain women, and they provide more hours of care than their male counterparts. An estimated 59 percent of women provide 20 hours or less of unpaid care per week compared to 41 percent of men. The difference between male and female caregivers providing more hours of unpaid care is much greater: 62 percent of women provide more than 20 hours of weekly care compared to 38 percent of men.

Before and during the COVID-19 pandemic, family caregiving responsibilities have fallen mostly on women. One in 10 women reported caring for a family member prior to the pandemic, and also, one in 10 women shared they gained new caregiving responsibilities as a result of the pandemic.

Black, Indigenous, and People of Color (BIPOC) women providing care are twice as likely as white women caregivers to only have a high school education or less.

—Caregiving.com

Let's begin with Betty's story, an all-too-common scenario for many middle-aged women caring for adult children and aging parents. Years ago, I took care of a young African American woman with a long list of co-morbidities ranging from depression and morbid obesity to cervical cancer. But it was her 51-year-old mother who I felt needed most of the attention during the patient's stay. The patient's mother, I will call her "Betty," was taking care of her daughter (there were multiple psychosocial issues as well) and caring for her 82-year-old mother with newly diagnosed Alzheimer's. Further,Betty had a heart attack five weeks earlier and continues to smoke (her "only release"). Her sister is not contributing to her care and is often an additional source of stress. The duties have fallen solely on Betty's shoulders.

I have learned over the years in the clinical setting that the "patient" includes the family unit; again, "dis-ease" occurs in context and often is situated within a more extensive interconnected network. Knowing this, often the most therapeutic thing I can do is simply listen. Betty was willing, almost anxious, to share her situation while her daughter was sleeping, and I could feel her palpable sense of relief when she finally felt heard. Her daughter was in the system with a diagnosis, she will recover following treatment, but Betty is now paying the price for what has been termed "informal caregiving."

Contributing author Amanda Singleton, in an article for AARP, wrote about the megatrend of informal caregiving. Called informal because friends and family versus paid professionals do the care. Singleton writes:

> *The majority of people with health care or functional (communication, transportation, supervision) needs will require some caregiving assistance. For those who are not living in an assisted living or nursing home, only 3 in 10 use paid help from housekeepers, aides, or other assistance. That is because most caregiving in the U.S. is done by informal caregivers — the friends and family of the person who needs help. These informal caregivers are often not paid for their work, often to great personal expense and risk.*
>
> *Caregivers, on average, spend $7,000 to $13,000 out of pocket annually to help their care partners. They devote 23.7 hours per week on average (even more since the COVID-19 outbreak). Simply said, they are the backbone of the U.S. health care system and the front line of care provided to the ill and aging. If we paid these caregivers for their hours and reimbursed them for their time, we would be shelling out tens of thousands of dollars each to every single one of the nation's approximately 53 million caregivers. The value of unpaid family caregiving services in the U.S. is estimated at $375 billion a year, more than twice what is spent nationwide on nursing homes and paid home care combined.*
>
> *At present, 29 percent of the U.S. population, or approximately 65 million Americans, provide care to an adult relative or friend, according to Caregiving in the United States, National Alliance for Caregiving. And nearly 10 million adult children over the age of 50 care for aging parents. These family caregivers are themselves aging and providing the bulk of unpaid care (hence the term "informal care") at a time when they also need to be planning and saving for their retirement. The effect of informal care on work, wages, and*

wealth has been well documented and studied. The toll on the human experience is what is endless in scope.

As previously mentioned, an AARP survey found about 90 percent of older Americans wish to live at home for as long as possible. Most prefer aging in place to institutional care, even in cases where physical or cognitive decline makes it challenging to live independently, and Betty's mom is no different. At 82, in the early stages of a brain-ravaging disease, her time at home may be coming to an end. Soon tough decisions will have to be made. Despite the best of intentions, informal caregivers like Betty also need to balance the demands of their own families and professional lives together with the needs of their aging parents. Sometimes aging in place is not possible—or even desirable.

Our Aging Parents

It seems every week I read a Facebook post from old friends about the passing of their parent(s). The tributes are viscerally moving, and many of them I knew personally. The loss is so final and unimaginable, and yet we all must go on without them. A professor I once knew had lost his father, and he described it as now being "the outer layer of the onion." He was now the patriarch; a role reluctantly thrust onto his shoulders. Watching the slow, steady decline of once vital and steadfast people in our lives is disorienting. We end up having conversations (often too late in the process) we never imagined we would have, or doing caregiving tasks that once were family taboos, such as changing our parents' diapers.

We do our best to live at the margins of our work and family obligations while attempting to respond to what seems like a steady stream of crisis interventions, each leading to a temporary fix. This reminds us of our own aging and thoughts of how it could be for us in the not-too-distant future.

I have been on this emotional rollercoaster, witnessing parents' aging, and I want to share some hard-won insights. I have had to negotiate difficult conversations with siblings, wrestle with the medical system, and negotiate the modern healthcare labyrinth. And eventually, de-clutter my childhood home, with all that it entails, imposed by a deadline of rapid Senescence, and did I mention guilt?

Caregiving is not for the faint of heart. Eventually, this ends with selling the family home, and I am still struggling with that one. The house I grew up in was the built environment where we shaped our lives, it sheltered us, and was a gathering place for life's most meaningful events. The home was an aircraft carrier for our lives—a place we took off and landed from birth to death. It is challenging to think it will not be in the family any longer, nor will the landline phone number that I called to report in my entire life. This structure will soon house a new family, with new events, and life will go on. The cycle continues. During this period, I read a book by Susan David, Ph.D., which has been a solace during this change and loss. Her work, *Emotional Agility*, is rich in concepts and a somewhat contrarian view of complex emotions:

> *Emotional Agility is a process that allows you to be in the moment, changing or maintaining your behaviors to live in ways that align with your intentions and values. The process isn't about ignoring difficult emotions and thoughts. It's about holding those emotions and thoughts loosely, facing them courageously and compassionately, and then moving past them to make big things happen in your life.*

The author speaks eloquently; her thoughts apply when coming to grips with our aging parents and eventually ourselves, with this following paragraph:

> *In fact, one of the great paradoxes of human experience is that we can't change ourselves or our circumstances until we accept what exists right now. Acceptance is a prerequisite for change. This means giving permission for the world to be as it is because it's only when we stop trying to control the universe that we make peace with it. We still don't like the things we don't like; we just cease to be at war with them. And once the war is over, change can begin.*

The challenges for informal caregivers are growing, and it has become a societal issue and has even been considered an "infrastructure" problem by some in the American government. Yet, it takes just one human encounter to bring it home—make it real. I have not been able to shake Betty's story since first hearing it. She and I were similar in age, and most everyone I know has their own story, or they will have. Caregiving will touch most of us sooner or later.

> ***Instead of Loving TRUTH, We Make True, That Which We Love.***
>
> —ROBERT RINGER *LOOKING OUT FOR NUMBER 1*

The Robert Ringer quote above is one of my all-time favorites because it is so relevant. When it comes to the older loved ones in our lives, we want to think they will be forever buoyant. The thought of our parents or grandparents giving way to the forces of time is unthinkable, yet with each visit, there is a lower bar, and new normals are established and reestablished. Often, we notice but either deny or rationalize until we can no longer dispute the reality of age-related declines. I know from firsthand experience that I went through the heart-breaking physical/mental breakdown stages in my loved ones.

In case you need assistance in recognizing when your family member(s) may need help, here is a list:

1. Lack or slipping of personal hygiene
2. Unexplained dents in the car
3. Falls
4. Wounds in various stages of healing
5. Unpaid bills
6. Clutter piling up
7. House/yard need care/maintenance
8. Expired/spoiled groceries in freezer and cabinets
9. Forgetting to take medications/on time
10. Trouble getting up from a seated position
11. Unsteady gait
12. Using furniture as support when negotiating the room
13. Depressed or irritable moods increasing
14. Loss of interest (neglect pets, plants, etc.)

15. Changes in bowel habits
16. Inability to ask for assistance
17. Confusion of time/dates/events
18. Repeating, repeating, repeating
19. Lack of concentration
20. Difficulty accomplishing daily tasks
21. Looking for "lost" items constantly
22. Increased time sitting
23. Excessive ordering of products/magazines/donating to charities
24. Increased calls to 911 for assistance
25. Weight loss/dehydration

Some of these changes can be subtle over time, others acute, but they accumulate and only progress to higher levels requiring interventions. We love; therefore, we sometimes see what our hearts will only let us see—but in the end, we act to make them feel cared for, loved, and safer. Reversing our parents' roles and parenting is one of the most soul-challenging experiences of a caregiver's life (the hardest thing I have ever done), but it becomes necessary.

Several Things to Keep in Mind

- Do your best to involve them in the decisions you make (buy-in equates to lower barriers to adoption).
- Have patience.
- Keep communication lines open with loved ones (and family/friends).
- Keep your sense of humor (this may save you).

Another consideration is a phenomenon called "care deserts"—or areas where it is difficult to access resources such as transportation or medical care—which leave older adults without the means to stay healthy, active, and independent. Communities of color are significantly affected by the lack of such services. I read an article by Meg Brown about a study led by Iowa State University concerning older adults living in rural states who are at risk due to lack of access to resources they need. The investigation uncovered an alarming trend in analyzing characteristics of states with the highest population of people over 50. They discovered that fourteen of the twenty oldest states were also rural.

The implications of these data are far-reaching and consequential. Rural communities are often without resources that define the urban environment. For example, public transit, assisted living, home-based care, clinics, easy access to shops, civic centers, and grocery stores. The unintended consequence of rural living is premature institutionalization. The article cites 76 percent of assisted living facilities in metropolitan centers, and to make things more challenging, assisted living centers in rural areas are 40 percent smaller.

The research shows that in Iowa, 93 percent of Iowans over 50 favor aging in place over institutional settings. At the same time, Iowa ranks second in the nation for many older adults entering long-term care facilities. Rural America is prime for home and community-based care; caring for older adults in long-term care (LTC) facilities is far more costly. Further, the research found that the funds required to keep one older adult in LTC could cover the costs of three living with home-community-based care.

The concept is worth considering because most baby boomers live in the suburbs or rural areas, and they prefer it (reoccurring theme). For many women, providing informal care for loved ones and possibly experiencing the challenges of living in care deserts, this should be a wake-up call to their future selves. Emerging technologies are rapidly developing to meet the need, and the trend is for healthcare to move from the clinical setting to the home. Living a long life that you will love should include a plan to either move closer to care before you need it or plan to compensate with technologies like these:

- Telemedicine
- Tablets for communication and entertainment
- "Smart" platforms that integrate electronic medical records (EMRs) and electronic health records with AI and analytics
- Wearables
- Voice, touch, motion, and other assistive technologies
- Connected IoT devices and sensors
- Technologies for safety (monitoring and alert devices)

- Sensory aids (e.g., hearing devices)
- Gig economy services (e.g., meal delivery)
- Self-driving cars
- Robots
- Drone delivery of medications / 3D printing

The good news is you will potentially have more choices about where you will receive care than your parents did, but this does not preclude planning for it in advance and keeping up to date on technological advances in-home care.

Story of Waiting Too Long

On occasion, I receive a thoughtful post from a visitor to my website, aginginplace.com; this is one of those. So heartfelt are these thoughts; I wanted to share them here. His is a cautionary tale of perhaps waiting too long but loving deeply enough to live with the consequences.

> *Aging in Place is a fine idea and I completely support it—until it isn't a good idea, and when it isn't, it may create real problems, especially for our children. I know this from personal experience. My mother was 73 when my dad died. She was strong, healthy, engaged in church and community, and she continued to live—by herself—in the family home. The years went by, and she gradually declined physically, but we, her children, did all the things necessary for her to remain in her home—accessible bathroom, grab bars and rails, ramps, help with transportation and shopping, etc. Now 97, she is still healthy, with some mild memory and balance issues, and still in her own home. But now she needs constant, around the clock care to be dressed, showered, fed, safe, and not feel alone at the end.*
>
> *She is too old to move to assisted living—it would likely be the end for her, and it would be against her wishes, which we're not about to do. And as you know, Social Security has in-home caregiver benefits only for skilled nursing, and most seniors simply can't afford to pay for care out of pocket, so that means children take on that responsibility. So, her children have taken on the responsibility for her care. I*

drive ten hours from my home every other month and stay a month, and my sisters leave their families to help out, too. My experience has taught me that there is a window of time during which an Elder can —and should—leave her home for a situation that will provide her the services and support she needs all the way to the end. If we don't move during that window, well, I am living with the consequences. And as much as I love my mother, I'm not about to pass this on to my children.

So, while you are providing us with all the tools for aging in place, I would hope you would use some of our Elder wisdom to address the question of planning for and knowing when it is time to leave our homes, and what kinds of new arrangements we can create to nurture and support us in our final years. I think Elder owned and staffed group homes—Elders caring for Elders—is an exciting idea, one that leaves Elders in charge of our lives, provides us with companionship, and perhaps most importantly, brings real meaning to our final years, as we help each other in the grand experience of conscious dying.

Many blessings and thank you for your work,
C.L. (name kept anonymous)

Caregiving as A Journey

As the COVID pandemic has gone into various progressing phases and vaccines, has become widely administered, more and more people are talking about travel. I have been listening to friends and coworkers describe trips to places near and far. I am also aware of others (like myself and maybe you?) who have been on another 'trip', the journey that is caregiving for our aging parents. There are common themes such as going somewhere you have never been, not knowing what to expect, how to plan for the optimal experience, leaving room for some uncertainty along the way, and of course, how to pay for it.

All this has me thinking about the value of guides when embarking on new and foreign lands (exotic destinations and eldercare). One of my favorite programs to listen to is *Travel with Rick Steves* as I take trips precariously listening. Steves always interviews guides from around the world, and these trusted insiders make travel a more meaningful experience while often easing the stress of the unknown.

> ***An exquisitely crafted trip can help release stress and be a better bang for the buck in that money you may appear to save as an 'independent' traveler can be quickly lost in hassles and inevitable mistakes. Bottom Line, a smartly designed trip is about economy and efficiency, which equates to an optimal experience.***
>
> —RICK STEVES, ON USING GUIDES

There are many types of guides, from Rick Steve's tour guides to mountain wilderness and fishing guides. There are even psychedelic guides called "trip-sitters," co-pilots who remain sober to ensure the safety of the drug user while under the influence of a drug. The practice is qualified as a means of harm reduction. A trip sitter is sometimes called a psychedelic guide. However, this term is more often used to describe someone who actively guides a drug user's experiences. In contrast, a sitter merely stands by to discourage bad trips and handle emergencies but otherwise does not take on an active role.

The main idea I am emphasizing is that employing someone who is an expert concerning the place (actual or psych) you will be going, is key to the success of your trip. Caregiving is in many ways a trip or journey—not unlike traveling to foreign destinations that are mysterious and life-changing. Given the staggering number of growing unpaid caregivers (approximately 43.5 million people in the United States), this "trip" is likely to be the one you are now on, or it will be soon. And it can be a long, strange trip because you will be going places and doing things you never dreamed of in your most exercised imagination—you are most likely woefully unprepared for it.

Caregiving often calls us to lean into love we didn't know possible.

—TIA WALKER, *THE INSPIRED CAREGIVER: FINDING JOY WHILE CARING FOR THOSE YOU LOVE*

For the caregiving trip, it is optimal to hire a guide if you can afford it. This eldercare guide is called a Geriatric Care Manager (GCM). These are trained professionals in social work, psychology, nursing, and gerontology. They are trained to assess, plan, coordinate, monitor, and provide services for the elderly and their families. Being an advocate for older adults is a primary function of the care manager. They belong to the National Association of Professional Geriatric Care Managers. They are certified by one of the three certification organizations for care management—the National Association of Social Workers, the National Academy of Certified Care Managers, or the Commission for Case Managers.

The GCM can be well worth the investment as someone to watch over you (aka guide) to make sure things do not get so out of hand you will be looking for a trip-sitter next (smile)! They can make it a smoother path so you can focus on what matters most–the journey and being there with them.

Anyone who has ever been on a plane and sat through the safety presentation before take-off can tell you what all attendants advise in case of cabin pressure dropping and oxygen requirements. You probably know where I am going with this—always place the oxygen mask on *yourself first* and only then attend to those in need. The message is clear; self-care first if you are going to be of any use to others. These are turbulent times; it feels like you need a seatbelt and helmet to get out of bed in the morning, and it seems to never let up. So now more than ever, self-care is essential to survival and thriving to do whatever you do in the world. For informal caregivers, this time is incredibly bumpy, and resiliency is the character trait needed so we can be available physically and mentally for loved ones.

For this discussion, self-care prioritizes your well-being and health by being gentle and kind with yourself—supporting your mind, body, and spirit with thoughts and activities that recharge and bring joy. Yes, this reads like something you would find in any edition of *Oprah Magazine*, and it sounds sage. Having noted this, I am as guilty as the next person in following through on self-care when over-tasked. It is seemingly impossible to live a "balanced" life as an informal caregiver. But the mantra *"self-care is health-care"* does frame it in a more digestible way—at least for me. It may sound self-indulgence (guilt aside); being there for yourself so you can be there for a loved one is more than pretty sentiment. The idea is not new and is not revolutionary; what it is, is required for the times we are now navigating. Here are some simple, actionable steps that can make a difference. They are easy-peasy and possible anywhere, anytime.

Take Deep Breaths

It sounds so simple, and it is. Three deep breaths, and you can do it anywhere, anytime. According to the American Institute of Stress,

> *20-30 minutes of deep breathing daily is effective in reducing both anxiety and stress. It must be breathing deeply through the abdomen to produce the best results. What happens during deep abdominal breathing is that the oxygen breathed in stimulates the body's parasympathetic nervous system. This, in turn, produces a feeling of calmness and body connectedness that diverts attention from stressful, anxious thoughts and quiets what is going on in the mind.*

(psychcentral.com/blog/why-deep-breathing-helps-calm-anxiety#1)

Practice Gratitude

I will often ask myself, *"What's good in my life right now?"* This simple question always sets in motion a cascading list of people and things that I am astonishingly fortunate to have in my life. I instantly feel better. I also tell myself to get out of comparison and get into creativity!

> *Studies on gratitude and appreciation found that participants who felt grateful showed a marked reduction in the level of cortisol, had better cardiac functioning and were more resilient to emotional*

setbacks and negative experiences. By reducing the stress hormones and managing the autonomic nervous system functions, gratitude significantly reduces symptoms of depression and anxiety.

(Source: psychologytoday.com)

Motion Changes Emotion

Move your body; it is as simple as that. Physical activity helps stave off depression and anxiety and boosts the immune system. The Kaiser Health Foundation suggests getting your heart rate up for thirty minutes a day. The Mayo Clinic reports that regularly exercising may help ease depression and anxiety by:

- Releasing feel-good endorphins, natural cannabis-like brain chemicals (endogenous cannabinoids), and other natural brain chemicals that can enhance your sense of well-being.
- Taking your mind off worries so you can get away from the cycle of negative thoughts that feed depression and anxiety.
- Regular exercise has many psychological and emotional benefits, too.

It can help you:

- Gain confidence. Meeting exercise goals or challenges, even small ones, can boost your self-confidence. Getting in shape can also make you feel better about your appearance.
- Get more social interaction. Exercise and physical activity may give you the chance to meet or socialize with others. Just exchanging a friendly smile or greeting as you walk around your neighborhood can help your mood.
- Cope in a healthy way. Doing something positive to manage depression or anxiety is a healthy coping strategy. Trying to feel better by drinking alcohol, dwelling on how you feel, or hoping depression or anxiety will go away on its own can lead to worsening symptoms.

(Source: mayoclinic.org)

Admittedly, it was challenging for me to carve out time to exercise. My energy was so drained during caregiving that the idea of it was daunting, but every time I exercised, the world was a better place, the sun shined a little brighter, and I felt a little more in control. I call this a "victory over self" and it has always paid positive dividends. It is worth emphasizing, as an informal caregiver, you feel so much of the time out of control, you are responding and reacting to an ever-changing landscape that defines elder care. The exercise provided time alone, a sense of purpose, and all the academic benefits listed above—but most importantly, a sense of control was re-established with each exercise session (if only temporarily).

Eating Well

I have heard of "emotional eating" during the pandemic with increased drinking and substance abuse reported. A business logo on a truck tailgate I was following down the freeway one day in the height of the pandemic seemed to capture the country's mood: DOOMSDAY BREWING. So, it is understandable folks are turning to comfort and escape in the form of consumables—but this can fall into that "secondary agers" (speeds up aging) category. Make nutrition a priority; consider the Mediterranean diet as a template for eating well.

Small Indulgences

A nurse colleague at work carves out time to enjoy vinyl records on their vintage audio system. Sitting and directing undivided attention to the music *only*—a focused awareness, if you will, is the key. The music is not a backdrop to some "productive" activity—it is the activity! Their description of the process, the aesthetics, the ritual, and the soul-stirring experience is another form of "home health." What is your potential small indulgence? Visit it as often as you deem feasible. I like to call these "Indulgence Shots."

Ask for Help

Call a friend who has your best interest in mind. Who is it that makes you a better person? I am blessed to have a couple of trusted friends who are supportive. Males tend to be less adept at building supportive communities, and I will offer myself as an example. On the other hand, my wife prioritizes staying in touch with a core group of women friends. She views her life-long caravan of friends (sisters) as a "systems approach" to health and time invested—not spent (as of this typing, I can hear her in the other room on the phone with a girlfriend laughing to the point of tears).

These few things are easy to do—which means they are easy not to do. We are all in this together, and our days consist of choice points—choose you, ultimately it will benefit others. The line, *This too shall pass,* has been a source of strength and is a good reminder nothing lasts forever. A friend recently suggested the line, "*DROP THE ROCK*" for a mantra to repeat when stubborn negativity invades their thought patterns. I liked that simple line so much I found a perfectly round river rock and wrote it on the surface. I now see that on my desk as a reminder to LET IT GO.

> ***There are days I drop words of comfort on myself like falling leaves and remember that it is enough to be taken care of by myself.***
>
> —BRIAN ANDREAS

My best analogy for the informal caregiver is what most baby boomers will recall. On the Ed Sullivan Show (circa 1960s), a frequent guest was the plate spinner. A man in a dark suit would have thin wooden support poles and a long table which he worked behind. He began by sometimes twirling white dinner plates or clear bowls on the top end of thin twisting rods—and suddenly, like magic, he would have a long row of plates and bowls all spinning at various speeds. The different stages of spinning caused him to have to run franticly from end-to-end of the table, keeping the spinning all going at once! What made for riveting black and white TV is a fitting analogy for my caregiving experience. The running from inevitable crisis to crisis, putting out fires, then beginning the process all over again with another loved one is much like the plate spinner—only the stakes are higher.

Healthy boundaries and duty sharing are the keys to your survival. Set limits on your time availability, delegate, if necessary, to other family members and try to play to their strengths. If someone is talented with setting up appointments and organization, have them do clerical duties like paying bills. If another has a strong back, let them do the physical aspects of caregiving, for example, transportation needs or clearing the house out.

If time is available to yet another family member, ask them to do the shopping. Perhaps a family member is not geographically compatible with caregiving but can cover the needed role in another way. Get creative in support; this requires INTER-dependence. Tempted as you might be to do it all and thus keep control and get things done; trust me, you cannot do it all.

Shared responsibility may mean letting go; often, things fall short of expectations, tempers flare, and feelings get hurt. And yes, there will always be that one who doesn't help no matter what or makes things worse; this is all part of the process. But do allow others to step up and appeal to their better angels. C.S. Lewis noted, "Hardships often prepare people for an extraordinary destiny." Do not deny them this. It is helpful to remember that the goal is to keep your loved one in need safe, cared for, and experiencing some quality of life. Caregiving is not the path of least resistance; it will call on your deepest reserves. You will be required to answer the call time and time again, do things unimaginable. Most of your victories will go unnoticed and often unappreciated by distant others (the accolades are not coming)—do them anyhow.

Solo Aging

Carol Marak, Author of SOLO and SMART, A Roadmap for a Supportive and Secure Future, knows firsthand these caregiving challenges. She helped her parents with their elder care needs and aging issues. Once her parents died, it occurred to her that she had no one to assist her with the things she and her sisters helped their parents with.

Carol is one of about 27% (14.7 million) of all older adults in 2020 living alone in the community (5 million men, 9.7 million women). They represented 20% of older men and 33% of older women. The proportion living alone increases with advanced age for both men and women. Among women aged 75 and older, for example, 42% lived alone, according to the

2020 Profile of Older Americans report published in May 2021 from the Administration for Community Living (ACL). These older solo agers have been termed "elder orphans,"

FORBES contributing author, Sara Zeff Geber, PhD, in her piece, New Census Report Reveals Growing Number of Childless Older Adults, provides insight into the historical beginnings of the now trend of female solo agers.

> *It started with the boomers. You might call the rise in childlessness among boomer women the result of a perfect storm in the waves of change that were taking place in the late sixties and throughout the seventies and eighties.*
>
> *Prior to that era, there was little acknowledged resistance to the traditional roles for women: they married, had children, and if there was time or financial need, they might also be teachers, nurses, or secretaries. That scenario blew up for good, starting in the late 60s with the equal-rights-for-women initiative. That led to a political movement to push the equal rights amendment (ERA) through congress and pass an increasing number of laws that prohibited discrimination against women in any institution that drew on government funding, mainly universities and large corporations. Soon, the doors of prestigious educational institutions that trained doctors, lawyers, engineers, architects, and scientists were opening wide and inviting women (albeit, often grudgingly) to apply. Subsequently, hiring managers were compelled to bring on the products of those schools and women found themselves being ushered into what had previously been almost exclusively the domain of their male counterparts.*
>
> *With all of the new opportunities within their grasp, a very large number of women decided motherhood (and sometimes marriage as well), were not going to be part of their future. In addition to new occupational opportunities, these women of child-bearing age in the 1970s and 1980s also had a brand-new weapon in their arsenal, one their mothers and grandmothers did not possess: THE PILL. For the*

> *first time in history, women could take complete control of their reproductive systems. Those who chose to avoid motherhood could still have an active sex life if they chose and not run the risk of ending up in the family way, by accident.*

Zeff-Gerber notes that when you fast-forward to the present these boomer women are in their 60s-70s-80s and childless. Data from The U.S. Census Bureau, partially supported by the National Institute on Aging, (August 2021) on the childless state of the older adult population, showed among adults 75 years and older (not boomers), 10.9% reported being childless; among those ages 65-74 (early boomers) 15.9% reported being childless; and among those 55-64 (late boomers), 19.6% reported being childless.

In the growing ranks of solo agers, Carol Marak realized once her parents died, she would have no one to assist her. So, she went to work and created her own life plan after investing thousands of hours helping parents, researching for resources, and writing hundreds of articles on aging-related topics for the senior care sector, Carol condensed her learning about what's needed to grow older confidently, even when living solo. She stated:

> *I learned over the past ten years after creating my plan is to gain as much knowledge about self-care, becoming self-reliant, and creating a family-like community. Because if you live alone, you will need nearby support and most importantly, to be in good health, have enough money to outlast you, and have someone who cares about you.*
>
> *Then in 2016, I launched the Elder Orphan Facebook Group because I wanted to know how many people are in a similar situation—living alone with no family to help with financial and medical decisions, long term concerns, personal care, estate planning, power of attorney and more. It was astonishing to discover there are many of us who live alone and likely will into old age. Whether a person is single, divorced, married, or widowed—each needs a plan!*

Dr. Marion Somers—A Life of Service

Elder care expert and award-winning, nationally recognized geriatric care manager, Marion Somers, Ph.D., "Dr. Marion," shares some caregiving insights. She is profiled later in chapter 11.

> ***There are only four kinds of people in the world—those who have been caregivers, those who are caregivers, those who will be caregivers, and those who will need caregivers.***
>
> —ROSALYN CARTER

From Marion Somers, Ph.D.

I have spent my life as a caregiver for my family, friends, students, and clients. I have always been cautiously incorporating the "look before you leap" saying into my daily rhythm. While preparing for my own aging process, I have written books and articles and talked to anyone who would listen to how to take care of themselves. I truly have listened to my own advice, mostly because I have gained wisdom from listening to the many seniors who have crossed my path. These elders have blessed me in countless ways because of their practical and varied years of wisdom and life experiences they so freely shared with me. My life has been enhanced, blessed, and filled with ancient wisdom from lives that have experienced wars, famines, displacements, and the loss of incomparable deaths. Yet, in the many stories I have heard and absorbed, there has always been unshakable faith that things will work out. Whatever the tragedy of the moment —it will pass.

I, as well as my seniors, have benefited on some level from the experience that was endured to the point that one can say I have conquered. So, in the same openness shared with me with humility and humor, I share with you how I have prepared for my aging process. I am following the ten steps from my book, *Elder Care Made Easier*, 2nd edition.

. . .

The steps are:

1. Communicate openly
2. Safety first
3. Improve the lifestyle
4. Make life easier with adapted equipment
5. Manage financial issues
6. Take care of legal matters
7. Find mobility and disability
8. Find the right housing
9. Hire help when it's needed
10. Learn to let go

1. Communicate Openly

Communication is an art form that we need to keep awareness of always to the forefront. No matter the individual's age, I speak to everyone from adult to adult and not from a sense of inferiority or superior at any time. I seek to honor all who have come into my presence, whatever their need or circumstance. This comment also includes the birth of my children, the family members that have been in and out of my life, any of my personal relationships, plus the bond that has been forged with many of my students, clients, and business associates.

As part of my communication process, I have sought to understand the individual before me, not from my perspective of who they may be, but of their own perceived concept of themselves. As a keen observer once told me of my interactions, I take everybody at face value, no matter how unusual or unique. Not all communication is easy, especially if there have been conflicts past or present; we come to a meeting of the minds and aim for a win, win outcome. Because I have found if somebody wins, then somebody else is losing; therefore, there may be negative issues either immediately or on the horizon or the future. My goal is always to be honest with myself and those with whom I interact. I didn't say it was easy, but it certainly is doable. Being honest with myself has taken a great deal of practice to reach where I now am, and I care to be.

When dealing with a client or professionals, I find the person or group before me, saying one thing but doing another—intentionally, I stop. I then ask everyone who is currently involved to pause and take a step back. I restate what I think they have said so that there is clarity. Because in the restatement of what they have said, the other person or persons often hears their comment with more clarity or at least an understanding of how I have interpreted what they have said. I have striven for truth and clarity, and I have found the effort worthwhile and rewarding. What I learned has been first to observe and then be clear within my thought and emotional process before speaking or going forward with the next segment to be addressed.

2. Put Safety First

I became aware that staying alert to my environment often afforded me safety and peace of mind at an early age. As a geriatric care manager and somebody fascinated with universal design, I am aware that sometimes just making minor adjustments can make one's life and home environmentally appropriate, more comfortable, and ecologically more livable. Wherever I have lived, I have always made sure that anything I would need in an emergency was planned for and made available, for example, like a simple thing like having a flashlight with working batteries in every room. All electrical equipment is checked periodically and is in working condition. Anything I might need in a car emergency is already tucked away in the trunk of my car. In this area of California where I live, we have earthquakes, floods, and fires, so, therefore, there is a packed satchel for every member of the household, including pets. There are websites full of charts and lists for every conceivable emergency that one can prepare for. What I learned was by putting safety first, I have reduced or eliminated anxiety, and I can usually entertain a sense of calm and dominion.

3. Improve the Lifestyle

I know my likes and dislikes, and I try to take in new interests where time and finances allow. I love to travel and have visited a vast array of interesting places that have been on my very long bucket list. It has been fun and frustrating to have these adventures, but not all have met my highest expectations. I have no sense of direction, and I refuse to admit I have ever gotten lost. I simply state that we are seeing scenery that was not on the agenda. I have long ago found if I am in a situation that I cannot change, I simply go with the flow as the expression goes. I make sure I eat holistic foods and understand how my body best functions. I try not to get tempted with foods or beverages that I know may be detrimental to my health. As a practical prescription for good health, I go to the doctor once a year to get a general checkup as well as dental, and eye care are attended to.

I think of myself as an old car with many moveable parts and keeping everything in working order is my primary goal both within myself and as well as my car. In the same way that I try to incorporate my elderly clients into expanding their horizons to meet new friends or try new experiences, I do the same for myself. I recently went to Alaska on a fishing expedition, I mean a real fishing boat. We fished for salmon, haddock, and trapped for shrimp. All catches caught during the day were eaten on board that night for dinner. I touched glaciers and watched a part of the glacier fall off into the water. Earth warming is a reality that we all must face and do something about now, where and when we can. I have taken the Monarch Butterfly under my wing so to speak and have planted in my garden the variety of plants that these beautiful creatures need to survive. I have reached out to my neighbors to think about and encourage them to do the same. The positive response to this project has been heartwarming. What I learned is that every day can be an adventure and to appreciate the uniqueness of each aspect of nature from sunrise to sunset.

4. Make Life Easier with Adapted Equipment

We are living at a time that is very sensitive to anyone with an affliction or disease that might keep them from fully functioning. With the help of artificial intelligence (AI), the world is only limited by one's ability to seek out information and resources. I have assisted many of my clients to a more involved and productive life. Sometimes the equipment or adjustments that are needed are not necessarily big or expensive. For someone with trembling hands to make feeding oneself more doable, there are special adapted utensils to help maintain one's independence. Clever items such as helping oneself put on their socks or pull a little button through a buttonhole.

I was hired as a consultant for a large corporation that was transitioning from being solely for children's toys to entering into the eldercare space. We devised an animatronic robotic cat and dog that were lifelike, could purr or bark and move in very realistic ways. These "Comfort Companions" were wonderful to give to anyone who could not have a live pet due to their living circumstances or allergies. These animatronic creatures served the same purpose as pet therapy without any negative aspects of a live pet that needed to be fed, walked, or cleaned up after. I have several of these animatronic Companions, and I enjoy the companionship without the work. What I have learned is that adapted equipment and AI are for every age and every need. I now hike with a hiker's staff (not a cane) as I treasure my travels in the countryside.

5. Managing Financial Issues

Sometimes financial issues or financial subjects are difficult to deal with either personally or when you are dealing with family members or financial advisors who are there to help or assist you. The most important, maybe the most obvious, is that these are your finances and therefore yours to spend, save or distribute as you deem appropriate. If you do not have cognitive impairment and are knowledgeable of your assets, I have found it wise to research and hire those I feel will be most helpful to address my needs. I have always thought I could handle money because as I was growing up, funds were very limited, and I started earning money at the age of ten.

I first started cleaning apartments for the elderly in the tenement building where I lived. Sometimes I didn't get money; I got food which was equally important to a growing youngster. The homemade stuff was delicious, but the food was also made with love and expertise I didn't understand. To my limited culinary taste buds, the flavors were foreign, exotic, and visually different from what I knew. I must state at this moment that my mother was the worst cook ever. She had no interest in food; fresh foods and vegetables were virtually unknown in our home. My mother was a master at opening a can of food; as a child, breakfast consisted of a slice of bread and a cup of coffee with milk. It's no wonder I love cooking, feeding people, not only nourishing their bodies but their souls.

I was 25 when I realized most people don't read cookbooks the way I do. Most people open a cookbook to get the recipe they need, and I read a cookbook from page one to the end. As I read a cookbook, I can visually see the end product and, gastronomically, taste the different flavors and textures in my mouth. The only time I am stumped is when I come across a different spice or herb I haven't been exposed to before.

Getting back to finances and my early entrepreneurial efforts. In my neighborhood, many people did 'piece work' at home. Often, they would send out an SOS when they had a rush job, and I was always called to help. I had a reputation for listening and following instructions. I was also very fast. I made a game of everything in my head, and I tried to do the project better, faster, and accurately no matter what the project was.

I also learned at an early age to manage my pennies, nickels, and dimes. When I first left home, I put whatever money I had into various envelopes designated rent, clothing, education, etc. I never bought anything on credit; I simply saved up the needed funds before I bought anything. This habit of not borrowing and carefully allocating funds stayed with me. I follow careful monitoring of all my assets no matter the category and am aware of something amiss in any of my accounts.

The same goes for my careful monitoring of my car and anything else I hold of value. Having been in the geriatric field caring for people who have been taken advantage of by friends, family, or simply fraudulent intruders via the phone, computer, or even unscrupulous professionals, one cannot be overly cautious. When reaching out for professional assistance, it is good practice to check on resumes, education, and professional qualifications. Including checking on letters of recommendation. As the old saying of carpenters and quilters goes, "Measure twice, cut once." I would rather be faulted for being overly cautious than for hiring someone who was not up to standards.

I have learned not to be hesitant to ask for guidance and assistance from professionals. Always asking that next question until you know you know everything you need for your immediate situation or your plans for the future. Sometimes our concerns go beyond ourselves and may extend to family, friends, or those who have been generous with their time and expertise. One might think about how they may be incorporated, or rewarded, or remembered if not now in some future time and benefit from your gratitude and generosity.

I know how to research any information I may need, whether it be about insurance, reverse mortgages, or any other subject that falls under the financial category. With today's resources so readily available with some time and effort, one can cautiously go forward with a wealth of information to seek appropriate professionals who may assist you. What I have learned with managing financial matters is to find the right computer, app, program, or have someone write a program that fits my specific needs. I have learned to ask.

6. Take Care of Legal Matters

As we age, we collect a wide variety of important papers. These include everything from the day we were born, birth certificates, marriage/divorce papers, etc., that we have accumulated that cover the significant events in our lives. Many sites will enumerate the variety and complexity that detail our life experiences. What is important is that these certificates, documents, records are up to date and are in a safe, waterproof, fireproof, easy-to-carry container. Having everything in one place keeps the burden of answering any legal questions and inquiries at your fingertips. There are computer programs that can keep a computer version of this material available in the event of some disaster.

Always be careful that whatever program you use is secure and tamper-proof. Having a USB device with the most important information can be an excellent way to be sure it is secure and portable. They are also easy to carry in an emergency. All appropriate materials need to be updated periodically. Just a reminder people move, retire, or pass away. What I have learned is that everything you sign you need to fully comprehend each word, each paragraph and overall content. Also, use caution when you empower others with any legal documents. There are basic legal terms to be familiar with.

. . .

Legal Terms to Know

Will: A legal document that states your intentions and what you wish to be done regarding disposal of your property after your death.

Advance directive: A legal statement signed by you, as a living, competent person, that expresses your wishes in advance of an emergency that makes you otherwise unable to convey your decisions. A living will is a type of advance directive.

Health care proxy: A legal document in which you designate another person to make health care decisions for you if you are rendered incapable of making your wishes known. Also known as medical power of attorney.

Durable power of attorney: A power of attorney is a legal document that assigns legal authority to another person so he or she can make a property, financial, and other legal decisions for you if you are unable to do so for yourself. In some states, health care decisions can be added to the responsibilities of the durable power of attorney.

Durable power of attorney for health care: A document allowing another or others to make health care decisions when you are not able to. Authorized by state law, this document allows you to designate another person to have powers which you specify in the document. These powers can be limited to health care decisions, or for general financial management, health and medical care, and emergencies. This document can be revoked by you, as the principal, at any time if you remain competent.

Scams to be aware of:

- Charity scams
- Construction and home repair scams
- Fake mail from the Social Security Administration, IRS, or Medicare
- Fake online pharmacies and Medicare scams
- Grandchild in trouble scams
- Investment seminar scams
- Jury duty scams
- Nigerian 419 scams and sweepstakes scams

- Opt-out negative option scams
- Phony fraud alerts

These fraudulent scams reach into your pocket. The perpetrators are clever and will use any means at their disposal to charm you, frighten you, lie to you, appeal to your compassion and sense of community, or your religious preferences. They will pull at your heartstrings in unimaginably clever ways. No matter how sophisticated or knowledgeable you may be, it is easy to fall, victim. One can never be alert enough because some scams may originate close to home and your community. Also, do not give out any information over the phone, computer, front door, or solicitations on your way to work. What I have learned is, you cannot be cautious enough. That is why I have listed all these because I want to underscore this point. None of us can afford to lose what we have worked so hard to secure for our futures, as well as the ability to take care of those we love.

7. Find Mobility in Disability

We all want to experience personal freedom, physically, mentally, and emotionally. But sometimes restrictions to our bodies happen, and we might have a loss of mobility or the onset of cognitive impairment. My experience has been to take care of my physical, mental, and emotional needs daily as best I can. I take great comfort in food and all its joyous manifestations. As someone who has always been an artist, painter, and sculptor, I trained my children, who I knew would someday go out on their own. I wanted them to look at a plate of food as though it was a colored artist's palette. There should always be a variety of colors and healthy combinations of vegetables, protein, carbohydrates, and fruit—to be washed with room temperature water.

I have personally never smoked or drank alcohol. I am a senior by definition which needs no medication. I exercise doing things that I enjoy, such as playing basketball on the court all by myself; I walk on the beach or in nature at every opportunity. I have a variety of interests, including fishing, reading, writing, gardening, and cooking. My spiritual life is quite intact. My kids laugh and say some people bar hop, but their mom church hops and goes to wherever she feels or is drawn to that has a religious or spiritual atmosphere. I find the concept of a spiritual life surrounds me in nature as well as informal religious settings.

I am confident with the breadth and depth of adaptive equipment in its many manifestations will be able to address any physical or emotional handicap or disability I may ever experience. If the need should arise for me to be supported in my future, I am sure answers will be found to help me lead a productive life. My life has been one of contribution and personal satisfaction. This includes my ability to continue to travel with the many adaptive devices and equipment that are constantly being upgraded or invented. We are also blessed to live in a time when artificial intelligence (AI) is on the frontier of ever-expanding horizons. What I have learned is that individuals can be transformed with assisted living devices and can appreciate their sense of self and potentially regain independence and renewal.

8. Find the Right Housing

There are many choices about how one wants to live, considering one's physicality, cognitive mental ability, and finances. My personal choice would be and is, to maintain my independence until such time as I cannot function on my own. The choices are: I want to maintain my own abode with all the adjustments that might need to be made, or do I want to live with an aide or assistance in its variety of forms? If I were going to move, would I want to be near friends and relatives or not? I would like to be close to family because, for me, family is very important. One can always move, and within the move there are options.

- Move-in with friends or relatives.
- Move into a like-minded community or spiritual group.
- Moving into an adult home.
- Moving into an assisted living facility.
- Moving into a nursing facility.
- And at the end of life, there may be a choice of Hospice.

Under all of these categories, one can find a wealth of information using your computer and the various elder/senior organizations that cater to a population that needs assistance and or complicated care. I have found housing and how one is to care for oneself, or another is a very personal independent series of choices. I have found with all the work I have done over the years is just to search one's soul and listen to one's inner voice. You know best what is right for you. I most certainly have made choices that were right for me, and I have no regrets because each choice was made with the information, I had available.

When I have worked with my seniors and their families, I have emphasized that the person being spoken about and cared for needs to be the person to primarily make the decision after considering all practical matters. I had one orthodox Jewish client, and because of family circumstances, we had to move her in with one of her adult children. It was also decided at that time to get a full-time live-in aide for her. We went through half a dozen aides over a six-month period before she found one that she and the family liked. This aide was a Muslim, and there was a lot of controversy around this choice. Both religions followed the same washing rituals, the many practices of the same food restrictions and the preparations of food, and their religious holidays often coincided. These two women had the most interesting conversations about child-rearing, family in general, and politics. Over the years they were together, there was an understanding of each other and a very deep appreciation of their differences.

In general, I think the United Nations and politicians could learn a very valuable lesson on understanding differences and appreciate the contribution made by others who were different yet made an advancement and shared different perspectives. What I have learned is to first figure out what your basic needs are and how to best fulfill those needs. Also, in the case of moving to a facility, it is wise to take into consideration not just the location and costs, but who will visit you and do you want a facility that might be closer and convenient to your potential visitor. This takes in not only friends and family but your spiritual group or your community support system.

9. Hire Help When It's Needed

The basic interviewing process is important if you are going to hire help, especially if they are going to be working inside your home or taking care of your senior in a care facility. You want to make sure the person is insured, has the education they claim, or has worked with a client like the one you are asking them to work with.

These questions can be long and formal, but you have to gather the information so that your client or family member is safe. I have found I am skilled at asking questions, but more importantly, I listen to people's answers, both what they say and what they don't say. I have found this skill is helpful whether I am hiring somebody for myself or for a client.

On a personal level, my ability to listen has stayed with me as a guidepost to listen to words and what my inner instincts are telling me. This is a skill set that takes a certain amount of maturity and life experience. With all I have learned and experienced, I make lists, charts, and graphs of anything I need to do or accomplish for the day, week, month, and year. I would go so far as to even say future goals in a breakdown of one year, five years, and beyond. This keeps me on task and always moving forward. I believe in the rewards system, and sometimes it can be as simple as a gold star I can stick on a calendar or a new something that I have had my eye on.

One of my most endearing memories happened at a time when I was living in New York City. I had a very dear male friend who was very politically astute and active. He needed "arm candy" for a big political gathering in Washington, D.C. He invited me to come to Washington to the gathering. My only job was to look good and stay out of his way as he "made the rounds" of the room shaking hands and doing all the things that politicians do. I quietly took a seat near the corner of this very large room with a plate full of food; I was going to enjoy this political soiree.

Within a moment, I had an older gentleman sit down next to me, and we immediately were talking about sports, fishing, camping, fishing, and camping sites around the country and how to tie flies. We chatted for over an hour, and I was somewhat aware that people gave us a very wide berth, and nobody came near us. Then this gentleman said, I have to get out of this place and do the room first. He said, "delighted to meet you," and off he went. Within seconds my friend rushed over to me and wanted to know what we talked about. Everyone was commenting that this gentleman never sits for any length of time at these gatherings. My friend was very frustrated with me because I never mentioned his name to my new unknown companion. It turned out I was sitting with Tip O'Neill when he was Speaker of the House. For me, this is a wonderful example of how you can extract a lot of information in a very casual way. What I have learned is to take whatever time is needed to check on this individual you wish to hire. You will probably see more of this person than people who have been close to you all your life.

10. Learn to Let Go

Dying, death, and bereavement are difficult subjects with a wide range of emotions. Having been in the geriatric profession for decades, I have found comfort in knowing that I am as prepared as a human being can be for the inevitable ending of one's life. A long time ago, when I was a youngster out camping and having traipsed around for hours in the soft, gentle rain, I sat up with my back against some rocks to take a short nap while enjoying the pitter-patter of the raindrops on my rain gear. I woke up and heard an unfamiliar cacophonous noise. I looked up to see a large blackbird swoop down and take a tiny bird out of its nest and fly off. The parent birds were squawking, as were all the other varieties of birds. I had never heard such a chorus of high-pitched screeching. This sound resonated with the pain that these parent birds and their neighbors were experiencing.

Within 15 minutes, there was silence in the woods and then the most beautiful chorus of birds singing their natural/native songs. This unique experience has never left me, and I realized at that moment that all are affected when death strikes. After we have mourned the death or passing of someone dear to us, our job is to sing their praises and resume continuing the life we have. Find the song within our soul and heal as these birds had done. Preparation and planning for the end of life are the very best we can do for ourselves and those who care about us. We can carefully outline all we want to have done for us, or to do for ourselves before we die. Many forms might be advisable to have at least investigated to understand if they are appropriate for you to fill out and complete.

Advance Directives basically direct those caring for you, how you want to be treated at the end of your life especially, if you are not capable of voicing your wishes at that time. A person you have chosen should be someone you have confidence in, has your values, and agrees to follow your directives. Advance Directives are available through an elder law attorney or physician. These forms may also be found on the internet under caregivinginfo.org or from your local funeral parlor. The Family Caregiver Alliance has a great deal of information regarding End-of-life-care. Hospice focuses on providing comfort for persons living with a terminal illness. Their goal is to ease pain and have someone in the dying process be comfortable at all times. The comforting process comprises five concepts: physical, practical, psychological, social, and spiritual. My experience with the Hospice Organization is that they are compassionate and practical. They help not only the individual but the family and friends in practical and supportive ways. They facilitate and establish a support system that the person who is dying prefers. They consider all the cues from the dying individual.

When my sister was diagnosed with cancer, she was young and had a husband and two children. The doctor and the medical profession gave her less than a year to live. My sister had asked me to come to this meeting as she stated I would be practical and stoic. I asked the doctor what our alternatives were? He listed the type of operations and procedures needed for this diagnosis. My sister was devastated. We walked out of the doctor's office. We went to the nearest coffee shop so that my sister could compose herself. I asked her what she wanted to do? We made a list of all the things she wanted to accomplish, to see, and to experience. Including seeing her children graduate from school, go on to college, have her children get married, see her future grandchildren, buy a piece of property in upstate New York, start a bed and breakfast, and open an antique shop.

I took my sister to every alternative therapy approach imaginable. We worked at her goals while being health-oriented, both in mind and spirit. My sister went thru chemotherapy and several operations. She also went to every alternative therapy (many of which are listed in my book, *Elder Care Made Easier*, 2nd edition).

My sister lived another seventeen years. She witnessed her children graduating, planned and attended their weddings, and opened bed and breakfast in upstate New York with an antique shop on the premises. I was there with her every step of the way. I believe strongly in setting goals and working with and through this process with my sister and many of my clients. I know that the will to live is very strong. One can prevail if we fan the fires of having a future and not give in to doubt and despair. There are many steps not only in the dying process but preparing for one's demise. The computer and the internet will give you a wealth of information; be specific about what you are looking for. Planning one's estate takes time, and you need to gather all your legal papers that need to be in order, up to date and current. Discuss your family inheritance issues and do an estate calculation, including estate taxes, final administration costs, and burial costs. Make sure that the spelling of all individuals in all papers is correct. Consider different states have different laws and regulations.

Grief is part of the dying process. For those who are in the process of dying and those who are emotionally, physically, or even financially attached to the dying person. Also, take into consideration children. Children and young adults grieve as well as adults and should be considered and cared for with loving attention appropriate to their education, level of understanding, and age appropriateness. Sometimes a child simply needs to be listened to, comforted, or physically held. When you are going through the dying or death process, seek out the avenues that will be of comfort to you and yours.

During this process, many of us learn to listen with our hearts and souls because we are in different places due to our own needs in the caregiving process. What I learned was at the moment of death, there is an energy that emerges and can often be felt by those in the room. My experience and what I have witnessed bring me to the conclusion that death is simply the transferring of energy as we discard our bodily form and become one with the universe. As long as we hold someone who has died close to our heart and in our thought process, they still live within us.

Millennial Caregivers Come of Age

The typical caregiver is still a 50-something woman feeding, bathing, and transporting her ailing mother. But it is estimated that about 10 million millennials now provide such help, usually to a parent or grandparents, according to recent reports by AARP and the National Alliance for Caregiving. Millennials, born between 1981 and 1996, make up nearly a quarter of the approximately 44 million caregivers in the United States.

There is an equal chance that a millennial caregiver identifies as male or female. According to the NAC and AARP report, the "typical" millennial caregiver is 27 years old and supports a parent or grandparent with a physical condition requiring care. Millennials may also provide care for spouses, siblings, close family, friends, and their children. The care recipient may have care needs related to a mental illness, substance abuse issue, developmental or learning disability, HIV/AIDS diagnosis, or an age-related disease such as dementia or Alzheimer's. In addition, millennials are increasingly providing care for their loved ones with injuries sustained in military service (e.g., traumatic brain injuries). In other words, the millennial caregiving landscape is vast and ever-changing.

As baby boomers age, the burden of care will fall even more on millennials. The term to describe this is the "caregiving cliff," in that the support ratios are expected to be three caregivers available for every one person needing care by about 2050. In short, millennial caregivers will be facing increasing physical, emotional, and financial strain in providing for their care. There is a reason for concern: the lack of support from employers or the government for caregivers nationwide will only increase the challenges facing millennial caregivers.

Debt, distance & divorce are likely to complicate how Millennials will care for aging Baby Boomers.

—JOSEPH COUGHLIN, *THE LONGEVITY ECONOMY: UNLOCKING THE WORLD'S FASTEST-GROWING, MOST MISUNDERSTOOD MARKET*

In the article, "5 Ways Millennial Caregivers Can Find Help," edited by Lauren Young and Bernadette Baum, practical points are made to assist this new generation of caregivers.

1. YOU ARE NOT ALONE.

Connect with support online. Remember, there are 10 million of you, and the numbers will only increase!

2. TAKE CARE OF YOURSELF.

The bottom line, stress, guilt, and over-extending will burn you out. When a caregiver is too focused on others, they can neglect their own needs and suffer. Get plenty of rest and take breaks when possible.

3. PLAN YOUR FINANCES.

Without preparation, millennials who take time off to care for a loved one may not have their own money set aside for the future, including retirement, said Grace Whiting, chief executive of the non-profit National Alliance for Caregiving. "Millennials have to plan for the financial part, as they're getting older, too," Whiting said. Organizations including the Alzheimer's Association (alz.org) and the Women's Institute for a Secure Retirement (www.wiserwomen.org) provide resources to help caregivers prepare for long-term financial sustainability.

4. KNOW YOUR STATE'S DISCRIMINATION LAWS.

The average millennial caregiver is employed and works 34.9 hours a week, according to the AARP. But caregiving can get in the way of career advancement. "Millennials are trying to get started in their careers," said Lewis. "If you need to take time off for work or if you're late for work, your caregiving is starting to impact the role you have." Different states have different laws protecting caregivers from discrimination. You can find more about your rights on AARP's website (www.aarp.org/caregiving/).

5. AVOID COMPARISONS WITH PEERS.

Every millennial caregiver's life change in different ways, so avoid comparing yourself with others. Some will get college degrees before you —there are different milestones and goals reached at different times than peers. Beeton, who got a college degree online to continue caregiving, reminds herself that it is okay if she hits milestones at different times than her peers. Remember your loved ones will not be around forever, and it helps to remind oneself, "This is what life's about right now."

. . .

Another Caregiver Story

One night, I was taking care of a woman admitted to the ICU after extensive surgery for cancer. She was a lovely, optimistic soul who wrote a weekly column for a senior newspaper; she was a gerontologist. We had professional interests in aging and much in common. She had written several books on gerontology, including one on caring for the caregiver. She sent her husband, Tom, out to the car for a copy of her latest book to give to me.

The next morning, at the start of my shift, I entered the room to find Tom asleep, precariously perched in a chair next to the bed. (I have encountered this scenario many times, and I tiptoed around to perform my initial assessments, trying not to disturb a much-needed nap by a loved one. Eventually, an alarm breaks the peace, and the napping family member is suddenly awake and reminded where they are.) Tom smiled and said, "I hoped you'd be here today. I have a story for you."

Tom relayed the story as his wife fell back to sleep, despite the beeps and noises of the ICU. Taking a break from his bedside vigil, he strolled over to the Starbucks across the street from the hospital for a much-needed cup of coffee. He sat down to savor the drink, consumed with thoughts of his wife; noticing a newspaper lying on the table next to him, Tom asked the man close to him if he could borrow it. They struck up a conversation, and Tom told the man about his sick wife. The generous man offered not only the paper but kind words, suggesting he be sure to take care of himself. The man then mentioned a book that helped him get through caring for a sick family member. The book was the very one written by Tom's wife!

Goodbye Myth: At some point,
you will be the one needing care.

Step 9

Who do you want holding your hand in your last moments on Earth? Have the conversation with them.

Have a conversation with that person about your future care-receiving needs, decide if a Geriatric Care Manager is right for you when the time comes. And remember, self-care is healthcare; this is essential to loving your long life!

Suggested Resources

Elder Care Made Easier, 2nd Edition Dr. Marion's ten steps to help you care for an aging loved one.

Approximately 43.5 million people in the United States are caregivers to a family member with a disability or illness (Family Caregiver Alliance, 2020). These people are termed informal caregivers as they are seldom trained for this role, nor did they necessarily desire it. These "informal" caregivers provide indispensable health services to their family members and are considered by many policy makers to be front-line health service providers (American Psychological Association, 2020).

The economic value of services provided by informal caregivers was estimated to be 470 billion dollars in 2013 (Family Caregiver Alliance, 2020). Sheth K, Lorig K, Stewart A, Parodi JF, Ritter PL. Effects of COVID-19 on Informal Caregivers and the Development and Validation of a Scale in English and Spanish to Measure the Impact of COVID-19 on Caregivers. Journal of Applied Gerontology. 2021. 40 (3) 235-243. The same figure was reported more recently in 2019 estimates from AARP Press Room.

Look into hiring a Geriatric Care Manager to help with a loved one: aginglifecare.org

Lainey Younkin, M.S., R.D. Mediterranean Diet for Beginners: Everything You Need to Get Started: Get a quick how-to, a shopping list and meal guidance for beginning this ultra-healthy way of eating.

When looking at caregivers for adults only, the prevalence of caregiving has risen from 16.6 percent in 2015 to 19.2 percent in 2020—an increase of over 8 million adults providing care to a family member or friend aged eighteen or older, primarily driven by a significant increase in the prevalence of caring for a family member or friend who is age 50 or older (aarp.org).

Senior Relocation Services

Senior Move Specialists are licensed with organizations such as the National Association of Senior Move Managers who can help with the seemingly overwhelming list of things to do:

- Develop a moving plan
- Sort personal belongings to keep, sell, and or donate
- Pack belongings
- Hire and supervise movers
- Help plan the new space with universal design for aging in place
- Unpack and get settled in new space
- Manage the sale of the old home
- Clean, un-clutter and remove/dispose of waste
- Or help with aging in place rather than moving

CHAPTER 10

Unfinished Business

> ***The possibility of the dream gives strength.***
>
> —LAILAH GIFTY AKITA, *PEARLS OF WISDOM: GREAT MIND*

MYTH: Dreams Deferred Will Stay Dreams Denied— You Are Too Old

Do you hear The Call?

Throughout your life, there is a voice only you can hear. A voice which mythologists label "The Call." A call to the value of your own life. The choice of risk and individual bliss over the known and secure. You may choose not to hear your spirit. You may prefer to build a life within the compound, to avoid risk. It is possible to find happiness within a familiar box, a life of comfort and control. Or, you may choose to be open to new experiences, to leave the limits of your conditioning, to hear the call. Then you must act. If you never hear it, perhaps nothing is lost. If you hear it and ignore it, your life is lost.

—Jennifer James, Ph.D., *Windows: Success is the Quality of Your Journey*

The Call

This idea of a mythological call is a personal favorite of mine and a reoccurring theme in my life. Perhaps in yours too? Stephen Covey once said, "What's most personal is most universal." In the past, when I did a "life review" and saw turning points when something was compelling me to take a leap of faith, I could only define it as a restless feeling. I had no language for it, until I read human potential researcher, Jean Houston's explanation of The Hero's Journey. Then I discovered Mythologist Joseph Campbell's description of The Hero's Journey in his book, *The Hero with a Thousand Faces*. Campbell found that many cultures have a sequential pattern to their myth-making—that is, the same steps play out in stories from different cultures.

The steps of the Hero's Journey

1. Innocence (comfortable with your situation)

2. The Call to Adventure (now aware of your challenge)

3. Initiation (you are tested)

4. Allies (finding help)

5. Breakthrough (getting new awareness or resolution)

6. Celebration (return home, changed)

George Lucas read *The Hero with a Thousand Faces,* and it inspired *Star Wars*. Many movies use this same template over and over (see any Kevin Costner movie). The Call is really about a passage, advancing from one stage to another. Many thinkers have written about this concept, but none more eloquently than Dr. H.R. Moody in *The Five Stage of The Soul*. Dr. Moody is one of the most innovative thinkers on gerontology alive today. His unique treatment of The Call (and subsequent stages) has a spiritual basis. He says, "Sometimes The Call reveals itself in dreams."

. . .

The Dream

In 2007, I was in contact with H.R. Moody concerning a significant passage in my life. I had a dream of standing in a batter's box awaiting my turn at-bat. A young batgirl in a brightly flowered dress mocked me as she handed me my bat. I gazed toward home plate and saw a young Ted Williams, in his prime. His cotton uniform was cinched tightly around his trim waist with a leather belt, and his hair was glossy black. He turned to look over his right shoulder at me standing in the circle—he winked and said," You're next, kid." In the dream, I glanced down at my right foot, wearing baseball cleats, as it broke the plane of the chalk line of the on-deck circle.

I seldom remember dreams, but this one was too meaningful. Moody, an expert in dream analysis, describes the Judas inside all of us as, "a heedless, worldly naysayer who looks for the slightest opportunity to abort our journey and betray our highest yearnings." In the dream, as I see it, the batgirl represented my Judas—the naysayer in me. The good news is I left the safety of the on-deck circle (the passage) and headed for home plate to take my turn at-bat. As Dr. Moody suggested, The Call to a larger self was revealed in a dream with a baseball metaphor.

Aging is a passage for all of us fortunate to live long enough to create histories. When we look back on turning points, we can determine how The Call was answered. When we look to the future, we may be more aware of the feelings of being constructively discontent as, *The Call.* Insights provided by scholars like H.R. Moody give us language for our experiences, and like a rock climber, we have a toehold (terms and concepts) from which to climb higher to a greater understanding.

Conquering any difficulty always gives one a SECRET JOY, for it means pushing back a boundary line and adding to one's liberty.

—HENRI FREDERIC AMEIL

Psychologist Albert Bandura developed a theory that is useful not only in the field of psychology but in aging, as well. The concept is called "Self-efficacy," a person's belief in their ability to succeed in a particular situation.

A weak self-efficacy:

- Avoid challenges
- Believe difficult tasks and situations are beyond your capabilities
- Focus on personal failings and negative outcomes
- Quickly lose confidence in personal abilities

A STRONG self-efficacy:

- View challenges and problems as tasks to be mastered
- Develop deeper interests in activities in which you participate
- Form a stronger sense of commitment to your interests and activities
- Recover quicker from setbacks and disappointments

Can you see how having a strong self-efficacy could be a benefit as one gets older? Self-efficacy has four primary sources; for this chapter, I will cover only the first, which is Mastery Experiences. When performing a task successfully, the potential for a Mastery Experience to strengthen one's sense of self-efficacy is realized. Taking on new challenges later in life allows for mastery experiences.

The concept is a psychological dividend for older adults (and others) living independently. Custodial environments, such as nursing homes and many assisted living facilities, limit the chances for mastery experiences. For some, this is the goal; for others, seeking out a challenge and new experiences well into old age is what they are after. Those souls who do not take the path of least resistance but instead choose to live fully to the end are examples of modeling for a new old age. No judgment, just a new reality for many who desire a new narrative of old age.

> ***So, what exactly does it mean to be a late bloomer? Simply put, a late bloomer is a person who fulfills their potential later than expected; they often have talents that aren't visible to others initially. And they fulfill their potential frequently in novel and unexpected ways, surprising even those closest to them. They are not attempting to satisfy, with gritted teeth, the expectations of their parents or society, a false path that leads to burnout and brittleness, or even to depression and illness. Late bloomers are those who find their supreme destiny on their own schedule, in their own way.***
>
> —RICH KARLGAARD, *LATE BLOOMERS: THE POWER OF PATIENCE IN A WORLD OBSESSED WITH EARLY ACHIEVEMENT*

Turning Points (late-in-life transcendence)

I have always been drawn to stories of personal transformation or "turning points" in people's lives. The appeal for me is in the notion of change—your foreseeable life suddenly takes a new turn. I had just such a moment in 1997 when an injury caused significant loss leading to a re-evaluation in my life as the scaffolding of my life crumbled around me. I had always been the athlete, and that was now threatened. Not having my body readily available to me caused me to consider physical frailty for the first time. I then learned; your challenges will come from what you most lean on in life. I had leaned on my physicality, and for a painful period, it was taken from me.

Someone close to me shared a story of a turning point in her life when she realized she was mortal and going to die someday. She lay in a fetal position on the floor of her kitchen weeping uncontrollably—alone. This was her "dark night of the soul." These were reality-confronting experiences that made both of us stronger in the long run.

. . .

Normative Transitions vs. Turning Points

As human beings, we all experience turning points in our lives. Several longitudinal studies have documented that most Americans report turning points. Clasen studied 268 subjects in their mid-50s or early 60s and found that "more than 85 percent did feel that there had been turning points in their lives, and most could identify more than one." For men and women, marriage and career events were most frequently mentioned as turning points; these were associated with greater personal autonomy, a different self-concept, and more confidence.

These normative transformations, like leaving home and choosing a vocation, are on-course and "appropriate" for the chronological age. But what interests me most are the turning points that are discontinuous with what would be predicted from past life-experience and move the individual in a different direction. According to Harven and Masoaka, normative transitions become turning points when:

1. They coincide with or are followed by a crisis
2. They are accompanied by family conflict
3. They lead to unexpected consequences
4. They require constant adjustments

Late-in-Life Discontinuous Changes

Since 1994 I have kept an article titled, "The Unflinching Eye of Elizabeth Layton." It is a tale of a late bloomer, the creative spirit, and the transformative power of turning points. Layton lived some thirty years tormented with the perils of depression in Wellsville, Kansas. This woman had undergone shock treatments, tried medications, and psychotherapy—all failed to bring her spirit alive. The death of a child in 1976 plunged her further into the darkness. And at the age of sixty-eight, she felt at the end of her rope. The turning point came when her sister suggested she enroll in a drawing class at the local university; she learned contour drawing (the artist draws while looking at the object, never taking her eye off the subject matter or lifting the pencil off the paper).

The Wrinkled-Self: Depicting Old Age Honestly and Passionately

One evening when her husband was out, she decided to follow through on her self-portrait assignment. Peering into a small mirror, she began to draw the contours of her face—at sixty-eight; it was not what she wanted to see. She had wrinkles, flabby skin, age spots, arthritic fingers, and a body too large, but she drew what she saw. The drawings were unlike anything her teacher, friends, or family had ever seen. Drawing obsessively for ten hours a day for the next six months, she realized at the end of that period the depression was gone.

Her drawings won worldwide acclaim and have been exhibited across the country, including the Metropolitan Museum of Art in New York City, The National Museum of American Art in Washington, D.C., and have been featured in People, Life, and Parade magazines. Layton's work takes head-on the social issues of the time—the homeless, capital punishment, racial prejudice, and women's rights. She is best known for her portrayals of old age.

Two works exemplifying her subject matter are "The Motherless Child," a series of sixteen drawings inspired by weekly visits to her 91-year-old aunt in a nursing home, and "My Own Gulliver in Lilliput," which shows Mrs. Layton tied to the ground, hamstrung by childishness, jealousy, timidity, laziness, and fear of her mother's disapproval—emotions that cause havoc in women's lives. Mrs. Layton died in 1993 at the age of eighty-three, but not before discovering that it is never too late to become what you might have been.

The space in which we live should be for the person we are becoming now, not for the person we were in the past.

—MARIE KONDO, *ORGANIZING CONSULTANT AND AUTHOR*

My Tuesdays With Jim

I had returned from a visit with a friend, "Jim," who was at the time 85 years old. He had been showing some signs of physical frailty but was mentally robust as ever. A trip to his home was always an immersion into the deep end of ideas and an intellectual challenge. Jim was an extraordinary man who fought with the allies against the Nazi invasion of France. He seldom spoke of his WWII experiences, and when he did, it was riveting. Most of his era stories focused more on time spent at the Sorbonne in Paris, studying French civilization, philosophy, and art history. He moved with alacrity between cultures and had earned the title of being one of "The Greatest Generation."

He once told me about sitting on a sidewalk café in Paris with friends, near his tiny apartment (his balcony provided a full view of the Eiffel tower) and looking up to catch a glimpse of Greta Garbo strolling by with a gentlemen friend, arm-in-arm. That is the kind of life he experienced before moving back to Oregon, earning his Master of Art's degree in English, and embarking on a teaching career.

As a lifetime artist, Jim had an insatiable appetite for creativity. I enjoyed visiting his home studio, and I delighted in seeing new project in the works. He was perpetually describing some dream that was the impetus for his latest creation. Even more extraordinary is that Jim had macular degeneration, and his central vision was gone; he was legally blind. Imagine losing your eyesight as an artist, and what that could do to your psyche at an advanced age. He expressed to me that he spent more time in meditation. The job now "is to remember," he said. But beyond memories, Jim continued to paint, and his home was in a constant state of creative flux.

And the space which is paramount for memory is the house, for it is within that space that we learned how to dream and imagine.

—HEIDEGGER

Over several years, until his death, I went to Jim's house weekly, and he taught me to paint. We would talk philosophy over coffee—then, soon after, place a blank canvas on a small table in his kitchen. With the soft morning sun filtering through the windows onto the awaiting canvas, he would instruct me (indirectly) by sharing stories about his past. Leaving me to my task, he would mysteriously vanish only to return sometime later to examine my work visually. With his head contorted sideways like a flounder and peering intently inches from the painting, he would examine the lines, textures, and colors as I awaited his comments. Later, I would tell others that a blind man was teaching me to see.

Creativity and aging together, are topics that have been neglected and treated as unlikely pairings by most gerontologists in the past. Creativity was traditionally viewed as the domain of the first half of life. Human development, especially of the creative variety, was thought to be in decline in old age. The problem is that historically, creativity was mistakenly measured as productivity—that is to say, the older the artists, the fewer works they produced. This reasoning failed to measure the degree of creativity; rather, it equated the amount produced as creativity. An exception was the late Dr. Gene Cohen, who wrote, *The Creative Age: Awakening Human Potential In The Second Half Of Life.* Cohen defines creativity as bringing something new into existence that is valued. The definition is good. Another aspect of creativity is that it can take you outside of yourself and into the work. The creative process is where the magic happens for many older adults.

Do not go gentle into that good night, Old age should burn and rave at close of day; Rage, rage against the dying of the light.

—DYLAN THOMAS

The Welsh poet Dylan Thomas wrote his famous poem for his father, a robust, militant man all his days, until in his eighties when he became blind and weak. The young Thomas was so disturbed by the creeping senescence in his father, Thomas tried to invoke him to become the fierce man he once was by telling him *to not go gently into that good night but to rage against the dying of the light* (aging and death). The poet's attempt to stop his loved one's decline is understandable; aging, by definition, means change and loss—that is undeniable. What is encouraging, however, is the potential for creativity at an advanced age.

Jim had not given up painting; instead, he had changed his subject matter and style to adjust to the loss of vision, which had taken him into new realms of creativity and an inexhaustible source of renewal. I could always count on him as a source of inspiration. For creative older adults like Jim, meaning is derived not by striving against aging or losses, but by accommodating them. The consciousness born out of the limitations is the actual source of creative production and meaning-making beyond losses.

The late psychologist Mihaly Csikszentmihalyi suggested, "Creative individuals are remarkable for their ability to adapt to almost any situation and to make do with whatever is at hand to reach their goals. If nothing else, this distinguishes them from the rest of us."

For example, I once got a message on my phone from Jim, it was one of those messages that just delighted me. So much so, I played it repeatedly to squeeze the "juice" out of it. Jim relayed an observation I once made during a visit to his home. He wore two different colored socks, something Einstein was occasionally known to do. It seems he made it through half a day without noticing his socks did not match!

At times like these (especially if you are older), the tendency might be to question your failing senses or rush to self-judgment, murmuring under your breath some self-deprecating comment about losing your mind. But not Jim; he instead graced the "mishap" with a different frame of reference (reframing aging). "The two different colors of socks," he said, "are a reminder that everything in life has its opposite—get comfortable with it!" He deliberately wore them the rest of the day.

Sometime after the call, I snuck over and placed one light tan and one dark blue "pair" of socks in his mailbox. We talked after the incident by phone, and I told him I had a "pair" just like them at home; we laughed heartily. Jim told me he wore them on the bus and the contrasting socks so entranced a woman next to him she asked him to autograph her garter belt; to which we laughed out loud again!

The two different socks remind me that opposites define and inform each other. It is hard to understand "hot" without experiencing "cold." Success is more rewarding when we have tasted defeat. To know aging is to have once known youth; if one did not exist, the other would have little meaning. From Jim's stance on embracing the necessity of opposites, I have gleaned three things:

1. To wear matching socks means, on some level, we succumb to the cultural construction of norms—that is, my culture defines my actions, and I follow them unconsciously. 'Over-culture' can lead to soul-diminishing ideals of ageism (especially privileging youth). And as a result, we are then aged by culture.
2. Everything in life has its opposite—get used to it (embracing the necessity of opposites).
3. Reframing can be a powerful tool for good or bad—the choice is yours.

Now whether Jim autographed a garter belt, only he knew; I guess that wearing two different colored stockings can potentially take you into uncharted territories.

Watching a peaceful death of a human being reminds us of a falling star; one of a million lights in a vast sky that flares up for a brief moment only to disappear into the endless night forever.

—ELISABETH KUBLER-ROSS

I was handed a sympathy card the other day and informed about the death of a coworker's parent, then asked to write something. Most of us have this experience; all the "usual" comments are there as you search for a space to add yours. You are left with the choice of emotional plagiarism ("Thinking of you at this time") or struggling to find meaningful words to express the loss. For me, it is challenging. Death is so final—it is much easier to sign birthday cards.

On occasion in the ICU/CCU, patients have asked me why they were still alive during quiet moments. My answer was always part science; I would describe the medical measures taken to stabilize the body—and part philosophical; I would also explain that whatever they were supposed to do in life was not done yet. This latter point was the dominant theme at many an American Society on Aging conference and dovetails with AARP's messaging about awakening human potential in the second half of life, or the well-worn: "Don't die with your music still in you."

One of the most inspiring books I have ever read was Josh Waitzkin's, *The Art of Learning*. The movie, *Searching for Bobby Fischer*, (1993) is based on Josh, an eight-time national chess champion and martial arts champion who holds national and world champion titles. The book is a life-affirming tale about the learning process which allowed him to achieve such extraordinary goals. In the chapter, "Making Smaller Circles," Waitzkin describes a passage from Robert Prisig's, *Zen and the Art of Motorcycle Maintenance*, (1974) as the inspiration (in part) for the principles lying at the heart of connecting chess and martial arts, and the learning process. The scene begins with the story's protagonist, a brilliant and eccentric fellow named Phaedrus, teaching a rhetoric student with writer's block. Her assignment is to write a five-hundred-word story about her town.

The town, to her, seems too small and incidental to write about, so there is a struggle. Phaedrus frees the girl from her block by changing the assignment. He suggests she write about the front of the brick opera house, outside her classroom on the small street in a small neighborhood of the dull town. And she should start with the upper-left-hand brick. At first, the student becomes incredulous, but soon a torrent of creativity turns into twenty pages of inspired writing which she brings to class the next day.

Waitzkin nails the message of this little narrative by identifying the theme as depth over breadth—which, he says, has the potential to distinguish success from failure in the pursuit of excellence. The message is coming from someone with a proven track record. He states the learning principle is, "to plunge into the detailed mystery of the micro to understand what makes the macro tick. Our obstacle is that we live in an attention-deficit culture." We never fully attend to the micro (awareness) and only skim the surface of the macro (half asleep).

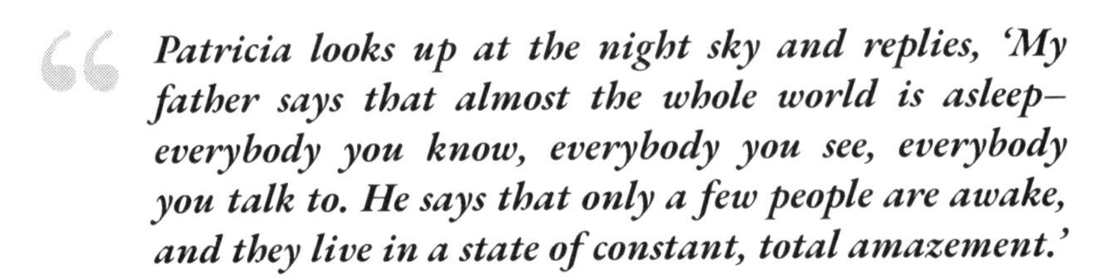

> ***Patricia looks up at the night sky and replies, 'My father says that almost the whole world is asleep–everybody you know, everybody you see, everybody you talk to. He says that only a few people are awake, and they live in a state of constant, total amazement.'***
>
> —*JOE VERSUS THE VOLCANO* (1990)

It is what Jennifer James, Ph.D., describes as an environment around us, the media in particular, that conditions us with a mechanism that both "speeds up our thought and limits its depth." I call it "provocative-surfacing," leading to an absence of systems thinking—that is, seeing how things are connected. Those minor daily choice points we make end up as larger patterns shaping our lives. In the speed culture, we are always in a hurry to go to the next thing sacrificing the present moment, which can be exhausting.

Focusing on the single brick (the detailed mystery of the micro) increases our awareness of what is present and puts us into the moment, where creativity lives. Perhaps this is one of the reasons I feel so strongly about aging in place and so love being home; a place for letting our guard down, self-expression, and where we can take the time to cultivate our uniqueness. Home can be a cocoon from the pace of the culture where we can rest, recharge, be in the moment, and dream a new dream.

> ***Life is never made unbearable by circumstances, but only by lack of meaning and purpose.***
>
> —VIKTOR E. FRANKL

What makes you want to get out of bed in the morning? Richard Leider asks this age-old and provocative question in a very worthwhile video from the Business Innovation Factory. Leider is the founder of Inventure, The Purpose Company, and listed by FORBES as one of the "top 5" most respected executive coaches. I share his ideas here, which emphasizes thinking that changes lives. Further, empowered aging has, at its core assumption, the notion of choice, the most basic of human freedoms. After forty years of studying purpose and meaning in life, Leider uncovered three themes when interviewing "elders" (sixty-five and older). He asked the question:

If you could do your life over again, what would you do differently?

Three themes emerged from his interviews:

- I would be more reflective the second time around, which means taking a step back to look at the BIG picture, not just at crisis times but throughout life.
- I would take more RISKS the second time around. Not the kind associated with sky diving or whitewater rafting, but the kind of risks of authenticity and voice. In the spirit of bringing more of the self into the equation.
- I wish I had discovered earlier in life my bottom line; what matters, and the kind of authentic legacy I want to leave.

Leider found transformative ideas in the work of Viktor Frankl's, *Man's Search for Meaning*. A key to Frankl's message was the notion of choice; moreover, the kind of choice that is moment-to-moment in daily life. When asked: What makes you get out of bed in the morning? Leider's research into the human experience guided by Frankl's Logotherapy Theory found that choosing something in the service of others, outside of one's self-interest, leads to a longer, more productive, and more vital experience of life.

To summarize Frankl's idea: the last of human freedom is choice. The first half of life belongs to biology (procreation for most, not all); and you are at choice in the second half. The potential pull that became you lay dormant for over three billion years. Ponder that for a moment—it's showtime!

> ***Tell me, what is it you plan to do with your one wild and precious life?***
>
> —MARY OLIVER

Bronnie Ware, the Australian nurse who worked in palliative care, caring for patients in the last twelve weeks of their lives, found inspiration for living in this experience. She uncovered insights from her dying patients that are good reminders on how to live. She reported, "The regrets touch upon being more genuine, not working so hard, expressing one's true feelings, staying in touch with friends, and finding more joy in life."

From my own experience, one night after arriving home from a long, tough night working in an inner-city trauma center, I collapsed into bed. When I woke up hours later, I had written these words on a piece of scrap paper on the bedside table:

The closer to death you are, the closer to life you are.

And such is the paradox of life.

Ace of Cups

I was in a Zoom meeting sponsored by Fielding University featuring the all-female band that started in the 1960s *ACE OF CUPS*. They were at the epicenter of the Summer of Love in1967. They continue ROCKING this foundation with a cause. They are in a new cycle of the life-long process that exemplifies creativity. They were being honored with an award from the University, followed by interviews. The wit and wisdom accumulated are inspiring—I took notes. Hold on to your stereotypes, they are about to be shattered.

Here are the top ten takeaways:

1. Put a woman in charge (opening video showed woman-after-woman in leadership positions of all ages and races making vital global differences in our world).

2. Intersectionality of Crone and Rocker (an unlikely pairing "busting myths").
3. It's never too late to become what you might have been.
4. Dreams deferred from childhood must be revisited.
5. Pushing the limits on gender norms from the summer of love to now.
6. Creativity across the lifespan (Continuity of Self Theory).
7. With age comes the wisdom to subordinate the self for a greater result to be open to intergenerational synergy.
8. Find a new friend who does not look like you—but the key here, also may not THINK like you (this is where divinity moves in).
9. "I own my age now."
10. With age comes the capacity for fierce forgiveness.

Listening to the collective wisdom of these wise women was such a tonic. They have unapologetically aged, there was no mention of "anti-aging," and the mission has remained to serve the greater good with music. Their art has evolved and is informed by accumulated experiences and enduring love of performing. Rock in the service of the greater good is something I can get behind, not to mention successful aging! I enjoyed the session and hoped to hear much more from these ladies. No rocking chairs here! I encourage you to visit aceofcups.com.

Goodbye Myth: It is Never Too Late to Become What You Might Have Been.

Step 10

At least one day a week (or more) wear two different color socks.

It seems like such a simple act, yet it can profoundly affect your thinking.

- This prompts you to question cultural norms. Start there, then ask what other cultural trances I have been operating under?
- It will encourage you to embrace opposites.

- It also reminds you reframing is your new superpower.
- It just might stir up some interesting conversations in your life—just try it.

Resources

Must Watch:

- I encourage you to watch *Joe Versus the Volcano*, a 1990 American romantic comedy film written and directed by John Patrick Shanley and starring Tom Hanks and Meg Ryan. It was not a big blockbuster, but if you are ready, the movie has a message not to be missed.
- Paul Brandt - Risk - Official Music Video (YouTube) I tear up every time!
- The Power of Purpose businessinnovationfactory.-com/video/richard-leider-power-purpose/

See: ElizabethLayton.com and GeezerGallery.com

Note: The English Victorian novelist and poet George Eliot is credited with penning the famous quote, "It is never too late to be what you might have been."

CHAPTER 11

Loving Your Long Life: Myth Busting Profiles

> ***It is good to have an end to journey toward; but it is the journey that matters, in the end.***
>
> —URSULA K. LE GUIN, *THE LEFT HAND OF DARKNESS*

Ten Examples of Aging Myth-Busters

Author Maureen Gaffney says, "Middle age—your 50s to late-60s—brings a new sense of confidence and a broader sense of wellbeing. Your life is more settled, and you feel a new stability. The combination of being settled and experienced is regarded as one of the best bits of being middle-aged. Over 70 percent of you feel that this stage of your life is exciting, enjoyable, a time when you have more personal freedom, when changes are still possible."

Her statement about women aging in middle age is right on target. There has never been a better era for women to age than today. Stereotypes of women past their prime, or "aging gracefully" are giving way to new societal realities. In fact, what has been called The Paradox of Aging: The

Happiness U-Curve is evidence that late-middle-age is some of the most happy and contented time of life.

Research suggests counterintuitive evidence for people after mid-life getting happier over time and often reaching a point where their happiness, or self-reported life satisfaction, exceeds all other periods of their life, including their youth. Jonathan Rauch, journalist, describes the phenomena in his book, *The Happiness Curve: Why Life Gets Better After 50.* Rauch reports that the U-shaped happiness curve (as previously mentioned in chapter 5) is valid based on research from economists, psychologists, neurologists, and others. It is observed across many cultures, countries, and even after screening for income, gender, education, employment, marriage, and health.

Laura Carstensen, Ph. D., director of the Stanford Center of Longevity, supports the Happiness U-Curve hypothesis. Carstensen notes that, "Research indicates that past midlife people often have lower stress, improved emotional regulation, less regret, and a general sense of positivity and contentment for their lives."

Further, Mary Pipher, author and clinical psychologist, concurs in her popular New York Times article, "The Joy of Being a Woman in her 70s." Pipher shares her thoughts about the benefits of aging and increasing life satisfaction that she and her peer group are experiencing:

> *Older women have learned the importance of reasonable expectations. We know that all our desires will not be fulfilled, that the world isn't organized around pleasing us and that others, especially our children, are not waiting for our opinions and judgments. We know that the joys and sorrows of life are as mixed together as salt and water in the sea. We don't expect perfection or even relief from suffering.*
>
> *A good book, a piece of homemade pie or a call from a friend can make us happy. As my aunt Grace, who lived in the Ozarks, put it, 'I get what I want, but I know what to want.' We can be kinder to ourselves as well as more honest and authentic. Our people-pleasing selves soften their voices, and our true selves speak more loudly and*

> *more often. We don't need to pretend to ourselves and others that we don't have needs. We can say no to anything we don't want to do. We can listen to our hearts and act in our own best interest. We are less angst-filled and more content, less driven and more able to live in the moment with all its lovely possibilities.*

From Pipher's book, *Women Rowing North; Navigating Life's Currents and Flourishing as We Age,* (2019) she tells the story of a vivid example of the happiness of older women. Pipher switched recreational centers from the university where she taught for many years to a gym "geared toward older people" and noticed a change in the locker room atmosphere. It seems the university locker room with its younger cohort of women was stress-filled and unhappy. Pensive talk dominated the phone conversations about weight, finances, studies, and relationships.

Many hid their bodies as they undressed, and the only happy talk came with the occasional topics of the weekend or school holidays. Other than that, it was primarily gloomy, according to Pipher. She contrasts this with the new locker room where older women did discuss health issues but predominately focused on family, travel, books, movies, and fun. The older women joked with each other and walked around "unselfconsciously naked with plenty of stretch marks, wrinkles, and cellulite, but do we care? Not so much," she said.

Women's experience of aging is summed up eloquently in this line by Pipher:

> "There is an ancient and almost universal cycle that involves trauma, despair, struggle, and resolution. This is the deepening cycle that prepares us for whatever comes next."

Aging is not lost youth but a new stage of opportunity and strength.

—BETTY FRIEDAN

Of course, not all individuals are happiest in old age—but for many it's free of all the turmoil of younger years. Recent evidence suggests that the U-shaped happiness curve is not universal (Bartram, D). However, the concept has support among many gerontologists.

Meet the Myth Busters

Each woman you are about to meet busts aging myths in their own way. They have gone through the universal cycle Pipher described to find purpose and rich meaning making in lives. They all have a story to tell and lessons to teach; take inspiration from them to live and love your long life.

1. The Myth of Ageless Aging

MYth 1: Successful Aging is Ageless Aging.

Goodbye MYTH: Aging is Not Defined as the Absence of Youth.

Step 1: Embrace Each Stage of Life.

Profile: Joyce Williams

I've traveled the world, written books, been a Physio & TV Presenter. Now I'm 80+, and I'm blogging about the fun and nonsense of being ancient in a modern world and experiencing everyday ageism in all its glory!

—Joyce Williams

Five years ago, this grandmother took on a new career as a blogger and social media contributor on the topic of aging; this is her story:

So, this is me, Joyce Williams, a Yorkshire-born retired physiotherapist who took up blogging recently. It was a challenge! I had heard of blogs but didn't know what they were. I asked my 25-year-old grandson how you did them, and he couldn't tell me. So, when I spotted a class called 'Blogging for Beginners,' I was there. Me, the only 80-year-old, in a class of the 20 to 30 generation—that took me through the technicalities. So, then I had to write. The usual travel waffle at first and childhood memories. Then enlightenment! "Find a niche and a voice," they said. And Grandma Williams was born . . . a quirky commentator on life as seen when you are ancient.

The fun, the enjoyment, the evolving serenity of later years was a great topic. But an increasing anger at the sad image of old age being portrayed by the media became an underlying theme. Old age is a happy period of life, and for most people one of the best! This media image is so wrong, so stereotyped, and unhelpful to everyone. Later years are the bonus years of a good life; they aren't to be feared! And someone needed to say so. I have always loved thinking and writing. Many were the unpublished "Dear Sir "letters. Though some made it, but blogging, it dawned: I could write and publish to the whole world! Haven't stopped since. I was determined to have a go at that stupid image of later years. Take out the fear and get some recognition of what a great, if different, period of a normal life it is—and challenge Ageism.

On Aging and Sex

What's delightful when you're old is you don't care anymore about wrinkles, what you're more interested in is twinkles!

I had to learn to tweet to promote the blog. As a result, I have lovely contacts with people from dozens of countries. But most importantly, I am being heard and recognized by the key influencers in the fields of 'Better Aging' and the media. Great fun! And it has completely changed my life. A new purpose, almost a career, at 80+! I've traveled the world, written books, been a Physio & TV Presenter. Now I'm 80+, and I'm blogging about the fun and nonsense of being ancient in a modern world and experiencing everyday ageism in all its glory! Much to my surprise and delight, being ancient is proving to be a great time of my life. Really! I found I wanted to challenge the unthinking ageism in today's world.

In Her Own Words

"I write about how great old age is—later years are great years."

Joyce Williams is active on social media and shares her thoughts on the joys of unapologetically growing older. Her insights are thought-provoking and counter the social narrative of ageism—especially for women. This is how she is loving her long life!

See "Proud to be old!" It was great to see Joyce Williams on @ThisMorning. She gave us the Friday Feeling by talking about positive aging!

Website grandmawilliams.com

2. The Future Feminized Gerontocracy

MYTH 2: Older Women are a Social Liability.

Goodbye MYTH: We Are now Entering the Era of a Feminized Gerontocracy.

Step 2: Employ the spirit of the "Grandmother Hypothesis" beyond just your immediate tribe—you don't need to be a grandmother to do so.

Profile: Robin Morgan, award-winning poet, novelist, journalist, activist, and best-selling author, has published more than twenty books of poetry, fiction, and nonfiction.

Robin Morgan has had many evolving roles, as her astonishing biography attests to, and is always a continuity-of-self that comes from a place of meaningful contribution. She is now living yet another chapter and is poetically meeting it with grace and a determination to fully experience and share. The following is a brief description of her works from her website, robinmorgan.net, which I encourage you to visit and marinate in her extensive offerings. She is a force for good in the world and an example of what is possible for the feminized gerontocracy future we are entering.

For me, it's always been about saving the world.

—ROBIN MORGAN

Biography

An award-winning poet, novelist, political theorist, feminist activist, journalist, editor, and best-selling author, Robin Morgan has published seven poetry collections (including her recent book of poems, *Dark Matter*), four novels, and eleven books of nonfiction on social justice issues--primarily feminism--including her best-seller *The Demon Lover: The Roots of Terrorism*, and the now-classic anthologies *Sisterhood Is Powerful*, *Sisterhood Is Global*, and *Sisterhood Is Forever*. Her fourth novel, *Parallax*, is now available everywhere. A recipient of the National Endowment for the Arts Prize (Poetry) and numerous other honors, and a former editor-in-chief of *Ms.* magazine, she co-founded The Sisterhood Is Global Institute with Simone de Beauvoir and co-founded the Women's Media Center with Jane Fonda and Gloria Steinem. An architect and leader of contemporary U.S. feminism, she has also been a leader in the international women's movement for thirty-five years (womensmediacenter.com/profile/robin-morgan).

A Life of Activism and Contribution

During the 1960s, Robin was active in the civil rights movement in CORE (Congress on Racial Equality), SNCC (Student Nonviolent Coordinating Committee), and in the anti-Vietnam War movement. But by the late 1960s she was already a founding member of such radical feminist organizations as New York Radical Women and W.I.T.C.H. (the anagram was adaptable, representing Women's International Terrorist Conspiracy from Hell, Women Inspired to Commit Herstory, Women Interested in Toppling Consumer Holidays, etc.).

Morgan organized the September 1968 protest at the Miss America Pageant in Atlantic City, the first major public action of contemporary feminism. That year she co-founded W.I.T.C.H., a radical feminist group employing guerrilla-theater actions to call attention to sexism. Morgan designed the universal logo of the women's movement, the woman's symbol centered with a raised fist. She coined the word "herstory" and has been credited with originating numerous famous feminist phrases, including, "The personal is political," and, "Pornography is the theory; rape is the practice."

With the royalties from her first anthology, *Sisterhood Is Powerful*, (1970) Morgan founded the first feminist foundation in the US, The Sisterhood Is Powerful Fund, which provided seed money grants to hundreds of early women's groups throughout the 1970s and 1980s. She led the women's takeover of the leftist newspaper *Rat* in 1970, memorably breaking with the "toxic sexism of the left" in the first women's issue of the paper, via her famous essay, "Goodbye to All That." (During the 2008 presidential primaries, Morgan wrote a fiery "Goodbye To All That #2" about the misogynistic rhetoric on and treatment of Hillary Rodham Clinton; the article quickly went viral on the Internet—as did her "Letters from Ground Zero" written after 9/11 and published at the back of, *The Demon Lover: The Roots of Terrorism*).

Traveling the world to report on women, she has met with female fighters underground in the Philippines, HIV organizers in the favelas of Rio de Janeiro, potters in the villages of Indonesia, Nepalese rice farmers, and generationally indentured servant women in the townships and farms of South Africa. In 1986 and 1989 she spent months investigating the conditions of Palestinian women in Jordan, Lebanon, Egypt, Syria, West Bank, and Gaza refugee camps. Co-founder (with the late Simone de Beauvoir) and President of The Sisterhood Is Global Institute, the first international feminist think tank, and co-founder (with Jane Fonda and Gloria Steinem) of The Women's Media Center, she co-founded or has served on the boards of the Feminist Women's Health Network, the National Battered Women's Refuge Network, Media Women, the National Network of Rape Crisis Centers, the Feminist Writers' Guild, the Women's Foreign Policy Council, and the National Museum of Women in the Arts.

A contributing editor to Ms. Magazine beginning in 1979, she served as Editor in Chief from 1989-1994, re-launching the magazine as an international ad-free bimonthly publication, leading to financial success for the magazine and numerous awards, including Editorial Excellence by Utne Reader, and the Exceptional Merit in Journalism Award by the National Women's Political Caucus. She resigned in 1994 to become Global Consulting Editor.

An invited speaker at every major university in North America, she has traveled—as organizer, lecturer, journalist—across Europe, to Australia, Brazil, the Caribbean, Central America, China, Indonesia, Israel, Japan, Nepal, New Zealand, Pacific Island nations, the Philippines, and South Africa. She has been a Guest Professor or Scholar in Residence at a variety of academic institutions. In 1973 she was Guest Chair for Feminist Studies at New College of Florida, and The Center for Critical Analysis of Contemporary Culture at Rutgers University hosted her as a Visiting Professor in 1987. She was a Distinguished Visiting Scholar in Residence, Literary and Cultural Studies at the University of Canterbury, Christchurch, New Zealand in 1989, Visiting Professor in Residence at the University of Denver, Colorado, in 1996; and Distinguished Lecturer at the University of Bologna in Italy, at their Center for Documentation on Women in 2000. She was awarded an Honorary Degree as Doctor of Humane Letters by the University of Connecticut at Storrs in 1992. The Robin Morgan Papers are archived at the Sallie Bingham Center for Women's History and Culture at Duke University (robinmorgan.net).

Quotes

For me, it's always been about saving the world.

Only she who attempts the absurd can achieve the impossible.

Carry yourself as one who will change the world because you will.

The subtlest and most vicious aspect of women's oppression is that we have been conditioned to believe we are not oppressed, blinded so as not to see our own condition.

Women are not inherently passive or peaceful. We're not inherently anything but human.

In the long run, Women's Liberation will of course free men—but in the short run it's going to COST men a lot of privilege, which no one gives up willingly or easily.

Women are a colonized people.

. . .

Women's Media Center Podcast

https://www.womensmediacenter.com/profile/robin-morgan/

In Her Own Words

"I do not feel diminished by Parkinson's; I feel distilled by it, and I actually very much like the woman I'm distilling into."

See her TED talk: When poet Robin Morgan found herself facing Parkinson's disease, she distilled her experiences into these four quietly powerful poems — meditating on age, loss, and the simple power of noticing. After a lifetime of activism, she is now living a new phase and sharing her experiences to evoke the will to live in others. This is how she is loving her long life!

3. **Bag Lady Fears: Should I be Concerned?**

MYTH 3: Aging will cause you to become a bag lady.

Goodbye MYTH: Greater financial literacy and starting a side hustle business can help end bag lady fears.

Step 3: Take the initiative to become more financially literate and start a side hustle business.

Profile: Angie Higa, CEO and Founder at Sky Dreams LLC.

Never give up on your dream.

—Angie Higa

SKY DREAMS STORY

Angie Higa, a grandmother in Mililani, Hawaii, became an entrepreneur as she began her fifth decade. "I love the freedom and creative aspect of my business," she says. She became a former banking vice-president and commercial branch manager when she retired to care for her eldest granddaughter after her daughter was deployed to Afghanistan. It all started when the family took a trip to celebrate her daughter's safe return; Higa discovered the airlines had stopped providing comfort items on the plane.

This got her thinking, "I wanted to design a travel blanket that was compact, convenient, and comfortable," she says. "So, I took a design my mother made over thirty-five years ago and redesigned it, and the Sky Dreams travel blanket that folds into a bag was born."

Higa had designed the blanket just for her family, and then a former client loved it so much she requested one. Soon, Higa had $1,000 worth of orders. This was not her first adventure into being an entrepreneur; at age eleven, she crocheted bikini tops and sold them at a local swap meet. Call it muscle memory or a track record of making money with her creativity —she drew on this experience and went for it!

"I converted my two-car garage into my workshop, and I work seven days a week and into the wee hours of the night," she says.

Sky Dreams LLC has now expanded to offer pillows, toiletry bags, and more, as Higa's dream is expanding and celebrating a decade in business. She has been featured on the local news and was a featured designer in Hawaiian Airlines' inflight catalog. Her products can be found in Kaiser Permanente gift shops. "I'm known as the Blanket Lady," she says. "I pride myself on my customer service."

Sky Dreams LLC took flight as an online retailer in July 2009. After thirty years in the banking industry, within six months of retiring, Angie rekindled her passion for sewing when she realized (as mentioned) there was a need for travel blankets and pillows when the airlines stopped providing these comfort items during air travel. As a frequent traveler who often travels with grandchildren in tow, she knew there needed to be certain elements to make the perfect travel blanket and pillow. The design needed to be compact, convenient, and comfortable, which Angie dubbed the "3 C's of travel." After several failed prototypes and countless yards of fabric wasted, she came across a blanket her mother made thirty-five years ago. She instantly knew that with just a few design changes, this could be the perfect travel blanket. The Sky Dreams travel blanket was born with a bit of ingenuity. It turned the pocket upside down, added a strap, and sized it perfectly, allowing the blanket to fold into the bag and fit a neck pillow.

What is the Sky Dreams travel blanket? It is a 40" x 58" blanket that conveniently folds into a bag. Nestled in the pocket of the bag is a matching neck pillow. Angie quickly learned from her customers that Sky Dreams travel blankets were not only used for air travel. Her customers said they were the perfect blanket and pillow combos used on road trips, watching movies in the theater, and busy moms loved the compact and fashionable way to carry a blanket and pillow for their baby—great nursing cover-up, too. The most notable additional use for the Sky Dreams travel blanket was when a customer mentioned her mother used it during her chemotherapy treatments. Angie now designs with versatility in mind.

Sky Dreams LLC is your one-stop-shop for everything travel-related. From travel blankets to travel accessories, travel totes, and more. Each design is authentically designed and made in Hawai'i by Angie. Angie's unique design aesthetic enabled her to expand her line of travel blankets to travel accessories, shopping totes, and purses. Her products were featured in several local magazines and newspaper articles. She was featured as a local designer in Hawaiian Airlines Duty-Free International Catalog for two years, selling an exclusive travel tote.

January 2016, she launched the "Aloha Collection by Sky Dreams LLC." A collection of island and beach-inspired tote bags, clutches, and accessories. Each design captures the beauty of the islands and allows her customers to share the "Aloha Spirit" in each design she creates from her atelier in Mililani, Hawai'i. On March 22, 2020, the Sky Dreams Giving back project was started. Angie shifted her focus, began sewing and giving away FREE face masks during the pandemic, and used her own fabric and supplies to meet that need. Since the sewing community was sewing face masks for Health professionals and First Responders, Angie focused her efforts on the community, focusing on essential workers, those with compromised immune systems, and our Kupuna (elderly). As of December 29, 2020, over 2,700 FREE face masks were given out.

(Reprinted with permission from Angie Higa)

In Her Own Words

Never give up on your dream. It took me 30 years to fulfill my dream of being a full-time entrepreneur at age 48. However, it was truly a Blessing since I was able to apply my work experience at the bank, leadership training and connections to my business. It truly enabled me to be a better businesswoman. As the saying goes, 'older and wiser'. Entrepreneurship is not for the faint of heart. I had to manage all aspects of my business and quickly had to adapt to work life balance. As a full time, grandmother, wife, and businesswomen it was truly tough at the beginning. However, I had to dig deep within to make it all work. I work harder now than ever before.

My advice to those who want to start a business at any age, is to DO it. You will have to make sacrifices and work harder than ever before. There will be times when the going gets rough and push you to the limit where you want to give up. Take a deep breath and know that perseverance and hard work is truly the key to success.

Please stay safe and keep on travel dreaming,
~ Angie

Angie Higa did what many successful entrepreneurs do—they solve problems. She recognized a deficiency in the marketplace and transformed it into beauty. And she did so after she retired! Angie designs with the belief that no matter how you travel, travel the fashionable way and with Aloha spirit. This is how she is loving her long life!

Her website: Skydreamsllc.com

4. Aging in Place for the Love of Home

Myth 4: Aging in place means independence.

Goodbye Myth: Aging in place takes inter-dependence.

Step 4: Use negative visualization to your advantage.

Profile: Rosemarie Rosetti, Ph.D.

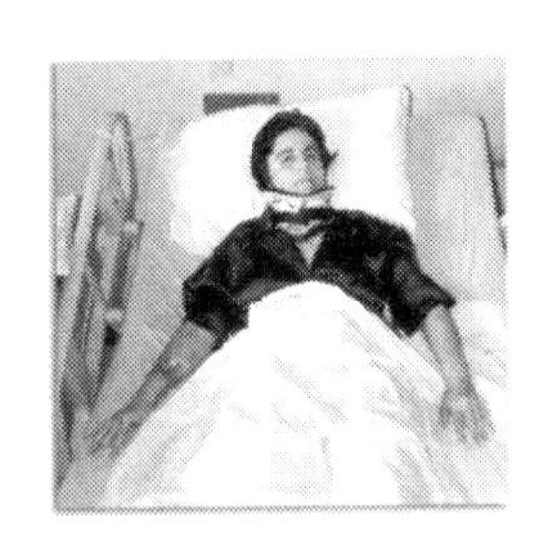

As I lay in the hospital, I was angry, scared, and mad at the world. I could not see myself living with this loss. I was in constant pain. I was so weak that Mark had to feed me. I saw my life as wasted! Everything that I had done in my life was a waste! My eight years of college were wasted! How am I going to survive? How are my businesses going to survive? My finances, my business, and my marriage are in jeopardy. I could lose Mark, our house, everything!

—Rosemarie Rosetti

Thriving After a Spinal Cord Injury

On June 13, 1998, Mark and I celebrated our third wedding anniversary by bicycling on a path," Rosemarie recalls. "It was a beautiful day with a clear blue sky. I was riding along the path ahead of Mark when he heard a loud noise and yelled, 'Something's falling! Stop!' A 7,000-pound tree crashed down on me, leaving me unconscious on the bike path. I was instantly paralyzed from the waist down with a spinal cord injury."

In the hospital after her injury, Rosemarie said, "In the days following the injury and emergency surgery, I was in the hospital—very angry, scared, and mad at the world. My life was catastrophically disturbed. I couldn't see myself living with this loss. I was in constant pain, my legs wouldn't move, and I couldn't even turn over in the bed. My hands were so paralyzed that Mark had to feed me."

Initially, Rosemarie saw her life and everything she had accomplished as wasted, including her eight years of college, and studying for a Ph.D. She wondered how she and her two businesses would survive and thought, "I could lose Mark, my house, everything! I cried over what I had enjoyed before my injury. Mark and I had found togetherness in our recreational activities—bicycling, skiing, hiking, dancing, and playing racquetball."

Rosemarie looked deep within herself to find a new resolve to rebuild her life. She was not about to lose the momentum that her years of hard work had provided.

During her rehabilitation at the Dodd Rehabilitation Hospital, part of Ohio State's Wexner Medical Center, she told her physical therapist, "I'll work hard and do anything you say. I want my life back." Rosemarie wanted a full recovery, an end to the pain, and the ability to do things for herself again and someday walk. Every day, she pushed herself harder to regain the most basic life skills for feeding herself, grooming, moving in her bed, sitting up, and eventually pushing a wheelchair.

A Not So Happy Homecoming

After six weeks of inpatient rehab, Rosemarie was able to return home. Her husband had built a temporary, but steep wooden ramp to get her into their home. Rosemarie remembers thinking, "How will I get up this stupid ramp? Someone will have to push me up to get me into the house." Once in the house, she discovered the carpet was too thick to roll across. The physical obstacles left her feeling frustrated and depressed on what should have been the happiest day of her recovery thus far. Rosemarie wondered if her injury was permanent and whether she'd ever walk.

For twelve years, Rosemarie and Mark were torn between staying in a home that would always need modifications or trying to find one that was already accessible.

Doors were removed. Furniture was moved. Shelving and storage were reconfigured so that Rosemarie could reach items in kitchen cabinets, closets, and bathrooms. She required some adaptive equipment to use the shower and the toilet. Later, they had an electric porch lift installed to enable her to get into the front door, and the wooden ramp was removed.

The couple finally realized they needed to build a new home and hired architect Patrick Manley, and found a builder who would agree to build a new home with input from their architect. Although Rosemarie and Mark already had a floor plan in mind, they learned from the architect that to accommodate all the accessible features, they would have to start from scratch. In 2006, they purchased a lot that would be the future site for their accessible home.

A New Life Direction Was Launched

Sometime later, Rosemarie was hired to give a motivational speech to a company that sells water garden and pond equipment for landscaping, and Mark went too. After her speech, she received a standing ovation. The president of the company who had invited her to speak asked, "Will you allow me the privilege of building a pond for you someday?" Rosemarie answered, "When we build a new home, I will contact you to build a waterfall."

The next step was to find help building their accessible dream home, so Rosemarie and Mark went to a mastermind meeting in Orlando, Florida, where a group of speakers, writers, and consultants got together to help support and grow each other's businesses. The mastermind members encouraged Rosemarie and Mark to pursue getting corporate America to sponsor their universal design and greenhouse. They suggested making their home a national demonstration house for people who wanted to build accessible and energy-efficient homes. The plan would be to "allow sponsors to put their products in our home, let other people come to our home and see the sponsors' products and tour our home," Rosemarie explains. Even if future home builders did not need accessibility, they could see the features in the home that made it energy efficient. The design of this home would save energy and the homeowners' money.

This seemed like a great idea, but Rosemarie and Mark had no idea how to get sponsors or other people involved. They thought the idea might be impossible; then it was suggested they find and hire someone who knew how to work with sponsors in the home-building industry who could help them sell this idea. After being referred to a professional in Denver, they worked with him to learn how to acquire sponsors. They also hired several other building and design professionals to join their support team.

The next big question that needed an answer was where they would get the money to put this team together and get this project underway. Rosemarie and Mark used their savings, asked their families for loans, and approached several banks to try and get a construction loan. "We looked for more than two years to find a bank that would give us a construction loan," Rosemarie emphasizes. "The housing market was down." They went to the International Builders' Show (IBS) for two consecutive years to meet with potential sponsors and continued to grow more contributors, who would provide products and services to help them drive down the cost of construction for their Universal Design Living Laboratory. Then in August 2009, they received the construction loan check from the bank. In September 2009, they broke ground for the construction and built their house, moving in nearly three years later.

. . .

A MODEL FOR UNIVERSAL DESIGN: THE NATIONAL DEMONSTRATION HOME AND GARDEN

Every entrance to the house is step-free. All entrances, including interior doors, are thirty-six inches wide. The floor space is open around the island and the appliances. The countertops and the shower are wheelchair accessible. An elevator allows Rosemarie to reach the loft and the lower level. "Today, our home is a national demonstration home and garden where people learn about universal design homes," says Rosemarie. She explains, "We have tours by appointment and a virtual tour on our website. From a computer, on our virtual tour, people can zoom into every portion of the house and look at the ceiling, the floor, and the wall treatments.

We have 2,000 square feet of landscape pavers in the backyard to make the garden and the patio accessible. Our wall cabinets are six inches lower than those typically installed. I have a large center island featuring three different heights and including an oven and a microwave at accessible heights. The dishwasher has been raised, making placing, and taking out dishes easier. The washer and dryer with front-loading doors are on raised pedestals and are hinged on the side, as is the oven for more accessibility. Some lights are on motion sensors and come on automatically, and so do some of the exhaust fans."

. . .

Inter-Dependence: A Love Story

Rosemarie's story is one of extraordinary grit and determination to create a living space that would accommodate them for the rest of their lives together (aging in place) took interdependence on multiple levels. First was her primary relationship with her husband Mark; he shared the vision and possibility thinking to overcome an unimaginable number of challenges; only love can explain this kind of determination. Next, the mastermind group is credited with generating the idea of sourcing vendors for the Universal Design Living Laboratory (UDLL). In addition, we were hiring architect Patrick Manley to draw the house plans for our new home in Columbus, Ohio, as well as kitchen and bath designer Mary Jo Peterson and Anna Lyon as the interior designer for our home. Not to mention all the builders, contractors, crew members, product vendors/installers, and all the unsung team members who made this happen.

The mission of the UDLL reaches beyond Rosemarie and Mark to an even more comprehensive and exceptional kind of service to the greater good. Their aging in place/Universal Design Home is a showcase for accessible products and a learning tool for students and professionals around the world. Rosemarie's life-altering event in June of 1998 was the call to a new path in life and one she answered in the spirit of coming from a place of contribution. She and Mark turned that spring morning into a magnificent purpose to build a home that embodies the mission to make the world a more inclusive place for all.

"Universal Design Living Laboratory," is the top-rated universal design home in North America, earning three national universal design certifications (view at UDLL.com).

THE UNIVERSAL DESIGN TOOLKIT

First and foremost, The Universal Design Toolkit is a love story between two individuals who risked turning a life-altering experience into a mission to make a difference. This is a book about resilience, contribution, and how to live fully—not in spite of limitations, but because of them. The book begins with Rosemarie's accident, but it is not the focus, rather it provides context for the journey to The Universal Design Living Laboratory, a showcase for those who seek the best practices in human-centered design and accessibility solutions for all. This is hands-down the most comprehensive work on Universal Design I have read. It is written from an end-user's point of view, so emphasis on practicality. For all of us who will benefit from this work, we should be forever grateful that Rosemarie and Mark took to heart the theme: "Failure is not an option."

Rosemarie kept very meticulous notes from the time of her injury through the completion of the house and its public tours and has compiled this information in a comprehensive resource and guidebook titled, "The Universal Design Toolkit: Time Saving Ideas, Resources, Solutions, and Guidance for Making Homes Accessible."

With The Universal Design Toolkit, people with accessibility needs can learn what products and services are available to modify their homes to fit them better.

The guide covers a range of helpful topics, including:

- The benefits of having Universal Design (UD) features in your home.
- The principles of Universal Design and 10 myths.
- A glossary of terms.
- Space planning dimensions for people who use wheelchairs or walkers.
- Sources of funding to repair, modify, remodel, or build a new UD home.
- A list of knowledgeable universal design professionals, including architects, home designers, builders, remodelers, interior

designers, lighting designers, occupational therapists, landscape designers, and realtors.
- Questions to ask when selecting a designer and builder/remodeler.

This toolkit also offers available house plans, floor plans, and room design for an accessible home, estimated construction and product costs, and a Universal Design feature checklist by room. Download the nearly 200-page *Universal Design Toolkit* by Rosemarie Rosetti here: universaldesign-toolkit.com.

In Her Own Words

Thriving after a spinal cord injury takes motivation, determination, perseverance, and a support team at home. Mark was my life-saving hero on the bike trail and my support at home. At no time did I doubt Mark's unconditional love for me. He demonstrated his love and support daily. Our home was a significant source of frustration, and I depended on Mark so often.

The path that I have taken for my life and career has been influenced by new ideas, guidance from others, and opportunities that I have pursued. I am persistent, resilient, determined, and hard-working. My advice to people who are recovering from an injury is to realize that life can be better once you know what you are looking for and find the people who can help you achieve what you want.

Rosemarie Rosetti transformed a tragic life event into a mission to serve humanity. Accessible environments for all are her life's passion. The world is a better place to be because of her and her husband, Mark's, determination to turn obstacles into solutions for living. The theme of Inter-Dependence is the support scaffolding of this incredible story. This is how she is loving her long life!

Thanks to Cure Medical and Rosemarie Rossetti for content related to this story. Contact: Rosemariespeaks.com

5. The Architecture of Happiness

MYTH 5: You have to go it alone.

Goodbye MYTH: You do not have to go it alone—you have options!

Step 5: Consider co-housing, home-sharing, accessory dwelling units (especially Age-Friendly ones), get to know **caring communities** and what they have to offer.

Profile: Marianne Kilkenny, Founder of the Women Living in Community Network.

We became fairly independent, then, at the end of the day, you're sitting in front of the TV eating your little ol' dinner, and you realize you would like to have someone say, 'How was your day?' I am no longer fiercely independent. I now can be interdependent, and this is by choice.

—Marianne Kilkenny

Our Purpose / Redefining Community

Recently I was asked to write a profile article about myself and my work. Writing about yourself is difficult but it did make me do some heavy thinking about my journey over the last (almost) ten years. There have been many times when I questioned my progress, especially when the future felt so unclear. But writing the article reminded me of the two reasons that started me on my journey almost ten years ago.

My Compelling 'Why':

1. The quest to honor the memory of my mother, Betty.
2. The desire to find or create a community of people with shared values to grow with, live with, and care for each other.

My Compelling Why

I last wrote about my mother in April 2014 for a Mother's Day article. You can read it on the website. Watching my mother age in a nursing home was like having cold water splashed on my face constantly. I was there, but it never felt like enough. When she passed away, I knew then that this was not the way to end what had been years of happiness and hard work. Honoring the memory of my mother meant finding a better alternative and spreading the word, so others did not share in that fate.

At the same time, I was caring for my parents; I was going through my own shift – my long career in Corporate HR was coming to an end. I was divorced, alone, and facing my future as a "boomer," like many others. I knew then I needed to find or create a community of people with shared values to support each other in good and bad times. Little did I know how long this quest would take.

A Morning Reminder of Hope

Always in a hurry for the quick fix, I had no idea the twists and turns my journey would take. The simple step of starting this website in 2007 turned into speaking, teaching, and then writing My Guidebook. Locally, I've become known as "The Community Lady." The media dubbed me the "real-life Golden Girls" when I was living with 3 to 4 women (and sometimes a guy here or there). In the last year, I've moved out of shared housing and am now exploring what to do with a 2-acre lot of land—do I build, what do I build, do I create a community? I have often doubted the progress I was making, but as I look back upon my journey, I realize that the last ten years have proven to be my own "School on Aging/Thriving." I learned about the pros and cons, options, and alternatives while testing and exploring different models, personally. While this journey is not yet over, I have come full circle to My Compelling Why.

I started honoring my mother the moment I took the big step to move to Asheville and founded Women for Living in Community. With each blog post I write and speech I give, or with every person who buys my Guidebook and takes that single step to finding their community, I am honoring my mother. I am sharing and will continue to share with others' ideas for a better way to age with grace and dignity than the nursing home model.

During all of this, I've realized that assets in dollars or possessions are not as important as assets in friendships, companionships, intimacy and belonging. The quest to find my own community was right there all along. In July 2014, I wrote and published a page on this website called "My Journey," and in it, I magically referred to the next chapter of my journey... "As I go forward into the future, there are many more chapters to this story. Finding my tribe and the place I can bring others to experience some of the things I have learned."

Women Living in Community

If you are considering your housing options as you age for yourself, your family, or your parents, then you have come to the right place. We are at a tipping point in this great discussion on aging. Everyone admits that we don't want to waste away alone in our homes, alone in a community retirement center, or just alone. There is a way to age in community with dignity, grace, friendship, support, and meaning. Women have always been the leaders, nurturers, and creators of home. We bring together family and community. Today, more than ever, our role is paramount as we redefine what it means to age and what it means to live. We need new community models. Models that provide companionship and support so that our loved ones and we can grow older with grace, love, and joy.

We have an extraordinary opportunity to lead the way in creating alternative community models that are based on more than just healthcare and insurance and don't cost an entire life savings. This is not just about "Golden Girls," and it is more than shared housing, and this is about being intentional in deciding for ourselves and our loved ones where we live and how we will live as we age. We invite you to join us, learn and make a positive impact through education and awareness as we develop and bring forth this new community model.

What We Do

Women For Living in Community brings together women, as natural leaders and nurturers, to create communities for growing older with grace and dignity. We also connect with existing community models and professionals to provide the necessary resources and alternatives. Women for Living in Community provides information, education, and awareness to women, community leaders, aging professionals, and healthcare providers about what it means to intentionally find or create a community for aging in grace and dignity. Our network, both online and offline, provides a framework for growing and learning.

Women for Living in Community provides the framework as a platform for women to learn about alternative models of community (co-housing, shared housing, etc.) and get guidance and support in creating those communities. We motivate and inspire women into action.

CONNECTION: To form connections with existing community models and professional partners.
INFORMATION: To provide information, networking, and a forum to meet.
ACTION: To inspire Boomer women with alternative living situations to take action.

3 P's

Marianne lays out the 3 P's for Living in Community: The People, the Place, and the Personal Skills. It takes all three to flourish while living in community. She helps audience members uncover the characteristics of the right people for them to live with, the perfect place that meets their specific needs, and both the skills they have and the skills they need to make it work

In Her Own Words

We are at a tipping point in this great discussion on aging. Women have always been the leaders, nurturers, and creators of home. We bring together family and community. We have an extraordinary opportunity to lead the way in creating alternative community models for aging with dignity, grace, and love. We invite you to join us, learn and make a positive impact through education and awareness as we develop and bring forth this new community model.

Marianne guides or facilitates workshops and training sessions, webinars for individuals, groups, and communities truly interested in designing, developing, and creating their own alternative housing model. If you're interested in incorporating an alternative housing model for living as we age, we urge you to contact us. She and her group have learned and gathered extensive information and feedback in this area as well as connected with individuals and professionals across the country that can assist in this important endeavor.

For example, *Who Will Leave the Light On For You?* In this important presentation, Marianne shares her own story that led her to found Women for Living in Community. She discusses the steps she is taking to promote, create and build alternative housing communities across the country. This is how she is loving her long life!

All her presentations are followed by question and discussion sessions. Starting the conversation is the first step. If you're interested in joining or building a community in your area, this is the first important conversation. You can inquire through the website for more information on workshops, classes, speaking engagements, join her Facebook page for live content and webinars.

Website: womenlivingincommunity.com

Email: Marianne@womenforlivingincommunity.com

Book: *Your Quest for Home: A Guidebook to Find the Ideal Community for Your Later Years*

6. The Meaning of Things

MYTH 6: The more things I leave for others, the greater my legacy of love.

Goodbye MYTH: Your family will be better off with a legacy of less and more time with you.

Step 6: Begin de-cluttering today, a simple napkin exercise can get you started.

Profile: Margareta Magnusson, author of, *The Gentle Art of Swedish Death Cleaning: How to Free Yourself and Your Family from a Lifetime of Clutter.*

I often ask myself, Will anyone I know be happier if I save this?

—Margareta Magnusson

She was born in Sweden, in her own words, between 80 - 100 years ago. A global citizen who has lived all over the world, Margareta is a mother of five children and currently lives in Stockholm. Her education was from Beckman's College of Design, and her art has been exhibited in galleries from Hong Kong to Singapore. *The Gentle Art of Swedish Death Cleaning* is her first book, and it has made her a media celebrity of sorts. As the population continues to age rapidly, many are finding themselves with the dilemma of a lifetime accumulation of material possessions and the challenges that presents—they are looking for answers and relief. A newfound movement has been sparked as minimalism is becoming the new thing. In Sweden, however, this has long been a cultural meme, and the benefits of a simple, minimalistic life is well known. This decluttering is known as "döstädning" (dö meaning "death" and städning meaning "cleaning") is embraced widely.

In *The Gentle Art of Swedish Death Cleaning: How to Free Yourself and Your Family from a Lifetime of Clutter*, Margareta instructs her readers on this surprisingly energizing process. Employing her own life as an example, she is digging through her late husband's tool shed and her own secret drawer of vices—guiding practitioners through the difficult conversations that pop up with elderly loved ones and offers suggestions for what to keep and what to get rid of. Her objective is to introduce the element of fun and humor into this otherwise daunting family task.

One Barnes & Noble overview of her book summed it up:

A charming, practical, and unsentimental approach to putting a home in order while reflecting on the tiny joys that make up a long life.

It is very much about letting go.

One of the most important things one can and should do is decluttering his/her house. Because, as our favorite modern lyricist Leonard Cohen says (quoted by Magnusson): "Putting your house in order, if you can do it, is one of the most comforting activities, and the benefits of it are incalculable." So, let's see what this means in practice and how tidying up your home can be—or even is—related to death.

In Her Own Words

"The only thing we know for sure is that one day we will die. But before that, we can do anything."

Writing a New York Times bestseller, helping start a movement, and freeing herself and her family from a lifetime of clutter, this is how she is loving her long life!

Key Lessons from *The Gentle Art of Swedish Death Cleaning*

- Decluttering: A Lesson from the Vikings
- Swedish Death Cleaning: The Art You Should Master
- Decluttering and 2 Questions to Ask About Each Item You Own

(https://blog.12min.com/the-gentle-art-of-swedish-death-cleaning-pdf-summary/).

The book has also been used as a conversation starter for children to approach this sensitive topic with their aging parents, as well as a guide for those starting the process themselves.

7. Compressing Morbidity

MYTH 7: Aging is a disease that can be cured.

Goodbye MYTH: Many of the things we blame on aging have nothing to do with getting older.

Step 7: Take a systems approach to healthy aging that includes: consulting an occupational therapist (aota.org) and an aging-in-place professional (nahb.org) for age-friendly home modifications, add environmental de-cluttering, then educate yourself on fall prevention, as well as incorporating physical activity, nutrition, sleep, and a framework of moral/ethical values that support your optimal aging and find a compelling purpose.

Profile: DeEtte Sauer

I was a heavy smoker, drinker, eater, and worker. I did everything wrong you could do.

—DeEtte Sauer

DeEtte grew up a self-proclaimed "tomboy" with a very active childhood. But as an adult, her health began to suffer from years of inactivity along with an addiction to tobacco and alcohol. Then in 1978, DeEtte discovered her faith and in turn, spiritual fulfillment. A robust belief system helped her overcome the substance abuse, but she soon found a replacement in food. "Once I put down those addictions, I took up food. I just started eating like crazy," she recalls. "I was 100 pounds overweight. I was miserable. I was 45 years old. I thought I was old." She remembers a vacation when—at 5-foot-5 and 230 pounds—she could not get into a boat with her kids. She looked at her life and where it was going, and she sat down and began to cry. "I was angry about what I'd done to myself," she said.

She began eating healthy and utilized a walking program at 46, which then graduated to a gym membership, and she eventually lost 100 pounds. Then she had a "best-worst" experience at the doctor's office. "In the late '90s, I went to the doctor for a checkup and was told that I had high levels of plaque in my arteries and if there was no intervention, I could expect a heart event in 5 years."

DeEtte got the message, and more lifestyle changes followed. In August 1999, she met a woman shot putter participating in the National Senior Games, an athletic competition held every two years for adults over age 50. DeEtte was intrigued by the idea of competition, so she decided to attempt competitive swimming (without experience or ability) at age 58. "The first time I tried it, I couldn't get across the pool. I wanted to quit, but I didn't. Then I started to love swimming. I loved learning a skill and technique at a later age. I have developed really good strokes," she says, adding with a laugh, "You can teach an old dog new tricks." The decision to take up competitive swimming and join a U. S. Masters Swim Team was life changing. In November 1999, she discovered she had a natural talent for this swimming thing at her first meet. That talent led her to the National Senior Games, where she has medaled. And the rest, as they say, is history.

> *DeEtte Sauer is now entering her eighth decade and continues to swim. A Houston based wife, mother, grandmother, AND nationally ranked swimmer, she's won a total of 57 national medals including golds at both Masters National Championships and National Senior Olympics with a ranking in the U. S. top ten in 175 events and several world top ten rankings. She's also a spokesperson for the National Senior Olympics and a member of the Texas Senior Athletes Hall of Fame. DeEtte talks about how she became a late in life athlete after years of sedentary living, and how swimming has brought her more than the thrill of competition—it has literally saved her life (seasonedathlete.me/episodes/013deettesauer).*

In talking with DeEtte about her incredible journey from pending health disaster to a champion swimmer and Texas Senior Olympics Hall of Famer, it becomes clear this is a tale of victory over the self. She describes her life in review as seeing patterns that have played out and were necessary to bring her to this point in life. When DeEtte received the sobering news from her doctor concerning her self-inflicted heart disease, she began to work diligently toward making some lifestyle changes. She credits Dr. Kelly Brownell for the theoretical scaffolding that helped guide her back to wellness. She employs the acronym L.E.A.R.N.:

- Lifestyle
- Exercise
- Attitude
- Relationships
- Nutrition

DeEtte says this model supports what she calls "Intentional Aging" versus aging by default.

> *What I mean by Intentional Aging is the concept of visualizing how you want your senior years to look and feel, and then be willing to take the necessary steps to ensure success. It ultimately develops your own personal 'bliss point.' Bliss Point is based on the procedure used in developing new food products. Extensive research is conducted attempting to bring together the perfect combination of sweet, salty, and savory that creates an almost euphoric experience for the consumer, creating a craving that causes them to return for the product again and again.*
>
> *This insures a profitable return for the food manufacturer. Similarly, if an older adult invests in all parts of their life (emotional, spiritual, social, financial, and physical health) they create an experience so desirable the behaviors are repeated daily. I feel like I am living in my personal bliss point. My life has evolved from no discipline to the necessary discipline required to sustain a sense of pretty much chronic wellbeing. I would strongly suggest that seniors seek out all the information they need to make the necessary changes.*

Her single overriding message is this: "Intentional Aging" led her to weight loss and then swimming—from these two, she gained the energy and discipline, respectively, to realize her purpose in life. The weight loss happened when she began integrating a healthy diet into her life with two fundamental changes: eliminating certain foods and finding healthy substitutes. For her, it was giving up any processed foods, fried foods, sugar, white pasta, and white bread, strictly sticking to whole foods with high nutritional value. Further, swimming was the cause for finding discipline in her life, getting up at 4:20 a.m. and in the pool by 5:15, swimming 120 laps daily. She soon found joy in the discipline. The bottom line, the lifestyle change ('L.E.A.R.N.') combined with swimming saved her.

Now DeEtte's body is available to her to do what gives life purpose and meaning. She is a giver; her story as a late bloomer Master athlete has inspired countless other seniors to intentional aging and lifestyle changes that make getting older a richer experience. She also volunteers to teach at-risk kids to read, and the stories of private victories with these children may be more meaningful to her than gold medals.

An example is this touching story about a young man with cancer in his leg. He walked unusually because of it, and this drew the attention of a bully. The bully ended up kicking the young man in the very leg that cancer had invaded. The disease caused him to be wheelchair-bound and he fell into depression. A dance coming up, and his thoughts took him down the dark path, worrying that no one would want to dance with a kid in a wheelchair. DeEtte, being the kind of person she is, took this head-on. She got online and searched for content showing kids dancing in wheelchairs. When DeEtte collected enough positive messaging about kids in wheelchairs dancing and having a ball, she then taught him how to recreate the same moves in the school hallway using her iPhone playlist. He did attend the dance with newfound confidence, and his dance card was filled the entire evening! She says, *"Don't let fear hold you back from experiencing great joy."*

The single best definition of healing I have ever encountered is this:

Healing is evoking the will to live in others.

—UNKNOWN

I have always loved it because you don't have to be a doctor, nurse, or therapist, to heal; you can be a grandmother who swims like a fish.

In Her Own Words

"I live younger. There is no such thing as aging gracefully; I believe in aging fiercely!"

October 2021 (email)

> *I won 5 National Championships. The great news is that my times were really good. My 800 free time was better than any time in the last nine years. That is crazy! Another time was the best in 7 years. The other times were 3-4 years out, but all were pre-pandemic. There were so many swimmers complaining that the pandemic had robbed them of valuable training time . . . either their clubs were shut or extremely limiting. So grateful for my club. I missed about 2 months in the beginning but stayed very active. Walking, doing weights at home, stretch bands, etc. My 100 and 200 fly will be at the top of the world rankings. It would be sooo nice to hit number one. I will really explode if that happens.*

DeEtte Sauer is an inspiration, period. Later in life, she made a 180 degree turn toward vibrant health and physical achievements that astound even her. The message she lives is simple, commit to empowered aging and live with purpose—the alternative is unthinkable. This is how she is loving her long life!

Update September 2022 (email)

> ***I had the best year of my life at 80.***

I think I told you that last October I went to National Masters Championship and won 5 titles. I ended up number one in US in 8 events total and number one in the world in 200 fly. I also had other top world rankings in 11 events. Crazy!! In May I went to the National Senior Games. We had a blast! I won 8 gold medals. There were 12,000 athletes there in 20 different sports. I won more medals than anyone. Incredible!! Shocked myself. It was a once in a lifetime experience. Was followed around by film crew from HBOMAX and was one of the featured athletes on Bryant Gumbel's "Real Sports." I am still training hard. Going to Louisiana next week for their state Olympics and then a large zone Meet in November.

God has been so good to me. Never imagined it would turn out like this but I'm loving it! Hope you are doing well! Wish you great success!!

Swimmingly yours,
DeEtte

. . .

8. The Long Goodbye

MYTH 8: I have Alzheimer's in my family, so there is nothing I can do to escape it.

Goodbye MYTH: Because you have family members with Alzheimer's disease does not necessarily mean you will get it, or you can do nothing to stave it off. You are more likely to have a genetic vulnerability than someone with a single occurrence in their family. But that does not mean Alzheimer's disease is in your future; it is a risk but not a guarantee. And there are things within your control to decrease the risk. An increasing amount of research supports the increased probability of dementia risk with physical inactivity, hearing loss, depression, obesity, hypertension, smoking, social isolation, diabetes, and low education levels. The good news is these are factors are modifiable (source: khn.org).

Step 8: Build novelty and complexity into each day and control modifiable risks.

Profile: Teepa Snow, Dementia Care, including Alzheimer's

My personal mission is to better the lives of people with dementia—as well as the lives of their caregivers—by sharing what I have learned. An occupational therapist by training, I have been called 'the horse whisperer of dementia.'

—Teepa Snow

Teepa Snow is one of the world's leading educators on dementia and the care that accompanies it. As an occupational therapist with over forty years of practice, she founded a company and a specific approach to support people experiencing changes in brain function. This Positive Approach to Care® emphasizes the use of retained skills while providing support and substituting our skills for theirs that may be no longer available. Teepa also created the GEMS® States model for brain change, which compares the various states to gemstones and focuses on retained abilities. She believes that with the right care and setting, all GEMS® can shine.

Teepa's company, Positive Approach to Care® (PAC), was founded in 2006 and provided training, services, and products to over thirty countries around the world. She has successfully integrated her education and extremely varied work experiences, recent medical and international research, and first-hand care support background into a program that guides others in effectively working with people living with neurocognitive degeneration. Using the phrase neurocognitive degeneration is an example of how Teepa works to change perceptions and common practices in the dementia care culture. "As people living with dementia at the World Health Organization summit indicated, language matters. So, let's try using the words that match what is actually happening for people, not the word that imposes judgment on another's mind" was Teepa's comment when asked why she is trying to get a complicated word into the vocabulary of people who have difficulty knowing the difference between the terms Alzheimer's and dementia.

Teepa's GEMS® State model and Positive Approach to Care® techniques are now used extensively by families, professionals, and community members who interact with those living with dementia or other forms of brain change. One core principle of PAC is that to obtain the relationships and outcomes that are desired, the first and most important change must originate with each person's own willingness and ability to change their healthy brain. Teepa believes that "Rewiring our own perceptions, attitudes, communication strategies, actions, and responses provides the shift that promotes change for the others around us."

Teepa's care strategies and techniques integrate what is known about brain changes that occur during various conditions with therapeutic approaches to foster positive outcomes, modified environmental supports, and altered task expectations that match retained or available abilities. She emphasizes the value of connection when primary verbal communication and interaction abilities are altered. Her teaching style is extraordinarily unique in that she can accurately demonstrate and model for her learners the struggle and challenges dementia creates for all parties involved. She is an enlightening, witty, entertaining, and energetic speaker who is much sought-after to present to agencies and organizations across the world.

Originally from West Virginia and western Pennsylvania, Teepa now lives outside Chapel Hill, North Carolina. She earned her undergraduate degree from Duke University. Then, she became the first graduate of the master's program in Occupational Therapy at the University of North Carolina in Chapel Hill. She has a wealth of clinical, teaching, and research experiences that have informed and influenced her philosophy, approach, and practice. Teepa has worked as part of Duke University Medical Center's Neuro-Rehabilitation Team, UNC-CH's Geriatric Clinic, as an OT director in a head injury facility, as a clinical specialist in geriatrics for a Veteran's Administration Medical Center, and as a therapist and restorative care coordinator for long-term care facilities.

Her hands-on caregiving experiences include providing direct care in community and wellness centers, day programming sites, home care settings, assisted living and CCRC communities, long-term care facilities, outpatient clinics, hospitals, hospice, and rehabilitation settings. Teepa currently has a clinical appointment at Duke University's School of Nursing. Previously, she held a clinical appointment at the UNC-Chapel Hill's School of Medicine, served as the Director of Education and Lead Trainer for the Eastern N.C. Chapter of the Alzheimer's Association, was employed as the Program Director of Durham Technical Community College's OTA program, served as an interdisciplinary team member and clinical associate professor at UNC-CH School of Medicine's Program on Aging, and worked as a coordinator and care manager for CAP Medicaid waiver services in North Carolina.

She has also served in a wide variety of leadership and advisory positions in professional organizations at both state and national levels, including the Alzheimer's Association, Alzheimer's Foundation of America, AOTA, and NBCOT. She is currently working on several national and international projects and with organizations. She is on the board of Senior Care for Orange County, NC, and the Alzheimer's Support Network in Naples, Florida.

She previously served on the board of the US Dementia Action Alliance. Teepa is a strong advocate for those living with dementia. She has made it her personal mission to help families, professionals, and the general public better understand brain change to reduce stigma and improve life for those living with brain change. Her goal is to change the culture of care, one mind at a time. This is how she is Loving her Long Life!

On a more personal note, Teepa has been married to Dick for over forty years. They have three grown children, Abby, Manda, and Drew. There are three grandsons named Sebastian, Benjamin, and Braden—and many grand dogs. She likes almost all forms of crafts and arts, although she is only good at some. She also enjoys time outdoors and various forms of activity, such as hiking, running, climbing, biking, canoeing, and exploring. When stressed, she cleans and cooks. She cooks, reads, walks, and gets into home or yard alteration or renovation projects when relaxing. The letters behind Teepa's name represent the following credentials: MS (Master of Science), OTR/L (Occupational Therapist, Registered and Licensed), FAOTA (Fellow of the American Occupational Therapy Association).

In Her Own Words

While various forms of dementia may not be completely preventable, there are certainly things that can be done to reduce your risk, as discussed. The choices we make every day about our diet, exercise, brain engagement, socializing, and stress levels can have a very significant impact on our risk for developing dementia and many other health conditions. What might appear to be a genetic connection may instead be a lifestyle pattern that is duplicated from generation to generation and family member to family member. Breaking the chain and doing something different for yourself and in your care, practices might make all the difference in the world. It is also essential to recognize the choices that you have control over and choose to let go of that you cannot control. Worrying about possible future diagnoses does not change the situation and may in fact have a negative impact on your immune responses.

It is also helpful to obtain a baseline cognitive function test so that you can be aware of any early development of brain change in yourself or someone with whom you are in a relationship. If there are early changes, create an action plan that involves education for yourself and those you love, and advance directives that specify how you would like to live. Recognize that a dementia diagnosis does not mean it is the end of life, as there are many, many individuals choosing to live well with dementia.

Teepa Snow understands how devastating Alzheimer's can be on individuals and their families, so she emphasizes the positive aspects of living with the disease—yet covers the realities with grace and clarity. In a world where growing dementia rates threaten the social fabric of an aging society, Teepa is a beacon of light and hope. This is how she is loving her long life! (teepasnow.com)

9. Someone to Watch Over Me

MYTH 9: You will always be the one giving care.

Goodbye MYTH: At some point, you will be the one needing care.

Step 9: Who do you want holding your hand in your last moments on Earth? Have a conversation with that person(s) about your future care-receiving needs. Decide if a Geriatric Care Manager is right for you when the time comes. And remember, self-care is healthcare.

Profile: Dr. Marion Somers, author of, *Eldercare Made Easier: Doctor Marion's 10 Steps to Help You Care for an Aging Loved One.*

Life is my playground and school; I'm a willing, perpetual student.

—Dr. Marion

Marion Somers (AKA Dr. Marion) is a Giver who has overcome adversity her entire life and employs it as fuel for serving. She is a captivating storyteller with a message that is designed to inspire others to use adversity as a steppingstone to happiness. She has a plan to make caregiving less traumatic for all involved because she knows firsthand the private challenges families face—she's been there. She is an unlikely pairing of kind-heartedness tempered with East Harlem, New York City grittiness—the ideal hybrid to be a guide for caregiving.

A Life Review / Lessons Learned

Elder Care Expert and award-winning, nationally recognized Geriatric Care Manager, Marion Somers, Ph.D., ("Dr. Marion") for the past four decades has provided care for more than 2,000 elderly clients while she owned and operated a thriving Geriatric Care Management practice. It is now Dr. Marion's goal to help caregivers everywhere by providing valuable insights and information.

Doctor Marion is regarded by the media as a leading expert on eldercare issues, topics, and solutions. She has been featured on The Today Show, Eyewitness News, The Wall Street Journal, Newsday, and a host of national radio programs. She completed national 50-city bus tours across the nation to talk about planning for long-term care. The bus tour was part of a national campaign called "3 in 4 need more," which was based on a study that said that three out of four Americans need long-term health care but are not prepared for it.

While others might avoid elder care issues at every turn, Dr. Marion has made caring for the elderly her life's work. She loves her work, and it shows. Dr. Marion does not focus on the grey hair or wrinkles of the elderly. Instead, she is inspired by the beauty of their life experience. "If an individual has lived to be 90 years old, he must have some real skills and smarts to get his needs met in life. It's vital we tap into the wisdom, strength, and life strategies of the elderly before they pass on," says Dr. Marion.

Dr. Marion knows that caregivers feel scared, angry, guilty, frustrated, overworked, and under-appreciated, but she is here to hold their hand through these demanding times. She passes on her knowledge and practical advice in a way that all caregivers can understand.

Dr. Marion's Story
In Her Own Words

My concept has always been no matter how many rocks are thrown in my path; I do not use them as deterrents but as steppingstones. I was born in East Harlem, New York City. Two working-class parents who never graduated high school. The chronological order of my siblings: I was the eldest, my sister Loretta was two years younger. Two years after her birth, my mother had a miscarriage which drained all the energy out of her, and then ten years after my birth, identical twins' sisters were born, Carol and Patricia. The apartment was a walk-up—the toilet was a water closet (WC), and the tub was in the kitchen next to the only sink.

The general environment outside the home was squalor, a community of heavy drinkers, smokers, and a great deal of anger in the overall environment. The nearest park had limited equipment, and what was there was mostly broken. There were two swings that could be sat on and swung, so I would pump the swing until it went over the portion that the chains were attached to. What I learned is that if I did not give in to fear, I could push myself further with whatever I was doing.

There was no privacy anywhere, but I found while exploring the Tri Brough Bridge that there were under bridges for the workmen, and I and some friends would hang out there until somebody would shoo us away. We also found wooden planks to build playhouses in various underparts of the bridge. What I learned is you can find joy, fun, and excitement wherever you are.

I learned to fish and swim in the Harlem River. Under the Willis Avenue Bridge, the currents were strong, and the whirlpools could suck you down. Twice I was rescued by two of the teenage boys that had grabbed onto my pigtails. What I learned is that I must stay physically strong.

There were large rats that ran up and down the pilings at the river's edge as we kids ran up and down the rocks; never did any child get bitten because we learned early the lesson of living and let live. What I learned is that if you do no harm to animals, they will not harm you. We found fun where we could. The local men during the winter would dig an oval ditch and fill this one-foot-deep hole with water that would freeze, and that became our ice-skating rink. No one had the money for ice skates, so we would 'ice skate' with the brown paper bags we had on our shoes that had strings on the bags to keep them tight and on. What I learned from this was when I first went to Wollman Ice Skating Rink in Central Park that had real ice and music that anyone can have fun when you change your mindset and accept what is before you.

My responsibility was to care for my sisters, and this included when my sisters were in diapers. The diapers had to be cleaned each night by rinsing the diapers in the toilet to flush down the residue, and the diapers were washed on an old-fashioned scrub board with soap and water. Then these clean diapers were put in a large cauldron on the stove, filled with water and boiled, and then hung on the outside line to dry. My responsibility was also to take my sisters to and from school daily. What I learned from this is not to put off any chores or responsibilities, but to get them done quickly, accurately, paying attention to details. I was always looking for a way to do my chores more efficiently without cutting corners.

We did not have adequate books at PS 39 Elementary School, so two and three children often read or share a book. The local library and librarian were my friends. The library was also a place to go in the winter because the library always had heat. What I learned from this was to be aware of what creature comforts are and how do we satisfy those needs. In the third grade, it was my turn to read in front of the class and as I was reading my teacher walked behind me. She realized I had memorized the reading book, and I was on the wrong page for what I was saying and supposedly reading. I knew I could not read, but I did not know how to learn, so I memorized everything I could. I had often asked to be in the back of the class because I was so physically active and did not want to disrupt anyone. But my real reason was that the words on the backboard constantly moved, jumped, and vibrated. When I said this to anyone, I got whacked. What I learned from this is I had to take care of my own needs in the best way I could without involving others.

I was determined to find answers. Our family never went on vacations, nor did the teachers take us on school trips, but our class was taken to the Metropolitan Museum of Art of New York City on one occasion in the third grade. We were shuffled into a school bus; told nothing about where we were going. My life to this point had been in the confines of 126th Street and 116th Street. Between the river and Lexington Avenue. That was my world. I walked into the Metropolitan Museum saw this huge abundance of flowers in the center of the entrance hall and I thought I had died and gone to heaven. With each painting, my world opened and was never the same. What I learned from this is that beauty and abundance are infinite, and I planned to explore more of life.

Somewhere in this education, I did learn to read, but I read in a very unusual way that worked for me at the time. Books became my friends and escape. The first book that truly touched my soul was *The Good Earth* by Pearl S. Buck. What I learned was that books could transport me to anywhere. In eighth grade, I was taken out of my class which was for gifted children and put in the retarded class (Dr. Marion notes that "retarded" was the label used at that time and is not appropriate now; today, students are called "special needs"). The logic was–there was no logic. While with these children who had IQs of 65 or below, I took it upon myself to teach them math, the alphabet, basic words, number recognition, and colors. I did this all by singing all the lessons I was teaching and having them move physically at each and every lesson.

What I learned from this is that everyone can learn. You just need to find their receptive methodology. What I learned is that my need to help those who have 'other' abilities was strengthened in a way that has impacted my life. My drive is to help those who are listening to another drummer or are dealing with a handicap that keeps them out of the mainstream, be it a physical, mental, or emotional (seeming) limited view and interaction with the world. In the Ninth Grade, there was a citywide IQ test for both private and public-school children. Each test was given in your homeroom with your homeroom teacher as the overseer/disciplinarian. About a month after I was called to the principal's office (which was not a good sign).

In the office were the principal, my primary teacher, and two women from the department of education who checked the test. In effect, they thought I had cheated on the IQ test, and they wanted me to retake the test again in front of them. I did exactly as I was told as all four watched. I thought to myself how could I have cheated when I am in a classroom of students with limited IQs? When I finished the test, the two women from the department of education checked right there in front of me. Then they gave the results to my teacher and the principal. Nobody said anything to me. The department of education ladies asked me a host of questions. The bottom line was I was being reclassified because my score put me in the top 5% of all the students in the ninth grade in New York City. This meant that grownups were not as smart as they thought they are and the value system they impose on others is not necessarily right for everyone.

I was not the least bit upset with this new news and category because I knew right along with that, I was smart in different ways, and I learned in unique ways. I went back to the ninth-grade gifted class immediately and was fully up to the class in every way. What no one asked me-- was, "how was I right on grade level having just spent a year with the retarded students." When I was put in the retarded class, they had taken away all my eight grade books. What I had arranged with three of my girlfriends was that I would help them with their homework, or we four would work together so that I could graduate and go on to high school. I still had the responsibility of my three sisters, but nothing deterred me from learning. What I learned from this is I had to plan and organize my own life and keep education foremost in my life.

When I was planning to go to college, I had limited funds, so I only put forth one application to City College of New York and was accepted. (This was before open enrollment. I got in and was accepted on my merits/abilities.) It was only later that I learned people practiced and took tests for these Entrance Exams, or they hedge their bets by broadening their outreach base for acceptance into a college. I have always focused on exactly what I wanted and know that the universe will provide what is right for me. What I learned from this is that I must value myself and not rely on how others value or assess me. When I wanted to go for my Ph.D.

I was accepted at both NYU and Columbia in New York. I, at the time, was teaching at Lehman College at the master's level. I audited some classes at NYU and Columbia only to find that they were basically what I was teaching at Lehman. So, I put the Ph.D. on the back burner, knowing it would happen but trusting the Ph.D. would unfold in the time that was right for me. A year later, I heard about Fielding; put in my application. Patrick, I already told you my story about meeting with one of the Fielding professors in my four-hour interview. What I learned from this is that time works out the way it is supposed to work out and not necessarily in my personal time structure. In the same vein, when I had accomplished my Ph.D. and wanted to become a nursing home administrator, I only applied to one nursing home in New York State.

The Hebrew Home for the Aged was considered the best, plus it has property on the Hudson River in Riverdale, and they also have an exquisite art collection. They only accept two applications a year, and I heard later they had had over 20 for those two positions. I got to spend a year on these fabulous grounds with outstanding nursing home administrators. What I learned from this is to not be limited by numbers or that it will come to me if a position is right for me. On September 1, 2011, and the collapse of the twin towers, I had a business appointment at the restaurant on the top floor. I had already had a successful geriatric care management business for many years. I was planning to have breakfast with two new clients from Chicago who wanted me to take care of their elderly aunt in Brooklyn. The entire day before our breakfast I had several of my clients in hospitals and I had been on the go from eight in the morning to about nine that night. I must state here that I have never canceled a business meeting.

That evening when I got home, I called these two potential clients to ask if they would mind canceling tomorrow's meeting (Sept 11) and move our meeting to the following day or later in the day. Their flight had been delayed, and they were happy to change not to later that day but to the following day (Sept 12). When I turned the television on the morning of September 11, I understood for the first time survivor grief. All my instincts were to cancel the business meeting, and I did. I would, in all probability, have been one of the statistics on that day. What I learned was to follow my instincts/my gut reaction, not my logic.

P.S. I did go on to get my New York nursing home license.

P.S.S. Along this timeline, I did have three children, three stepchildren, three grandchildren, four great-granddaughters, and three husbands, plus three divorces. I have also helped raise my sister's two boys.

> ***There are many common issues that caregivers face when dealing with the elderly. The language or the culture may be different, the values or the color of skin may be different, but many issues are universal, and it's my goal to make a positive impact.***
>
> —DR. MARION

Dr. Marion Somers is an extraordinary woman who has a lifetime of life-affirming and death-denying experiences and has transformed them into life lessons. From humble beginnings, she has created a life rich in accomplishments and contributions. Marion works tirelessly in the cause of older adults and caregivers. She toured the country speaking on TV and media outlets, wrote books, gave lectures, developed apps, and was active on social media—not to mention being a grandmother and helping raise children in her family.

Seeking out physical and intellectual challenges, she exhibits a growth mindset; every encounter with life is lived fully and turned into a lesson. Priorities are taking care of herself, having adventures, supporting family, and remaining engaged professionally. She has a plan for her family when the time comes to care for her. After all, she wrote the book. This is how she is loving her long life!

As the co-founder of Dr. M Media, LLC, Dr. Marion Somers has dedicated her life to providing caregiving and guidance to aging individuals, as well as the families who take care of them. A former private geriatric care manager for five decades, she holds expertise in gerontology and family therapy. She also worked as a coordinator and staff trainer at Hasbro, where she produced "Comfort Companion Pets," lifelike interactive animatronic pets created to bring companionship to aging loved ones. Receiving a BA, with honors, from the City College of New York, DR. Somers subsequently earned an MS in recreational therapy from Lehman College and a PhD in human and organizational development from Fielding Graduate University.

She holds a residential care facility for the elderly administrator certification in California and completed postgraduate training in neurolinguistics programming (NLP). She has been trained as a nursing home administrator in New York. Dr. Somers was an observer at the White House Conference on Aging and a grant reader for the U.S. Department of Health and Human Services. She is also an accomplished author, having written numerous books and articles regarding gerontology, including her recent book, *Elder Care Made Easier: Doctor Marion's 10 Steps to Help You Care for an Aging Loved One*, Second Edition in 2020. She has also appeared on "The Today Show," "Good Morning America," "The Nightly News," and on NPR and Retirement Living television.

A speaker at cross-country tours, Dr. Somers twice received the Mature Media Award, as well as the National Therapeutic Recreation Association Award "for starting National Therapeutic Recreation Week." Additionally, she earned the Lehman College Alumni Achievement award and was nominated for the President's Annual Points of Light.

Website: doctormarion.com

10. Unfinished Business

MYTH 10: Dreams deferred will stay dreams denied—you are too old.

Goodbye MYTH: It is never too late to become what you might have been.

Step 10: One day a week, wear two different colored socks. It seems like such a simple act, yet it can profoundly affect your thinking. Just try it.

- This prompts you to question cultural norms. Start there, then ask what other cultural trances I have been operating under?
- It will remind you to embrace "opposites."
- It also reminds you reframing is your new superpower.
- It just might stir up some interesting conversations. All four will add to your joy; try it and see!

Profile: Siobhan Daniels, AKA "shuvonshuvoff", author of, *Retirement Rebel: One Woman, One Motorhome, One Great Big Adventure.*

Follow my motorhome journey around Great Britain as I challenge ageism, change the narrative and champion pro ageing for all!

—Siobhan Daniels – shuvonshuvoff

LEADING RETIREMENT REBELLION

Siobhan Daniels is, as they say, living her best life. For so many, retirement means disengagement from life—not so for Siobhan; she has a mission to change cultural assumptions around what it means to no longer be working at your job. For some men, retirement has been termed "the roleless role." Women have traditionally been better at living beyond being defined by career status and meaning making derived from making a living. Yet, she feels traditional retirement for many women has greater potential for life-affirming experiences, contribution to a greater good, and aging well within one's age (this is not about anti-aging).

Siobhan is determined to show other women a different way with what she calls "Retirement Rebellion." What is that you might ask? It is traveling around Great Britain in a motorhome, championing positive aging and challenging ageist stereotypes. She has also been invited to speak about her experiences and her positive aging campaign.

"This is good news for me because when I started my adventures just under two years ago, I was not sure how I would get my message across; that it is good to age and we should be doing it positively, retirement should not mean that we are put out to grass. For me, retirement is a chance to become the person that I always knew I was. I have the freedom to do what I want when I want, be kind to others, and try to inspire others to live life to the fullest no matter how long they have on this Earth. I want people to listen to that voice urging them to have an adventure, no matter how big or small, we only have one shot at this living lark." Siobhan's thinking on aging echoes that of the late David Bowie when he said, "Ageing is an extraordinary process whereby you become the person you always should have been."

Her Story

I'm a retired journalist traveling the UK in my motorhome, raising awareness for positive aging, and changing the current outdated narrative. When I hit 60, I retired from the BBC after thirty years as a presenter, reporter, and producer. I gave up my home, bought a motorhome, and embarked on a journey around Great Britain to champion positive ageing and challenge ageist stereotypes. I want to help change negative narratives, like anti-aging and inappropriate images around aging that do not reflect ageing nowadays. I had always believed in living my best life, even when the going got tough.

> *After feeling bullied at work during menopause and facing ageism in the workplace, I took a gap year from the BBC in my late 40s and backpacked solo around the world for a year. Since turning 50, I've run two marathons, climbed 'The Three Yorkshire Peaks,' traveled to Malawi, and climbed Mount Mulanje. In my 60s, I have spent two years on the road in my motorhome, writing a book and giving talks. I have weathered storms and a pandemic along the way, and I feel the highs and lows have been worth it.*

Her Values

Authenticity: It is important to know your own worth and to speak your truth.

Bravery: Seek to be brave in all you do, in what life throws - know you are brave within and can conquer the challenging stuff.

Kindness: Always be kind, even though it is often mistaken as a weakness. I believe it is a true strength.

Community: I love people joining together to age positively and challenge ageist stereotypes.

In Her Own Words

> *I hope my experiences inspire people, young and old, to embrace ageing (UK spelling) and not to fear retirement. I want to inspire older women who may want to be adventurous but are too scared to say 'Yes' to that challenge. I also want to inspire younger women that ageing and retirement is not something to fear but to embrace. Ageing is a privilege. So, I'm grateful for the chance to age disgracefully at a time when we are ageing differently. I am proud to be part of the retirement rebellion!*

Siobhan Daniels is living a life of rich adventure, no rocking chairs for her. The open road, new people, and places await around the next corner. She has also embarked on a book promotion tour! "Re-tirement" to her is putting on new tires and talking off again! This is how she is loving her long life!

> I am passionate about positive ageing, pro-ageing, and challenging ageism. I work with organizations delivering talks, media interviews, panels, webinars, Facebook and Instagram Lives, and I've also been commissioned to write blogs and articles on the subject of aging and positive retirement.
>
> I cover:

- Why I'm leading the Retirement Rebellion
- What it means to be an ageless, fearless woman – and what you can achieve
- What has motivated me through my life to embrace this chapter wholeheartedly
- My perspective on ageism in the workplace and how to call it out
- Aging disgracefully and enjoying the ride
- How to find your inner strength and channel it for good

Shuvon Shuvoff Logo

Her website: shuvonshuvoff.co.uk

Instagram: @shuvonshuvoff

Email: Siobhan.m.daniels@gmail.com

New Book: *Retirement Rebel: One Woman, One Motorhome, One Great Big Adventure*

Review the Ten Steps to Loving Your Long Life

Step 1 Embrace each stage of life.
Step 2 Employ "grandmother hypothesis".
Step 3 Take initiative to become more financially literate and start a side hustle business.
Step 4 Use aging in place negative visualization to your advantage.
Step 5 Consider co-housing, home-sharing, accessory dwelling units, and get to know caring communities.
Step 6 Begin de-cluttering today with a simple napkin exercise.
Step 7 Take a systems approach to healthy aging.
Step 8 Build novelty and complexity into each day; control modifiable risks.
Step 9 Have a conversation about your future care-receiving needs; decide if a GCM is right for you when the time comes.
Step 10 One day a week, wear two different colored socks. Just try it!

The themes in this book are meant to be life-affirming, hopefully inspiring as well, and useful to you and your network. I wish to conclude with a poem I wrote as a young man on the journey of a lifetime.

INSPIRATION

Inspiration, like rain, falls on everyone
Some may shield themselves with an umbrella
Failing to take heed
Still others run indoors
Avoidance altogether
Then there are those who walk freely amongst the pour
Sensing every drop and giving reverence
Recognizing the passion and the splendor
Exerting its existence manifested through you
With consciousness raised and mind open to cosmic
proportions
Restoration of the deeply sleeping soul occurs
And you're released from artificial obstacles
Then embracing possibilities with dimensions still unknown
Messages from the heavens rush to you like lightning to
the rod
Ideas embraced, recorded . . . then shared

—PATRICK RODEN, CHRISTCHURCH
NEW ZEALAND, 1987

Epilogue

My final thoughts on aging. Strategically, avoiding the word "aging" is not doing any favors to the cause of countering ageism; aging is living. Reflect honestly for a moment on why this occurs. What has your historical experience of aging been? Being part of the solution means not re-enforcing negative images by denying aging. I am not talking about *"Happy Gerontology"* here, no sugar-coating it. But if we are determined to nip ageism in the bud, treating the word [aging] like the plague to be avoided at all costs sends a dog-whistle message providing oxygen to gerontophobia (fear of aging).

I was recently accused of "making the unacceptable aspects of aging acceptable," by emphasizing what goes right with aging and not focusing on the inevitable physical declines that might someday be cured with science. I found the accusation ironic after a lifetime of caring for the elderly in various stages of physical and mental decline—including my loved ones. I've lived all the "unacceptable" aspects of aging and make no attempt to deny them. Instead, I choose to support the best experience of aging for all—and women especially in this book.

I encourage you to be part of the solution, question assumptions about aging in general, and women's aging more specifically. So much of the cultural "anti-aging" messaging is soul-eroding and misleading. Each stage of mid-life and beyond has something unique to offer. To deny what I like to call "possibility aging" is to miss the lessons of lifespan development. The ranks of those who understand this are thankfully growing. As gerontologist and marketing strategist Ken Dychtwald recently noted in an interview, we (society) need more grown-ups. Join us in this meaningful endeavor. We have work to do! And remember, aging is denied to many.

Nancy Gnatz, RN, PhD; Patrick Roden, RN, PhD; Diane McLean, RN.

These two women were my first nursing supervisors and examples of the positive female influences in my life. Thank you, ladies, for your kindness and guidance.

My beautiful Aunt Ann at 94. I love you.

References

Chapter 1

Bergeron-Boucher, M., Alvarez, J., Kashnitsky, I., et al. *Probability of Males to Outlive Females: An International Comparison from 1751 to 2020.* BMJ Open 2022;12: e 059964. doi: 10.1136/bmjopen-2021-059964.

Berman and Goldman. (1992). *The Ageless Spirit: Reflections on Living Life to the Fullest in Our Later Years.* New York: Ballantine Books.

Diggs, J. (2008). *The Continuity Theory of Aging.* In: Loue S.J., Sajatovic M. (eds) Encyclopedia of Aging and Public Health. Springer, Boston. https://doi.org/10.1007/978-0-387-33754-8_103.

Dychtwald, K., Founder & CEO, Age Wave (agewave.com).

Estes, C.L., Binney, E.A. (1989). *The Biomedicalization of Aging: Dangers and Dilemmas.* The Gerontologist, 29 (5), 587-596.

Friedan, B. (1993). *The Fountain of Age.* Simon & Schuster.

Gillick, M.R. (2006). *The Denial of Aging: Perpetual Youth, Eternal Life, and Other Dangerous Fantasies.* Harvard University Press.

Kaufman, S.R. (1986). *The Ageless Self: Sources of Meaning in Late Life.* The University of Wisconsin Press.

Langer, E. (2009). *Counterclockwise: Mindful Health and the Power of Possibility.* Ballantine Books.

Levy BR, Slade MD, Kunkel SR, Kasl SV. Longevity increased by positive self-perceptions of aging. J Pers Soc Psychol. 2002 Aug;83(2):261-70. Doi: 10.1037//0022-3514.83.2.261. PMID: 12150226.

Peterson, G.P. (1999). *Gray Dawn: The Global Aging Crisis,* Foreign Affairs Vol. 78 (1) (Jan.), pp. 42-55. Council on Foreign Relations.

Popcorn, F., Marigold, L. (1998). *Clicking: 17 Trends that Drive Your Business and Your Life.* Harper Business.

Steele, A. (2021). *Ageless: The New Science of Getting Older Without Getting Old.* Doubleday.

The Administration on Aging, Administration for Community Living, U.S. Department of Health and Human Services. (2018). *Profile of Older Americans.* (2021). Retrieved from: https://acl.gov/sites/default/files/AgingandDisabilityinAmerica/2018OlderAmericansProfile.pdf).

Walter, C. (2020). *Immortality, Inc.: Renegade Science, Silicon Valley Billions, and the Quest to Live Forever.* National Geographic; 1st ed. January 7.

U.S. Department of Health and Human Services. (2018). *Profile of Older Americans.* Administration on Aging, Administration for Community Living.

Chapter 2

Bennett, J. (2019). *I Am (An Older) Woman. Hear Me Roar.* The New York Times, Jan.

Bush, A. (2019). *The Invisibility of Older Women.* FEBRUARY 27 / theatlantic.com, Feb. 27.

Conejero,I., Olié, E., Courtet, P., Calati, R. (2018). *Suicide in Older Adults: Current Perspectives*. Clin Interv Aging, 13, 691-699.

Friedan, B. (1993). *The Fountain of Age*. New York: Simon & Schuster.

Vaillant G. E. (2014). *Aging Well: Surprising Guideposts to A Happier Life From the Landmark Study of Adult Development*. UK: Hachette.

Wallis, V. (1993). *Two Old Women: An Alaska Legend of Betrayal*, Courage, and Survival. Epicenter Press.

Chapter 3

Allianz, L. (2016). *Women, Money & Power Study*. Retrieved from: https://www.allianzlife.-com/-/media/files/allianz/documents/ent_1462_n.pdf.

Cao, R. (2017). *80% of Older Women Can't Pass This Financial Literacy Quiz*. Retrieved 4/24/21 at: https://www.cnbc.com/2017/07/24/80-percent-of-older-women-cant-pass-this-financial-literacy-quiz.html.

Chinn, J.J., Martin, I.K., Redmond, N. *Health Equity Among Black Women in the United States*. Womens Health (Larchmt). 2021 Feb;30(2):212-219. doi: 10.1089/jwh.2020.8868. Epub 2020 Nov 25. PMID: 33237831; PMCID: PMC8020496.

Drucker, L. (2014). *How to Avoid Bag Lady Syndrome (B.L.S.): A Strong Woman's Guide to Financial Peace of Mind*. Drucker Wealth Management.

Frey, W.H. (2003) *Boomers and Seniors in the Suburbs: Aging Patterns*. Brookings.edu. Retrieved from:

https://www.americanprogress.org/article/basic-facts-women-poverty/

Godman, H. (2018). *Divorcing After 50: How Gray Divorce Affects Your Health*. Retrieved from: https://health.usnews.com/health-care/patient-advice/articles/2018-09-21/divorcing-after-50-how-gray-divorce-affects-your-health.

Leap, D. (2020). *The Tragedy of Gray Divorce*. Retrieved from: https://www.thetrumpet.-com/21750-the-tragedy-of-gray-divorce-its-not-about-finances.

Masedo-Gutiérrez, A.I., Swenson N. (2015). *Past, Present and Future of Caregiving*. AASCIT Journal of Health. Vol. 2, No. 1, pp. 1-6.).

Roark, A. (2009). *With Friends Aplenty, Many Widows Choose Singlehood*. The New Old Age blog NYTs, JULY 13, Retrieved 4/23/21 at:

https://newoldage.blogs.nytimes.com/2009/07/13/with-friends-aplenty-many-widows-choose-singlehood/.

Scherer, Z. and Anderson, L. (2021). *Larger Share of People in Same-Sex Couples Have Graduate or Professional Degrees Than People in Opposite-Sex Couples*. Retrieved from: https://www.census.gov/library/stories/2021/04/how-people-in-same-sex-couples-compare-to-opposite-sex-couples.html

Walsh, C. (2021). *The 5 Elements of Financial Freedom*. christinemwalsh.com.

Weaver, F. (1996). *The Girls with The Grandmother Faces: A Celebration of Life's Potential for Those Over 55*. Hachette Books.

The authors' calculations are based on the official poverty measure using the 2019 Current Population Survey, Annual Social and Economic Supplement. See Steven Ruggles and others, "Integrated Public Use Microdata Series, 2019 Current Population Survey, Annual Social and Economic Supplement" (Minneapolis: Minnesota Population Center, 2020), available at https://doi.org/10.18128/D010.V10.0.

Chapter 4

Agochukwu-Mmonu, N., Malani, P.N., Wittmann, D., et al. (2021). *Interest in sex and conversations about sexual health with health care providers among older U.S. adults*. Clin Gerontol. 44(3):299-306. doi:10.1080/07317115.2021.1882637 / Retrieved from: healthyagingpoll.org

Bo'sher, L., Chan, S., Ellen, I. et al. (2015). *Accessibility of America's Housing Stock: Analysis of the 2011 American Housing Survey* (AHS) (March 1). https://ssrn.com/abstract=305519.

Fried, C. (2021). *Aging in place could inflict a huge burden on your family*. Startribune.com retrieved from:

https://www.startribune.com/aging-in-place-could-inflict-a-huge-burden-on-your-family/600006029/.

Fulton, S. (2021). Visit Scott Fulton's website: homeideations.com

Hadler, N.M. (2011). *Rethinking Aging: Growing Old and Living Well in an Overtreated Society*. University of North Carolina Press; 1st edition (August 1).

Irvine, W.B. (2009). *A Guide to the Good Life: The Ancient Art of Stoic Joy*. Oxford University Press.

Jen, S., Jeong, M., Lafountain, O., Doll, G., Cornelison, L. (2022). *Sexual Expression, Policies, and Practices in Skilled Nursing Settings Serving Older Adults: An Updated Assessment in the State of Kansas*. Gerontol Geriatr Med., Jul 19;8:23337214221113137. doi: 10.1177/23337214221113137. PMID: 35874434; PMCID: PMC9301106.

Jordan, W.A. (2014). *'Aging in Place' Features for the Home Gain Higher Profile as Baby Boomers Get Older*. Washington Post/Real Estate. Retrieved from: https://www.washingtonpost.com/realestate/aging-in-place-features-for-the-home-gain-higher-profile-as-baby-boomers-get-older/2014/03/06/9f590d34-67fb-11e3-a0b9-249bbb34602c_story.html

Mandell, L. (2019). *Recommendation No.1 for a Secure Retirement: "Age in Place."* PBS News Hour. Retrieved from: https://www.pbs.org/newshour/economy/recommendation-1-for-a-secure-retirement-age-in-place.

Mattson, K. (2018). *Why Seniors Could Be Priced Out of Aging in Place Across US*.(October 11) Retrieved from: https://homehealthcarenews.com/2018/10/why-seniors-could-be-priced-out-of-aging-in-place-across-us/.

Pipher, M. (2019). *Women Rowing North: Navigating Life's Currents and Flourishing as We Age*. Bloomsbury Publishing.

Rosofsky, I. (2009). *Sex, Drugs, and Rocking Chairs*. Retrieved from: https://www.latimes.com/archives/la-xpm-2009-aug-03-oe-rosofsky3-story.html.

Zipkin, A. (2018), *Guidance for Aging in the Right Place*. The New York Times retrieved from:
https://www.nytimes.com/2018/03/03/business/retirement/aging-in-the-right-place.html
Zippia.com/advice/nursing-home-statistics.

Chapter 5

Goodpaster, B.H., Park, S.W., Harris, T.B., Kritchevsky, S.B., Nevitt, M., et al. (2006). *The Loss of Skeletal Muscle Strength, Mass, and Quality in Older Adults: The Health, Aging and Body Composition Study*. Health ABC Study. The Journals of Gerontology: Series A, Vol. 61 (10) 1059–1064. https://doi.org/10.1093/gerona/61.10.1059

Hansen, J.C., Scharlach, A. (2012). *Independent for life: homes and neighborhoods for an aging America*. University of Texas Press.

Mahoney, S. (2007). *The New Housemates.* AARP The Magazine, July 2007.

Nelson, T. (2020). *Boomers Aren't Flocking to Cities After All.* Architecturaldigest.com January 28 retrieved from: https://architecturaldigest.com/story/boomers-arent-flocking-to-cities-after-all.

Chapter 6

Csikszentmihalyi, M., Rochberg-Halton, E. (1981). *The Meaning of Things: Domestic Symbols and the Self.* Cambridge University Press.

Frost, R.O., Steketee, G. (2010), *Stuff: Compulsive Hoarding and the Meaning of Things.* Houghton Mifflin Harcourt.

Kondo, M. (2016). *Spark Joy: An Illustrated Master Class on the Art of Organizing and Tidying Up.* (The Life Changing Magic of Tidying Up).

Popcorn, F., Marigold, L. (1998). *Clicking: 17 Trends that Drive Your Business and Your Life.* Harper Business.

Postrel, V. (2017). *The Power of Glamour: Longing and the Art of Visual Persuasion.* Simon & Schuster.

Rowles, G. D. (1984). *Aging in Rural Environments.* In Altman, M.P. Lawton, J. Wohlwill (Eds.), Elderly People and the Environment (pp. 129-157). New York: Plenum Press.

Rubin, G. (2019). *Outer Order/Inner Calm: Declutter & Organize to Make More Room for Happiness.* Two Roads.

Span, P. *The New Old Age Blog*: https://www.nytimes.com/column/the-new-old-age.

For more on the study, see: Home and Identity in Late Life (2005). Eds: Graham D. Rowles and Habib Chaudhury, chapter 4.

Chapter 7

Frankl, V. (1992). *Man's Search for Meaning.* (4th ed.). Boston, MA: Beacon Press.

Fried, L. (2021). *Physical Frailty Syndrome: A Cacophony of Multisystem Dysfunction.* Retrieved from: https://www.publichealth.columbia.edu/public-health-now/news/physical-frailty-syndrome-cacophony-multisystem-dysfunction

Gunderman, R. (2014). *The Challenge of Treating 'Frailty'.* The Atlantic. Retrieved from: https://www.theatlantic.com/health/archive/2014/12/the-challenge-of-treating-frailty/383327/

Hales, C.M., et al. (2018). *Prevalence of Obesity and Severe Obesity Among Adults: The United States.* Data Brief No. 360, Feb. Retrieved from: https://www.cdc.gov/nchs/data/databriefs/db360-h.pdf

Stepko, B. (2020). *Get the Facts on Women and Alcohol: Why heavier drinking can be bad news for their health and well-being.* Retrieved from: https://www.aarp.org/health/healthy-living/info-2020/women-alcohol.html

Weller, R. (2016). *A Happier Hour.* Mod By Dom.

Whitson, H. (2009). *Women Live Longer, Not Better, Largely Because Of Obesity And Arthritis.* ScienceDaily, 7 May. Retrieved from: https://www.sciencedaily.com/releases/2009/05/090502183231.htm

Wright, V. (2015). *Fitness After 40: Your Strong Body at 40, 50, 60, and Beyond.* AMACOM.

Chapter 8

Arbor, A. (2020). *Doing Good Does You Good*. Retrieved from: https://www.elsevier.-com/about/press-releases/research-and-journals/doing-good-does-you-good.

Christian, A. *Granny Dumping*. Retrieved from: antonchristian.com.

Cotman, C. *Miracle-Gro for the brain*. See: The research of the Cotman laboratory is aimed toward understanding the mechanisms causing neuronal degeneration in Alzheimer's disease (AD) and the development of interventions to promote successful aging. Retrieved from: https://www.universityofcalifornia.edu/news/should-doctors-write-prescriptions-exercise.

Luks, A., Payne, P. (1991). *The Healing Power of Doing Good: The Health and Spiritual Benefits of Helping Others*. iUniverse Publisher.

Prior, R. (2020). *Belly Fat in Older Women is Linked to a 39% Higher Risk of Dementia Within 15 Years, Study Says*. Retrieved from: https://www.cnn.-com/2020/06/23/health/belly-fat-dementia-link-wellness/index.html

Rowe, J., Kahn, R. (1989). *Successful Aging*. Dell Publishers.

Snowdon, D. (2003). *Aging with Grace: What the Nun Study Teaches Us About Leading Longer, Healthier, and More Meaningful Lives*. Bantam Books.

Webb, G. (2001). *Intimations of the Great Unlearning: Interreligious Spirituality and the Demise of Consciousness Which Is Alzheimer's*. Cross Currents, Vol. 51 (3), The Ecology of Compassion (FALL), pp. 324-336. University of North Carolina Press.

Chapter 9

Brown, M. (2015). *Iowa State researchers urge rural states to prepare for aging*. Retrieved from: https://archive.hs.iastate.edu/news/2015/02/11/aging/.

Cohen, G. (2001). *The Creative Age: Awakening Human Potential in the Second Half of Life*. William Morrow.

Januta, A. (2018). *YOUR MONEY-Five ways millennial caregivers can find help*. Retrieved from: https://www.reuters.com/article/money-millennial-caregivers-idINL2N1QA17V.

2020 Profile of Older Americans from the Administration for Community Living. 2021. Retrieved from: https://acl.gov/sites/default/files/Aging%20and%20Disability%20in%20America/2020ProfileOlderAmericans.Final_.pdf

mayoclinic.org/diseases-conditions/depression/in-depth/depression-and-exercise/art.

Psychologytoday.com/intl/blog/being-your-best-self/202010/practicing-gratitude-is-important-now-more-ever.

Sheth, K., Lorig, K., Stewart, A., Parodi, J.F., Ritter, P.L. (2021). *Effects of COVID-19 on Informal Caregivers and the Development and Validation of a Scale in English and Spanish to Measure the Impact of COVID-19 on Caregivers*. Journal of Applied Gerontology. 40 (3) 235-243. Retrieved from: https://journals.sagepub.com/doi/full/10.1177/0733464820971511.

Singleton, A. (2021). *Planning for Aging and Illness Includes Budgeting and Paying for Care: Explore long-term options now so family caregivers don't face costs later*. AARP, May 4.

Steves, R. (2021). Retrieved from: ricksteves.com /tours/guides.

Unknown. (2021). *2020 Profile of Older Americans from the Administration for Community Living*. Retrieved from: https://acl.gov/sites/default/files/Aging%20and%20Disability%20in%20America/2020ProfileOlderAmericans.Final_.pdf

Walker, T. (2013). *The Inspired Caregiver: Finding Joy While Caring for Those You Love.*

Chapter 10

Campbell, J. (2008). *The Hero with a Thousand Faces* (The Collected Works of Joseph Campbell). The New World Library.
Clausen, J.A. (1995). *Gender, contexts, and turning points in adults' lives.* In P. Moen, G.H. Elder, Jr., & K. Lüscher (Eds.), Examining lives in context: Perspectives on the ecology of human development (p. 365–389). American Psychological Association.
Clausen, J.A. (1990). *Turning points as a life course concept.* Paper presented at the American Sociological Association meeting, Washington, DC
Frankl, V. (2006). *Man's Search for Meaning.* Beacon Press.
Hareven, T., Masaoka, K. (1988). *Turning points and transitions: Perceptions of the life course.* J Fam Hist. 13:271–289.
James, J. (1986). *Success Is the Quality of Your Journey.* The Newmarket Press.
Moody, H.R. (1998). *The Five Stages of the Soul: Charting the Spiritual Passages That Shape Our Lives.* Anchor.
Prisig, R. (1974). *Zen and the Art of Motorcycle Maintenance.* William Morrow.
Waitzkin, J. (2008). *The Art of Learning: An Inner Journey to Optimal Performance.* Free Press.
Ware, B. (2019*). The Top Five Regrets Of The Dying: A Life Transformed By The Dearly Departing.* Hay House.

Chapter 11

Bartram, D. (2022). *Is Happiness U-Shaped In Age Everywhere? A Methodological Reconsideration For Europe.* National Institute Economic Review, 1-15. doi:10.1017/nie.2022.1.
David, S. (2017). *Emotional Agility.* Penguin Random House.
Freedman, M. (2002). *Prime Time: How Baby Boomers Will Revolutionize Retirement and Transform America.* Public Affairs.
Masterson, M. (2021). *Females Behind Bars.* March 27, Retrieved from: https://www.nwaonline.com/news/2021/mar/27/females-behind-bars/
Orwell, G. (1983). *1984.* Berkley; 60th Anniversary edition.
Selig, M. (2015). *Older but Happier? 5 Amazing Findings from Recent Research Whoever dubbed old age "the golden years" was right.* Psychology Today Jan 07.
Unknown. (2019). *Social isolation, loneliness in older people pose health risks.* April 23, 2019. Retrieved from: https://www.nia.nih.gov/news/social-isolation-loneliness-older-people-pose-health-risks.
Walpole, H. (2016). *The Invention of Serendipity.* The Paris Review. Retrieved from: https://www.theparisreview.org/blog/2016/01/28/the-invention-of-serendipity/.

About the Author

Photo by Kate Singh

Patrick holds a bachelor's degree in Nursing and a Ph.D. in Gerontology; he was given the Lloydena Grimes Award for Excellence in Nursing from Linfield College School of Nursing (first male ever) is a member of Kappa Delta Pi: International Honor Society in Education, and was inducted into Sigma Theta Tau International Honor Society of Nurses Beta Psi chapter.

His professional organizations include the Oregon Nurse's Association, Oregon Gerontological Association, and the American Society on Aging. For more information, visit his website at aginginplace.com.

Made in United States
Orlando, FL
17 April 2023